The Scientist, The Madman, The Thief and Their Lightbulb

THE SCIENTIST,
THE MADMAN,
THE THIEF
AND THEIR LIGHTBULB

KEITH TUTT

**POCKET
BOOKS**

LONDON • SYDNEY • NEW YORK • TORONTO

First published in Great Britain as *The Search for Free Energy* by
Simon & Schuster UK Ltd, 2001
This edition first published by Pocket Books, 2003
An imprint of Simon & Schuster UK Ltd
A Viacom Company

5 7 9 10 8 6 4

Simon & Schuster UK Ltd
Africa House
64-78 Kingsway
London WC2B 6AH

www.simonsays.co.uk

Simon & Schuster Australia
Sydney

A CIP catalogue record for this book is available from the British
Library

ISBN 0-7434-4976-2

Typeset by SX Composing DTP, Rayleigh, Essex
Printed and bound in Great Britain by
Cox & Wyman Ltd, Reading, Berkshire

Contents

Foreword

In March 1989, two respected chemists, Drs Pons and Fleischmann, claimed to have achieved nuclear fusion in their modest private laboratory. Naturally, this claim caused a worldwide sensation, but numerous attempts to repeat the experiment ended in failure. Pons and Fleischmann were laughed out of court, and that was the last anyone heard of them for several years.

From the mid-90s however, there was an underground movement of scientists who believed that their claims should be looked into more seriously, and started experiments of their own – often in defiance of their employers. There have now been several international conferences on so-called 'cold fusion' which have been derided by sceptics as congregations of deluded disciples worshipping a false religion.

To complicate matters still further, there are several reports of excess ('over-unity') energy which apparently can have nothing to do with nuclear reactions. Some reports involve systems of magnets, which appear suspiciously like the 'perpetual motion' devices that have obsessed generations of inventors. More convincing are machines – several now being manufactured on a commercial scale – which depend upon liquids under extreme conditions, where it is known that the phenomenon of micro-cavitation can produce million-degree bubbles.

Whatever the final verdict on this whole affair – and despite all claims to the contrary the jury is still out – it is almost certainly the biggest scandal in the history of science.

Keith Tutt's *The Search for Free Energy* is a fascinating – and often highly amusing – account of a quest which has been under way for at least a century, and has involved dozens of bizarre characters. He has even discovered some fine examples of a species much rarer (luckily) in fact than in fiction: genuine mad scientists.

I do not believe that any unbiased reader will put down this book without feeling that something strange is happening at the fringes of physics. Exactly the same thing happened just a century ago, when a new and totally unexpected source of energy was discovered. From Becquerel's 1896 fogged photographic plate to nuclear power took less than fifty years. Now another revolution is urgently needed; let us hope it will be even swifter.

In 1973, when OPEC started to multiply the price of oil, I predicted: 'The age of cheap power is over – the age of free power is still fifty years ahead.' Now that the price of oil is rising once again, I hope this will be only a slight exaggeration.

Sir Arthur C. Clarke, CBE
Colombo, Sri Lanka, 23 September 2000

Preface

The Scientist, The Madman, The Thief and Their Lightbulb is aimed at people with an interest in the ways we create our electrical energy, and in the impact this process has on our planetary environment. This is not a 'science book' as such, although it is a book about science and technology and the people who function (and 'dysfunction') in this strange and esoteric world.

My intention is that anyone with a school qualification in physics and/or chemistry should be able to understand nearly all of it. Even if you don't understand every word, this shouldn't put you off the process of reading it. Whenever things get complicated, they usually get simple again soon after. It's also worth remembering that just because someone says something complicated, it doesn't mean that they understand it themselves! Einstein was keen on reminding people (not that he always stuck to his own dictum), that if something is true it should be possible to explain it in a way that makes sense to an eight-year-old child.

Most of the more difficult concepts and technical details are explained in a glossary at the end of the book, and for those who want to understand the basics of energy and energy transformations there is an 'energy primer' in Appendix 1.

List of Illustrations

Acknowledgements

I'd like to thank all the people who have helped this book along the way with independent technical and editorial advice. They know who thy are.

My thanks are also prolific for the team at Simon & Schuster who have supported *The Search for Free Energy*, particularly Helen Gummer and Katharine Young. I also want to thank Nick Webb for his commitment to this project – it's meant a lot.

Thanks are also due to those organisations and individuals who have supplied information, or been willing to permit use of material in these pages. I have endeavoured to give due credit to everyone, and hope that if anyone feels uncredited that they will let me know so that they can be fully acknowledged in further editions.

CHAPTER ONE

Introduction

'We ought to be able to obtain the energy we need without consumption of material.'
    Nikola Tesla, *Century Illustrated Monthly Magazine* 1890

We have become fossil addicts.

While we may deny it, our need for a daily fix of fossil power has become a problem. We have become caught up in a self-destructive spiral which will eventually, if we keep using the stuff, threaten our lives, our livelihoods and our means of survival. Even if we were to quit today (and as addicts we know we could, if we really wanted to) the best estimates tell us that it would take around a hundred years for our climate to recover from the abuses of the last century. Cold turkey will still be pretty warm.

In mid-2000 the US government released a report entitled 'Climate Change in America', which had been commissioned in 1990. A pre-publication article from Associated Press writer H. Josef Hebert painted a grim picture of the already toned down report:

> Alpine meadows will disappear, along with many coastal wetlands and barrier islands. Cities will be hotter and more humid . . . the demand for air conditioners will increase, and scientists will have to combat a likely resurgence in insect-borne diseases such as malaria.
>
> This is the weather forecast for the late twenty-first century, when average US temperatures will have risen by 5 degrees to 10 degrees. [1]

In the UK the Royal Commission on Environmental Pollution's report 'Energy – the Changing Climate' sounded an even more urgent note:

> The concentration of carbon dioxide in the atmosphere is already higher than for possibly 3 million years . . . The present concentration of carbon dioxide in the atmosphere is bound to increase further because emissions are continuing to rise, and because carbon dioxide remains in the atmosphere for 50–200 years. There is no precedent in recent geological history to help us understand precisely what consequences will follow . . . [2]

Globally the picture painted by the influential report is much worse. Most climate models now predict that tidal flooding will displace millions of people who live close to sea level:

> Deltas such as those of the Nile and Ganges/ Brahmaputra in Bangladesh would be especially at risk. So would coral atolls; the rate at which sea level is predicted to rise may outstrip the growth capacity of coral and they are liable to be damaged by the higher temperature of the sea. The rise in sea level . . . has been estimated to increase the number of people in the world affected by coastal flooding from 13 million each year to 94 million each year by the 2080s, unless there were to be large-scale migration away from threatened areas. [3]

Our food sources will also come under threat, as many agricultural crops are likely to suffer from unpredictable combinations of long droughts and sudden rains.

Even if we keep on consuming at today's levels, we will experience increasingly extreme swings of weather patterns: floods and storms will become more regular, as will, paradoxically, extended droughts.

Yet we are neither stopping nor slowing down our consumption of energy. Global energy use at the start of the twenty-first century is ten times what it was at the beginning of the twentieth. Each day we invent new devices and machines to consume more and more of the addictive stuff. Countries that have not so far benefited from an electricity grid, such as China, are now, understandably, keen to catch up and make energy luxuries – such as television, computers, electric kettles and fridge-freezers – available to all its citizens. With current technology this would unleash a massive increase in carbon dioxide pollution over the next twenty years at a time when some Western governments have committed to cutting emissions by as much as 20 per cent in the next fifty years.

Electricity production from 'clean' sources is still a tiny proportion of our overall supply. In the UK – Europe's best-sited wind recipient – wind energy makes up only around 3 per cent of the country's supply. At the same time, however, demand for energy is increasing by as much as 3 per cent per year – or a doubling every twenty-three years – thus wiping out any of the benefits the wind might bring. And while nuclear power, despite its other disadvantages, may not produce carbon dioxide, many countries have decided that it is simply too expensive and dangerous to keep going – a victim of high running costs and the huge liabilities of decommissioning the radioactively contaminated generators.

The prognosis does not look good.

The Impact of Electricity

A hundred years ago the electrification of Europe and the US was in the midst of its luminous heyday. With the arrival of new transmission technology, electricity was able to travel over hundreds of miles to people's homes without suffering significant losses in power. The marvels of the electric light and the benefits of new labour-saving devices would soon be available to everyone.

All that was required was an enormous supply of coal to power the generators.

This revolution in technology had occurred as a result of a number of major technological leaps forward during the nineteenth century: James Watt's kettle-watching had led to steam engines; Michael Faraday's laws of electromagnetic induction had led to the invention of electric motors which turned electricity into motive power and dynamo-generators which performed the reverse; Nikola Tesla's envisaging of the 'rotating magnetic field' had led to alternating current (AC) and the creation of electricity grids spanning whole countries. And yet, even in 1900, Tesla was sounding a warning of the dangers of the over-dependence on the new drug, fossil-fuel-driven electricity:

> In some countries, as in Great Britain, the hurtful effects of this squandering of fuel are beginning to be felt. The price of coal is constantly rising, and the poor are made to suffer more and more. Though we are still far from the dreaded 'exhaustion of the coal fields', . . . it is our duty to coming generations to leave this store of energy intact for them, or at least not to touch it until we shall have perfected processes for burning coal more efficiently. Those who are to come after us will need fuel more than we do.[4]

Whether it was coal, gas or more latterly oil, the message still remains the same: the reserves are finite. Even a hundred years ago Tesla believed that there were better ways to harness energy which did not involve the use of fuels:

> It now seems to me that to burn coal, however efficiently . . . would be a mere makeshift, a phase in the evolution toward something much more perfect. After all, in generating electricity in this manner, we should be destroying material, and this would be a barbarous

process. We ought to be able to obtain the energy we need without consumption of material.[5]

Tesla's ideas for this 'fuelless' energy generation have played a significant part in a very slow-burning technology revolution which goes by the name of 'free energy'. It is, most freely admit, a misnomer. No energy will ever be strictly free – just as nuclear electricity never fulfilled its promise of the 1960s that it would be 'too cheap to meter'. Fuelless technologies still have capital costs, whether they are borne by individuals directly via their own generating capacity, or indirectly through a centralized grid. Nevertheless the name free energy has caught on.

So What is Free Energy?

This book is about the inventors, machines and technologies that claim to be ushering in a new energy revolution: a revolution which – if it comes around – will offer solutions to the biggest climatic challenge this planet has faced since the last Ice Age. For we now know, more clearly than ever, that clean, cheap, pollution-free energy technologies are the only means we will have of preventing the earth from suffering the extreme weather fluctuations that already threaten millions of people's lives and livelihoods, and may well go on to affect billions.

These free energy or new energy technologies are not renewable in the normal sense. They are not based on solar heating or solar photo-voltaic energy, which are still highly inefficient and expensive; they are not based on wind energy, which, while it has its merits, is still unpredictable, capital intensive, unsightly (some say), and unlikely for practical reasons ever to fulfil more than a minority of our energy needs. These technologies do not involve the burning of waste (which many do not view as 'renewable' or clean); nor do they employ expensive geothermal energy whereby we tap the heat from the hotter layers of the planet. Nor are they biomass energy – the digestion of green and 'brown' waste to form gases for burning. They are not fuel cells, which, though more efficient than fossil fuels, will still be a significant carbon dioxide polluter. These free-energy technologies do not produce harmful radioactive waste which remains dangerous for many thousands of years, and is a potential source of fissile materials for nuclear weapons.

'Free energy technologies' or 'new energy technologies' are names given to an unusual collection of diverse technologies which share at least one major trait. They are all, generally, fuelless technologies that do not consume a substance in order to produce energy. There are scientists, researchers and inventors around the world who are wholeheartedly convinced that they have discovered non-conventional ways of producing useful amounts of electrical energy from devices, machines, inventions which they have originated, and that it is only a matter of time before their technologies are developed to a point where they become important means of producing electrical energy. These inventions involve magnets, electromagnets, electrostatics, solid state electronics, water cavitation, low-energy nuclear reactions, catalytic nuclear reactions, charge clusters, pulsed plasmas, radiant energy. The list is long, but not exhaustive.

The second common claim of these technologies is that they are somehow gaining energy from a new source. Many claim to be 'over-unity': in other words, when provided with an energy input, they subsequently generate or release an output that is larger than their initial input. There are also machines which claim to have 'closed the loop' and used some of their excess output to feed their input – so creating a self-sustaining machine. These machines have committed the ultimate heresy of appearing to be 'perpetua mobiles' – perpetual motion machines. The most common disagreements in this whole field result from questions about the accuracy and validity of measurement techniques employed by the scientists involved.

In all claims for over-unity the key question arises: where is the 'excess' energy coming from? There is no such thing as a cosmic free lunch, just as it is not possible to create energy out of nothing. The law of conservation of energy works – energy cannot be created. So, argue the detractors, the measurements must be wrong, and the developers deluded.

But the arguments of the developers run along different lines: they are not creating any new energy. The systems are doing at least one of two things: they have either found – as in the case of some cold fusion cells – a new way of accessing chemical, nuclear or other forms of energy locked up in the system's components parts; the other possibility is that they are getting their energy from the 'zero-point fluctuations of the vacuum'. This zero-point energy is the 'background' or 'ether' energy of the universe, and is also called vacuum energy, or the 'quantum fluctuations of the vacuum'.

While it may come as news to many that empty space is, in fact, teeming with energy, it's a fact that's accepted by mainstream science. In the 1960s John Archibald Wheeler, a Nobel-Prize-winning physicist at the University of Texas, measured the energy density of our universe and came to the shocking answer that each cubic metre of the universe contains the equivalent of 10^{94}g – in other words more than all the matter in the universe. If only there were a way to mine it. That, say some of the free energy researchers, is what they've done in their technologies.

For many mainstream scientists, though, this is still a highly controversial idea which challenges the current status quo. New technologies, even if they function successfully, may well require a reworking, a reframing or even an overturning of conventional understanding of physical theory before they are accepted. In other words, if they work as claimed, they may work in spite of our current understanding of energy transformations governed by laws of conservation of energy and thermodynamics.

Guidelines for the Search

Before we can look at the evidence we need to establish some guidelines for the search – the search for truth about these new energy technologies. Otherwise how will we know what we are looking for?

It is sometimes difficult, sometimes impossible, to apply the normal rules of scientific research. First of all it is important to distinguish between science and technology. Science tends to proceed by the publication of peer-reviewed articles in established mainstream academic journals such as *Nature* and *Science*. Technology, on the other hand, is not always interested in such approbation. It is interested in whether something works and whether it can be developed commercially. If something works, it may be more important to an inventor to secure patent protection, which can be a complex and drawn-out process. People can also apply for patents for things that don't yet work – there is no requirement to demonstrate a working model in order to receive a patent. These two approaches – journals and patents – are not mutually exclusive, and many technologists still seek the peer approval that published papers bring. As you'll see from some of the cases in this book, some inventors opt to avoid both.

Searching for truth in the area of energy research is fraught with pitfalls, lay-bys and dead ends. Things are not always what they seem. People do not always say what they mean. There is bias and prejudice everywhere. Greed and jealousy rear their ugly heads regularly and fear and frustration are never far behind. Motivations are mixed, and mixed up, and it's sometimes hard to know why people act the way they do. Not all scientists and inventors are willing to hand over their life's work for someone else to 'independently test' and possibly steal it. There is a huge amount at stake, and the rules of 'normal science' do not always apply. Just because inventors don't play by the rules of peer-reviewed science, though, does not mean that they are necessarily wrong.

In 1899, Charles H. Duell, the then Commissioner in the US Office of Patents, announced to the world that: 'Everything that can be invented has been invented.' He is now best remembered for this quotation. Did people believe him at the time? It's hard to know, but it's likely that some did.

Theory, or at least current interpretation of theory, does not necessarily support, or even allow for, what is claimed by some of the technologies presented here. That doesn't mean that the claims are wrong. Science and technology move forward through the observation of new phenomena, and the expansion of our scientific model to encompass these new phenomena. This is, in fact, a definition of science: the perfection of a model of knowledge through the incorporation of new observations, new discoveries and new achievements. If science itself did not evolve, we might still believe that the sun travelled around the earth.

In order to progress scientifically, we need an open-mindedness, a willingness to allow clearly observed and measured phenomena to guide the search for scientific truth. We know that scientific paradigms can and do shift, and that today's status quo may not – and probably *will* not – be next century's. As Thomas S. Kuhn made clear in his book *The Structure of Scientific Revolutions*, science is not a steady, continuous accretion of knowledge, but a discontinuous set of steps from one paradigm to another.

At the same time we have to be on our guard for bad science, the ever-present possibility of self-delusion (by the scientists as well as the observers of science) and out-and-out fraud. I have no doubt that in the free energy field as a whole only a relatively small percentage of what is claimed is incontrovertibly true.

The technology and research featured on this book is only the quality tip of a sometimes 'mixed' iceberg. I know, for instance, that in the search for new energy sources, there have been very clear abuses of people's trust. I know of a number of scams and con tricks based on the promise of future financial returns from new free energy technologies. Some of these have left many gullible people thousands of dollars out of pocket.

There have also been a number of very genuine scientists who, out of the sheer hope that they are right, or the need to see their life's work fulfilled, have lost their scientific objectivity and deceived themselves that they have achieved more than they actually have. Indeed, it is the first assumption in this search that the potential for self-deception is limitless. The second assumption is that the first assumption has to be applied to the majority as well as the minority. Only in this way can open-minded science flourish.

The big question is, though: do any of these technologies really work? And if they do, can they be made to work commercially? Can they really offer a better, cheaper, safer and non-polluting alternative that is capable of overcoming the barriers to being adopted into the current energy market? And if they can, how quickly? These are the most urgent questions.

As a detective mystery the search to get to the truth of free energy can be a frustrating and confusing journey – and you may not even know when you have reached it. Nevertheless it's a journey well worth the taking.

Let the search for free energy begin.

CHAPTER TWO

Nikola Tesla –

Electricity's Hidden Genius

'I have harnessed the cosmic rays and caused them to operate a motive device.'
Nikola Tesla, *The Brooklyn Eagle*, 10 July 1931

'Ere many generations pass, our machinery will be driven by power obtainable at any point in the universe . . . Is this energy static or kinetic? If static, our hopes are in vain; if kinetic – and this we know it is, for certain – then it is a mere question of time when men will succeed in attaching their machinery to the very wheelwork of nature.'
Nikola Tesla, 'Experiments With Alternate Currents of High Potential and High Frequency,' 1904

In 1884 a young Croatian immigrant stepped ashore at the Castle Garden Immigration Office in Manhattan, New York. He was a sharp-featured 27-year-old with a glamorous shock of black hair, named Nikola Tesla. In his coat pockets he carried a few coins, some papers with drawings and calculations on them and, perhaps most importantly of all, a letter of introduction to Thomas Alva Edison, the incumbent king of electricity.

Behind Tesla there was already an extraordinary past filled with invention, hardship and a series of near fatal accidents and afflictions. Ahead of him lay a future in which many of the things he had already imagined would come to pass for the benefit of the world. And yet his greatest wish – of freely available electrical energy for all – would be denied him.

*

Blessed with an extraordinary mind capable of extravagant and yet detailed visual imagination, Tesla was a complex prodigy who suffered from strange over-sensitivities and symptoms of what we would now call an obsessive compulsive disorder. As well as one of the most highly developed forms of photographic memory, Tesla claimed to possess a superhuman, almost supernatural, power of hearing which enabled him to hear conversations hundreds of yards away and – in a few instances – to hear thunder up to 500 miles away. During a teenage nervous breakdown Tesla could hardly go out of his home, as he had become hyperaware of sounds, atmospheric pressures and sunlight. He seemed to feel the impact of natural phenomena directly within his body. His compulsive side brought long periods of needing to count physical actions he performed – steps along a road, mouthfuls of food, even breaths: he behaved like a self-monitoring machine, a mobile laboratory which his psyche had decided to investigate. Later, when he was able to bring the exercise of his will power to bear over these compulsions, he would make good use of this internal observation.

Invention came naturally to Tesla from an early age. When he was five he modelled a waterwheel which worked without the use of any conventional blades; he was later to recall this when he designed his bladeless turbine.[1] He designed a device in which imprisoned beetles powered a wheel with the flapping of their wings. He tried to fly from the top of the family house using an umbrella – a feat which nearly killed him. He tried to take apart and reconstruct his grandfather's clocks, a skill which had its limits: 'In the former I was always successful, but often failed in the latter.'[2]

In 1875, at the age of eighteen, he enrolled at the Austrian Polytechnic School in Graz, Austria, where he studied mathematics, physics and mechanics. He was determined to complete the two-year course in one year, and worked most days from three in the morning until eleven at night. One aspect of his compulsion was a need to complete anything he had started.

While it later became a helpful force within his creative production, it often drove him to despair. At college he had started to read the works of Voltaire when he discovered that there were nearly one hundred volumes in small print. Such was the strange conscience of his psyche that he could not rest until all were read.

It was during his time at Graz that his ideas about alternating current first started to surface. Professor Poeschl, a German, was Tesla's inspirational teacher of theoretical and experimental physics. One day Poeschl showed the class a new electrical machine that had just arrived from Paris: called a Gramme Machine, it could function as both a direct current (DC) motor and a dynamo. Tesla reported later that he felt strangely excited by the machine's arrival. When it was operating the machine's brushes sparked wildly. Tesla suggested to his teacher that the machine could be improved if the commutator were done away with, and if it were to run instead by alternating current. He didn't know how this might be done, and yet he had an instinct that somehow the answer might lie within his own mind. The professor was less confident: 'Mr Tesla may accomplish great things but he will never do this. It would be equivalent to converting a steadily pulling force, like gravity, into a rotary effort. It is a perpetual motion machine, an impossible idea.'[3] However, Tesla's need to complete things would not let this idea rest: 'With me it was a sacred vow, a question of life and death. I knew that I would perish if I failed.'

With this motivation burning away inside him, it was a few more years before finally a burst of creativity hit the young Tesla. He was taking a walk in Graz's city park with Anital Szigety, a mechanic friend, at the same time reciting a passage from Goethe's *Faust*. Then, as Tesla reported it: 'The idea came like a flash of lightning, and in an instant the truth was revealed.' Tesla started to draw in the dirt with a stick for his friend to see: 'See my motor here; watch me reverse it!'[4]

He had hit upon a whole new system of electrical operation based on the totally novel concept of producing a rotating magnetic field by running two or more alternating currents out of phase with each other. The rotating magnetic field completely did away with the need for the conventional brush contacts and commutator of the normal DC motor. In his creative flash he had discovered multiphase alternating current (AC) – a leap forward which would make possible the high-voltage widescale generation, transmission and distribution of electricity that is still the worldwide standard today. In that same moment he had also shown Professor Poeschl the error of his sceptical ways. Over the next days, Tesla designed most of the new machines and devices required by the multiphase AC system: particularly the induction motor and all the equipment required for the generation and supply of AC electricity. He wrote of his work: 'It was a mental state of happiness about as complete as I have ever known in life. Ideas came in an interrupted stream, and the only difficulty I had was to hold them fast.' His work also provided an example of his extreme gift of visualization: 'The pieces of apparatus I conceived were to me absolutely real and tangible in every detail, even to the minutest marks and signs of wear. I delighted in imagining the motors constantly running.'[5]

As well as an extraordinary intuitive gift for new technological ideas, Tesla was blessed with this extreme form of 'mental practicality', by which he was able to save himself many hours of wasted effort in engineering time. Instead of building real, physical devices, he would usually design and construct them in the workshop of his creative imagination. In this virtual testbed, he would set them running, later returning to see what had happened, what had worn or broken down, what had functioned correctly or incorrectly. He would then make imaginative improvements in order to make the devices more efficient or effective, before continuing this refining process. When he was absolutely happy with his mental creation, he would then, and only then, commit his idea to physical reality. It was this gift above all others that enabled him to be so prolific as an inventor.

When in 1884 the confident Tesla set off for America, however, with the AC system and its components firmly embedded in his mind, he had little idea of the difficult path that lay between him and acceptance of his technology – a path that threatened to both make and break the young Tesla.

The War of the Currents

Straight off the ship in New York, Tesla headed for the offices of the Edison Electric Company, where he found the 32-year-old dynamo of the new world Thomas Edison. Already the inventor of hundreds of products and the owner or co-owner of many electrically related companies, Edison was a self-educated genius with the street smart of an alley cat. Tesla presented his letter of recommendation to the short-tempered Edison – a letter from Charles Batchelor, one of Edison's trusted officers in Europe. The note, addressed to Edison, was entirely flattering: 'I know two great men and you are one of them; the other is this young man.'

Within moments Tesla was attempting to explain his new induction motor and the development of the multiphase alternating current, but was stopped dead in his tracks by an angry Edison. His response was short and sharp: 'Spare me that nonsense. It's dangerous. We're set up for direct current in America. People like it, and it's all I'll ever fool with.'[6]

Edison was totally opposed to anything but his own DC system, believing, erroneously as it turned out, that his incandescent light bulbs would not work with AC current. Nevertheless he offered the crestfallen Tesla a job on his workshop crew. It was hardly the last he was to hear of Tesla's AC breakthrough. Once Tesla left his employ – following a broken promise over a $50,000 bonus owing to Tesla – he would team up with George Westinghouse, the Pittsburgh business magnate. While Tesla was a scientific genius of the highest level, he faced a continual challenge to fund the great, but expensive, plans that his imagination provided. When he joined George Westinghouse in 1888 to bring AC electricity to the whole of America, he signed a contract which gave him royalties of $2.50 for each horsepower of generating capacity licensed. The War of the Currents – the battle to electrify America – had begun in earnest.

While Edison had managed to electrify the wealthier parts of New York with a series of local coal- and steam-driven generating stations, his stubbornness could not allow him to think that there might be a more electrically efficient and more cost-efficient solution. With the backing of J. Pierpont Morgan, one of the wealthiest and most ruthless businessmen of his time, Edison had pinned his colours firmly to the DC mast, and there was no turning back. For him it was a battle to the death – although the fatalities were, in the end, innocent and unlikely victims.

In the War of the Currents Edison became a sinister P.T. Barnum figure: dogs and cats were collected off the streets and publicly electrocuted by Edison to demonstrate that AC electricity was dangerous – even lethal. Edison even convinced the New York State prison service to employ early AC electrical equipment in the world's first electrocution of a convicted murderer. AC was so dangerous, he contended, that all it was good for was killing.

Despite Edison's propaganda, the 1893 Chicago World's Fair saw Westinghouse and Tesla emerge as victors in the War of the Currents, with a combination of showmanship and technical superiority. The same year Westinghouse was awarded the contract to manufacture the generating equipment for the electrification of Niagara Falls, and Tesla was to be in charge of the design. In a compromise, General Electric, which had taken over the Edison Electric Company, was to supply the transmission and distribution lines for the twenty-six miles from Niagara to Buffalo – the nearest major city. Yet even General Electric's proposal was now based on alternating current technology. For Tesla this was a double triumph: not only had alternating current been accepted for its technical superiority, but he had also been given a strange confirmation of the power of his mind.

At the time he had modelled his first waterwheels, while in school in Gospic, Croatia, he had seen some pictures of Niagara

Falls in a school book. He had experienced a powerful reaction, and – as often – further associated creative pictures had appeared in his mind. He saw a huge wheel with water cascading over it. He told his uncle that one day he would travel to America and make this waterwheel. Some thirty years later his prophecy had come true.

By 1897 his royalties from AC were already worth some $12 million, and had they continued they could have reached billions. Tesla would have been the Bill Gates of his day. It was not to be. Westinghouse came under pressure from his commercial enemies. The General Electric Company managed a dirty tricks campaign that lowered the Westinghouse Company's stock and made it close to impossible for it to continue independently. George Westinghouse had to go back to Tesla and ask him to forego all his royalties – past, present and future – in order that the company could survive independently. Tesla, who believed that Westinghouse could still fulfil his dream of AC for all, gave up his right to the millions he was due, and accepted a single payment of just $216,600 for the outright purchase of all his AC patents. A large sum, perhaps, but not enough to independently fund Tesla's researches into the even more radical energy technologies that were already spinning around his mind.

Westinghouse survived to fight another day with General Electric over the country's seemingly infinite energy needs, even though court fights over patents would sap the company financial reserves for many years to come. From that time on it would be others who would benefit from Tesla's genius.

Forgotten Genius?

To demonstrate the genius of Tesla, we only need to list some of his patented inventions apart from those related to AC electricity: the arc light; the speedometer; the first radio-controlled boat; superconductivity; and the first tube light. He also laid the ground for radar, cryogenics, wireless radio and telephony, the use of X-rays and our understanding of the sun's cosmic rays.

Cosmic rays were at the heart of some of Tesla's later ideas about energy production. In his own time, though, there were few who could accept his concept that the sun threw out showers of tiny, highly energetic, fast-moving particles. Although no record remains of his methods he claimed that he had measured their energy at hundreds of millions of volts.[7] Thirty years after he first aired his controversial theories, two Nobel laureate physicists, Dr Robert A. Millikan and Arthur H. Compton, admitted their debt to Tesla's work, even though they disagreed violently about the nature of the rays – whether they were in fact photon (light) rays or, as Tesla had believed, charged particles. Millikan, though, managed to measure their potential at 64 million volts, close to Tesla's figure. We now know that cosmic rays, which are many and varied, result from the formations, decays and collisions of many different kinds of particles – some from the sun and some from other, more distant stars, novae and supernovae. Nevertheless, Tesla's principal concept was closer to the truth than any of his contemporaries knew.

Many of Tesla's discoveries and inventions are often mistakenly attributed to better-known names. While most lay people still believe that Marconi perfected the transmission and reception of radio waves, there is no longer reason to believe this: in June 1943 the US Supreme Court ruled that Tesla's patents predated Marconi's claims on the prize of radio. Popular history is, though, still slow to catch up. Errors committed in print can take many years to correct. The just do not always get to write the history books, and even during his lifetime Tesla became an object of ridicule and derision for his 'outlandish ideas'.

There were times when he may have contributed to this – for instance when he agreed with Lord Kelvin in 1902 that Mars was trying to make contact with America. (It is now believed he may have been the first person to have measured – without realizing its origin – the pulsing of distant stars.) However, Kelvin and Tesla also agreed on a further, more prophetic point: that the world's non-renewable resources – such as coal and oil – should be conserved and that wind and solar power should be developed.[8]

Tesla's creative scientific skills seemed to know few boundaries; yet many who saw him work were scared by his radical approach to natural forces. In public demonstrations he would often wreathe himself in sparks and crackling bolts of high-voltage electricity without ever seeming to do himself harm:

> I still remember with pleasure how, nine years ago, I passed the discharge of a powerful induction-coil through my body to demonstrate before a scientific society the comparative harmlessness of very rapidly vibrating electric currents, and I can still recall the astonishment of my audience. I would now undertake, with much less apprehension than I had in that experiment, to transmit through my body with such currents the entire electrical energy of the dynamos now working at Niagara – forty or fifty thousand horsepower. I have produced electrical oscillations which were of such intensity that when circulating through my arms and chest they have melted wires which joined my hands, and still I felt no inconvenience.[9]

A famous photograph of Tesla captures him sitting on a chair in the laboratory he built at Colorado Springs in 1899. From the huge electrical coil in the centre of the room, white arcing sparks – some over twenty feet long and as thick as a man's arm – squirm and leap around him. With millions of volts of electrical charge appearing to surround his posing figure, he seems perfectly, archly, 'at home' – and to prove it he is calmly reading a book. It is a seminal image of the man who was more comfortable with the awesome power of natural electricity than perhaps anyone else – either before or since. The image is, in fact, a double exposure, a flashy kind of hoax; nevertheless, it demonstrates a key part of Tesla's personality – his love of showmanship.

Transmission Without Wire . . .

While many of Tesla's dreams were achieved, his most ambitious visions remained unfulfilled during his lifetime. It is a matter of some considerable speculation, given his great achievements, as to why some of his plans did not reach fruition. While Tesla had gained great respect as an engineer and inventor, there were always those – like his professor in earlier times – who did not believe that his imaginings could really come to anything. There were others who were in commercial and technological competition with Tesla – Edison, for example – who were willing to ridicule him and to diminish his standing as a way of promoting their own interests. And then there were the backers, the moneymen, who both fed and starved him according to their preference. Tesla's individual wealth was never enough to finance his own projects, and when his projects cost more than expected, as they inevitably did, he would throw himself on the mercy of a series of investors and benefactors. Throughout his life Tesla's finances swung from copious amounts of cash – which were soon invested in new machinery and inventions – to mountainous debts.

In early 1899 Tesla secured new investment from a number of wealthy individuals including Col. John Jacob Astor, owner of New York's Waldorf Astoria Hotel. With this money he set up an elaborate laboratory in Colorado Springs, where he unleashed artificial lightning discharges of several million volts (blowing up the local generating station in the process). Tesla was convinced that he could transmit radio signals hundreds, even thousands of miles around the globe. In the 1890s he had secured patents on many aspects of radio transmission. In late 1900 Tesla needed a large investment if he were to get his Worldwide Wireless Telephone Transmitter to deliver its promise. After false starts with a number of investors he approached J. Pierpont Morgan, who had been Edison's backer during the early days of Edison's DC developments. Morgan's habit was to own 51 per cent of everything he became involved in, and when Tesla approached him with plans for his worldwide radio broadcasting system, the magnate Morgan was happy to forward him $150,000 secured on 51 per cent of Tesla's interests in his own radio patents.

Tesla did not tell Morgan his hidden agenda, which he had earlier confided to the now unsupportive Westinghouse:

> You will know of course that I contemplate the establishment of such a communication merely as the first step to further and more important work, namely that of transmitting power. But as the latter will be an undertaking on a much larger and more expensive scale, I am compelled to first demonstrate such feature to get the confidence of capital.[10]

Through his experiments he had become convinced that there were ways to transmit unlimited amounts of electrical energy to any point on the globe without using any conventional transfer medium such as copper cable. Writing later in 1900, he described how he had developed his ideas:

> For a long time I was convinced that such a transmission on an industrial scale could never be realized, but a discovery which I made changed my view. I observed that under certain conditions the atmosphere, which is normally a high insulator, assumes conducting properties, and so becomes capable of conveying any amount of electrical energy.[11]

But in order to carry out all the experiments, he needed to first put in place the worldwide radio broadcasting station. He had already proved to his own satisfaction that he could broadcast and receive signals over seven hundred miles, and now he offered Morgan the possibility of both transatlantic and transpacific radio communication. Tesla quickly purchased 200 acres of Long Island, which he christened 'Wardenclyffe'. The money was soon being spent on the transmitting tower that would be Tesla's landmark, the symbol of his life's vision. Wardenclyffe tower was 187 feet high and topped with a massive fifty-five-ton mushroom-like dome. This contained Tesla's most important component – the magnifying transmitter capable of generating oscillating signals of some hundreds of millions of volts.

In the two years or so that it took Tesla to build the transmitter he had developed two major problems. With escalating costs and long delays he was now in desperate financial straits. His second problem was Marconi, who had, on 12 December 1901, sent the first wireless signal from Cornwall, England, to Newfoundland. What Morgan, and many others, did not know was that Marconi was using Tesla's radio patents, which were to become the focus of much dispute before Tesla's primacy was established in 1943.

Nor did Morgan appreciate how Marconi was able to achieve this with much less equipment and cost than Tesla was employing. He also didn't know, but was about to find out, Tesla's hidden power agenda. Tesla had already filed a patent relating to the wireless transmission of power (US Patent No. 787,412 'Art of Transmitting Electrical Energy through the Natural Medium') and would later apply for a more important US Patent, No. 1,119,732 'Apparatus for Transmitting Electrical Energy', based on his work at Wardenclyffe. In his comprehensive vision every person on the planet would have a receiver which, just like a radio, they could tune to receive unlimited, unmetered power.

When, on 3 July 1903, Tesla made his final plea for more finance, he threw himself on Morgan's mercy, a quality that the magnate had never shown in any abundance: 'If I could have told you such as this before, you would have fired me out of this office ... Will you help me or let my great work – almost complete – go to pots?'[12]

Morgan's reply came on 14 July: 'I have received your letter ... and in reply would say I should not feel disposed at present to make any further advances.'[13]

In a Promethean display of anger, the next night saw the

skies around Wardenclyffe tower lit up with massive streaks and bolts of Tesla's artificial lightning, powered by the magnifying transmitter. But it was to be the last show of its kind. Neither Morgan nor Westinghouse, and none of the other big money people, were willing to start a new electrical revolution when they were still reaping the profits of the first revolution that Tesla had played his part in.

In the end, Wardenclyffe tower was demolished for scrap and Tesla moved on to more 'acceptable' projects. Yet his desire to make energy freely available would never go away.

Tesla's Free Energy Devices

The wireless transmission of power was, essentially, a distribution technology. It still relied on a conventional power generation method such as coal and steam turbine to produce the enormous amounts of power it would have required. Since many years earlier, however, Tesla had been fascinated by the idea of new, untapped energy sources. In one of his famous lectures of 1892 he told an astounded audience:

> Ere many generations pass, our machinery will be driven by a power obtainable at any point of the universe . . . Throughout space there is energy. Is this energy static or kinetic? If static, our hopes are in vain; if kinetic – and this we know it is, for certain – then it is a mere question of time when men will succeed in attaching their machinery to the very wheelwork of nature.[14]

In June 1900 in *The Century Illustrated Magazine* Tesla wrote what he considered to be the most important of all his articles, 'The Problem of Increasing Human Energy'. The article was radical, even sensational, in its ideas and caused a significant controversy amongst both scientists and the general public at the time of its publication.

Whatever our resources of primary energy may be in the future, we must, to be rational, obtain it without consumption of any material. Long ago I came to this conclusion, and to arrive at this result only two ways . . . appeared possible – either to turn to use the energy of the sun stored in the ambient medium, or to transmit, through the medium, the sun's energy to distant places from some locality where it was obtainable without consumption of material.[15]

Among many ideas for energy generation in the future, Tesla put forward a radical thought experiment:

It is possible, and even probable, that there will be, in time, other resources of energy opened up, of which we have no knowledge now. We may even find ways of applying forces such as magnetism and gravity for driving machinery without using any other means. Such realizations, though highly improbable, are not impossible. An example will best convey an idea of what we can hope to attain, and what we can never attain. Imagine a disk of some homogeneous material turned perfectly true and arranged to turn in frictionless bearings on a horizontal shaft above the ground. This disk, being under the above conditions perfectly balanced, would rest in any position. Now it is possible that we may learn how to make such a disk rotate continuously and perform work by the force of gravity without any further effort on our part: but it is perfectly impossible for the disk to turn and do work without any force from the outside. If it could do so, it would be what is designated scientifically as a 'perpetuum mobile', a machine creating its own motive power. To make the disk rotate by the force of gravity we have to invent a screen against this force. By such a screen we could prevent this force from acting on one half of the disk, and rotation of the latter would follow. At least, we cannot deny such a possibility until we know exactly the nature of the force of gravity. Suppose that this force were due to a movement comparable to that of a stream of air passing from above toward the centre of the earth. The effect of such a stream upon both halves of the disk would be equal, and the latter would not rotate ordinarily; but if one half should be guarded by a plate arresting the movement, then it would turn.[16]

A screen against gravity? Even now such an idea delights and tantalizes – as does his other assertion that all we needed for free energy was a magnet with one pole, or else a way of shielding magnetism. This assertion has led to much experimentation into 'permanent magnet motors' – motors that have no motive force apart from that of their own magnetism. In the 1920s Werner Heisenberg, one of the fathers of quantum mechanics, and the progenitor of the Uncertainty Principle, put forward the idea that we would indeed use magnets as a power source, despite the conventional theory that says magnets are incapable of doing physical work.

One of Tesla's many patents (No. 685,957 filed on 21 March 1901 and granted on 5 November 1901) was for an 'Apparatus for the Utilization of Radiant Energy' – a machine to capture the sun's cosmic rays and turn them into electricity. The concept for the device was relatively simple, and involved putting an insulated metal plate as high as possible into the air. A second metal plate is inserted into the ground. Wires are run from both into a capacitor.

> The sun, as well as other sources of radiant energy, throws off minute particles of matter positively electrified, which, impinging upon [the upper] plate, communicate continuously an electrical charge to the same. The opposite terminal of the condenser being connected to ground, which may be considered as a

> vast reservoir of negative electricity, a feeble current
> flows continuously into the condenser and inasmuch as
> the particles are . . . charged to a very high potential,
> this charging of the condenser may continue, as I have
> actually observed, almost indefinitely, even to the point
> of rupturing the dielectric.[17]

This simple design for capturing a large electrical charge, and
potentially an electrical current, may well have been the starting
point for T. Henry Moray (see Chapter 3) and those who have
followed his work to turn 'radiant energy' into electrical current.
(In Chapter 9 I look at how the radiant energy or 'ether' concept
has now been updated in the light of modern physics.)

Another fuelless energy device Tesla mentioned in his
Century Illustrated article 'The Problem of Increasing Human
Energy' was a mechanical oscillator, which first appeared in public
at the Chicago World's Fair in 1893. 'On that occasion I exposed
the principles of the mechanical oscillator, but the original
purpose of this machine is explained here for the first time.'[18]
Tesla describes how large amounts of heat can be extracted from
the ambient medium using a high-speed oscillator, a steam-driven
engine used for producing high-frequency currents.

> My conclusions showed that if an engine of a peculiar
> kind could be brought to a high degree of perfection,
> the plan I had conceived was realizable, and I resolved
> to proceed with the development of such an engine, the
> primary object of which was to secure the greatest
> economy of transformation of heat.[19]

Tesla envisioned the mechanical oscillator as part of a technology
to capture differentials in energy – a form of energy pump – but
he was, it appears, finally defeated not just by the complexities of
the other components that would be required, but also by the
economics of the project:

> I worked for a long time fully convinced that the practical realization of the method of obtaining energy from the sun would be of incalculable industrial value, but the continued study of the subject revealed the fact that while it will be commercially profitable if my expectations are well founded, it will not be so to an extraordinary degree.[20]

One of the initial spurs for his work on 'energy pumps' had been Lord Kelvin, who had stated that it was not possible to build a machine which could extract heat from its surrounding medium and utilize the energy gained to run itself. In one of his many thought experiments Tesla pictured a very tall bundle of metal rods, extending from the earth to outer space. Since the earth is warmer than outer space, heat would be conducted up the metal rods – together with an electric current. All that would be required to capture the current would be a very long power cable to connect the two ends of the metal bar each to an electric load such as a battery or motor. A motor should keep running continuously, Tesla believed, until the earth had cooled to the temperature of outer space – something which, depending on the size of such a device, might never happen: 'This would be an inanimate engine which, to all evidence, would be cooling a portion of the medium below the temperature of the surrounding, and operating by the heat abstracted.'[21] By such means, Tesla contended, such a machine could produce energy without 'the consumption of any material' – his key ideal.

Tesla and Faraday's Unipolar Dynamo

Michael Faraday, discoverer of the laws of electromagnetic induction, was the inventor of the first electric motors in the 1830s. One of his stranger, and often neglected, devices was the unipolar dynamo (which I discuss in Chapter 4), consisting of a metal disk rotating between magnets in order to produce electrical current. Tesla's involvement with the unipolar, or homopolar generator, led him to believe that it might be capable of acting as a 'self-activating' generator. Indeed, in 1889 he filed and received a patent for the 'Dynamo Electric Machine' based on Faraday's original design, but with an improved design intended to increase its efficiency by reducing its drag or back torque. Tesla was postulating that if the back torque could be engineered to work in the direction of movement, rather than against it, then the machine could be made self-sustaining. While Tesla was not able to achieve such a feat in his lifetime, his, and Faraday's, ideas were to be picked up by a number of researchers including Bruce DePalma – inventor of the N-machine – in the 1970s and '80s.

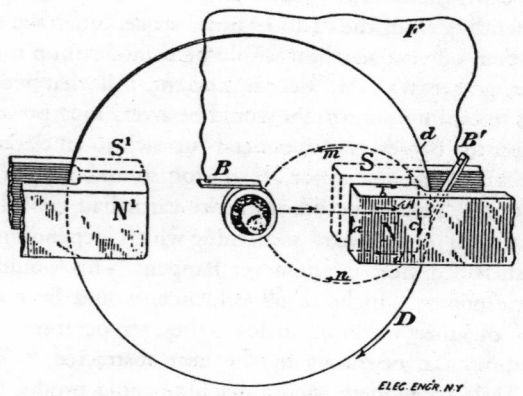

FIGURE 2.1 Early unipolar dynamo.

These are not the only attempts Tesla made to develop a fuelless energy generator, but just how far he got in his quest is far from clear. Tesla himself clearly stated that he had achieved energy generation from a new energy source on a number of occasions, although he was not always forthcoming about the technology behind his claimed achievement. On 10 July 1931, for instance, *The Brooklyn Eagle* carried an article in which Tesla was quoted: 'I have harnessed the cosmic rays and caused them to operate a motive device . . . More than twenty-five years ago I began my efforts to harness the cosmic rays and I can now state that I have succeeded.'

On 1 November 1933 Tesla made a similar claim in the *New York American*, under the headline 'Device to Harness Cosmic Energy Claimed by Tesla': 'This new power for the driving of the world's machinery will be derived from the energy which operates the universe, the cosmic energy, whose central source for the earth is the sun and which is everywhere present in unlimited quantities.'

These two articles, written during Tesla's later creative phase, demonstrate his concern to solve 'the energy problem' which he saw before him. While he had been critically responsible for the expansion of electricity use, he also felt a passionate need to conserve the coal reserves for future generations.

In November 1933 he was asked by a journalist from the Philadelphia *Public Ledger* whether his fuelless technologies would upset the present economic system. 'Dr Tesla replied, "It is badly upset already." He added that now as never before was the time ripe for the development of new resources.'

Summary

So why haven't we seen any of these free energy technologies working? There is little doubt that Tesla was one of the great scientific geniuses not just of his own time, but perhaps of the entire twentieth century as well, but the reasons why his technologies were not developed may be complex.

Some researchers have claimed that, like Leonardo da Vinci, he was not just fifty or a hundred years ahead of his time, but perhaps many hundreds of years in advance of contemporary thinking. Scientific and technological ideas need support, both intellectual and financial, if they are to thrive.

Is it possible, then, that new generations of scientists have not been able to develop his visionary ideas into physical technologies? This question bears on the notion of genius in science, as opposed to genius in the arts and other fields of endeavour. While we accept that no one else could have written Beethoven's symphonies or Shakespeare's plays, it seems harder to accept that science is subject to the same vagaries of human beings. Even though Galileo Galilei, Michael Faraday and Albert Einstein possessed unique minds, we often assume that if they hadn't 'come up with' their discoveries someone else would have done the same pretty soon after. Perhaps that assumption is erroneous, or at least, highly limited. If it hadn't been for Tesla it is quite possible that we would have developed a much more primitive and limited electrical system based on small generating stations every few miles.

Once Tesla had brought about one electrical revolution, the world was not ready for another, even more radical development of electrical power. The commercial powers that controlled the electrical landscape – based as it was on a distributed network of copper cable – had no interest in throwing away their investment in favour of the wireless, and potentially costless, transmission and reception of electricity. They seem to have had even less interest in Tesla's ideas of free-energy technologies. T. Henry Moray, who adopted some of Tesla's ideas in his radiant energy device (see Chapter 3) faced many of the same oppositions that Tesla faced. While we can thank Tesla's genius for bringing distributed AC electricity to most of the world, we have yet to receive the gift he really wanted to give. In his more enlightened times Tesla himself maintained a balanced view:

> I anticipate that many, unprepared for these results, which, through long familiarity, appear to me simple and obvious, will consider them still far from practical application. Such reserve, and even opposition, of some is as useful a quality and as necessary an element in human progress as the quick receptivity and enthu-siasm of others . . . the scientific man does not aim at an immediate result. He does not expect that his

advanced idea will be readily taken up. His work is like that of the planter – for the future. His duty is to lay the foundation for those who are to come, and point the way.[22]

Eventually on 7 January 1943 Tesla ended his days, alone and poor, in a shabby New York hotel where only a few pet pigeons shared his thoughts.

CHAPTER THREE

T. Henry Moray – Capturing the Energy of the Universe

> '*It is the belief of the writer that all space is saturated with energies which are doubtless electrical in their ultimate energies or very closely allied to electrical action. The relation of matter to energy and energy to matter then becomes the potential of the universe, one continuous series of oscillations, oscillating to and fro like a great pendulum across the universe.*'
>
> T. Henry Moray, 1914

There are a number of photographs of T. Henry Moray which show him demonstrating his Radiant Energy Device in the 1920s and '30s. Many of the images show a glowing array of thirty-five light bulbs and a clothes pressing iron – estimated to be a total load of 3000 watts. What was particularly remarkable to those who witnessed the device was that it appeared to achieve this without any conventional power source. Instead, Moray claimed, it operated by capturing the 'radiant energy' of the universe via an antenna and then, through a combination of complex detection and oscillation circuitry, turned this into a usable, stabilized power supply.

Dozens of highly respected scientists, lawyers and politicians – including secretaries of state – who witnessed and carried out detailed and extensive examinations of the Radiant Energy Device were unable to discover any batteries, hidden wires or other external inputs. Neither was the machine's power output ever found to be explicable by electromagnetic induction from electric power lines. Some witnesses made sworn statements, testifying that the machine ran continuously for periods of three or four days. Many were utterly convinced that this new technology spelled the end of one era and the start of a new golden age of free electrical power. There were others, though, who opposed Moray's invention, and – if the Moray family is correct – may have been willing to kill to make their point.

The evidence to support Moray's claim is truly remarkable, and yet we do not have Moray's Radiant Energy Devices running our homes today. So what happened? Was Moray a fraud, as some have suggested, or was he simply unable to develop and commercialize his groundbreaking, yet sometimes unreliable technology? Was Moray really the object of death threats, and, if so, from whom? Did the real secrets of his machine die with him as some believe; or will any of the scientists currently attempting to replicate his work manage to produce a machine that homeowners will one day buy and use to power their homes?

T. Henry Moray was born on 28 August 1894 in Salt Lake City into a Mormon family. His father was a well-known pioneer in the mining industry. From a very early age Moray was interested in electricity: often when school finished in the afternoon, he would run to the public library to read the works of the early electrical pioneers such as James Clerk Maxwell, Michael Faraday and Nikola Tesla. Moray was particularly inspired by the writings of Tesla, and by his idea that the earth floated in a vast sea of unlimited energy. Tesla's dream that we could 'mine' this 'radiant' energy by capturing, manipulating and amplifying its inherent oscillations became a scientific obsession for Moray – an obsession that would last his entire life. He was also to face similar difficulties to those Tesla faced, and in particular the scientific wrath reserved for inventors who not only claim to have a device but also have a theory to support it.

As a young boy growing up in Salt Lake City, Moray

became fascinated by the early technology of radio broadcasting, which was still in its infancy. If the accounts are to be believed he started experimenting with electricity at the age of nine and with high-voltage, high-frequency phenomena at the age of eleven.

In 1911, when he was only nineteen, Moray's first successful foray into capturing what he believed was radiant energy reportedly resulted in the powering of a 16 candlepower carbon-arc lamp with an electrostatic charge from an aerial and an earth connection. The following year Moray travelled to Uppsala in Sweden on a Mormon church mission. As it is for all Mormons, a two-year mission was part of Moray's induction into adult religious life, and Moray accepted the challenge gladly. It was, after all, a chance to see the world. He would also be studying his beloved electrical engineering at the University of Uppsala. While he may have anticipated that it might be an opportunity to pursue his deepest passion – crystal radio – he certainly didn't know that the adventure would also bring him into contact with new substances that would change his life for ever.

In his later writings Moray recounted how he discovered mineral materials which he believed could work as 'crystal-like' radio receivers. The first was believed to be galena, found raw in the hillsides, while the other was a white, powdery, stone-like material which was normally used in the building of roads. This second material – which became known as Swedish stone – is thought by some to have been some form of silicon dioxide. Moray is said to have heated this material with a welding torch to form fused silica – a substance already known to be a good radio receiving crystal. When he put these two together, along with a silver 'cat's whisker' tuning device familiar to early radio buffs, he found he was able to power a small horn loudspeaker without any further power source.

After he returned from Sweden in 1915, Moray held positions as an electrical engineer in a number of large corporations including the Utah Power and Light Co., Phoenix Construction Co. and the Mountain States Telephone and Telegraph Co. During this period he designed electrical layouts and circuitry for new power plants and for some of the largest buildings going up at this time in the West. At the same time, though, he continued to experiment with the Swedish stone. His experiments would lead him to develop the first semi-conductor valves, or detectors, more than twenty years before they were finally developed commercially by the Bell Telephone Labs.

In 1921 Moray decided to devote himself full-time to his researches into radiant energy, and in the next few years applied himself fully to the task of building the first functioning radiant energy device, using the Swedish stone as the key component of its 'detector tube'. The device apparently produced about 25 watts and was able to power a light bulb, The machine itself, which had no moving parts, was contained in a box some 30 inches long, 16 inches high and 16 inches wide. As well as the detector tube – effectively an early electronic 'valve' – the box contained two further oscillator tubes, two coils of wire, several condensers or capacitors of various sizes, as well as some other proprietary parts. The machine was connected to an antenna, which supposedly 'captured' the radiant energy, and also to a ground connection which completed the circuit. Moray sometimes referred to the machine as an 'energy pump' which was able to extract energy from the 'sea of energy' that he believed pervades space. In this description he may actually have been referring to the cosmic rays that continuously bombard the planet with high-energy particles. It may even be compared with zero-point energy (which is described in Chapter 9).

By 1925 he had managed to increase the output of the machine to about 100 watts, and felt that he had a prototype that would adequately demonstrate his technology. By this time he had well appreciated the potential of such a machine to offer benefits to humankind. As *The Sea of Energy in Which the Earth Floats*, Moray's own record of his researches with radiant energy later edited by members of his family, makes clear:

Dr Moray realized the magnitude of his discovery and has felt the burden of responsibility for what could well be the future of mankind. He has a sincere desire to place his knowledge where it would do most good for all and not into the hands of a few who were selfish for power and wealth . . .

On 24 July 1925, while conferring with Senator Reed Smoot at the senator's invitation in his offices in the Hotel Utah in Salt Lake City, Dr Moray offered his radiant energy discovery to the United States government gratis. The senator thanked Dr Moray for his offer but stated that the US government would decline such an offer on the grounds that the government was not running in competition with public utilities.[1]

Following this rebuttal Moray decided to run a series of demonstrations to respected scientists and politicians in an effort to establish the credibility of the device, and in order to raise investment funds to further develop the technology to a commercially available product.

One typical demonstration was witnessed by the Secretary of State for Utah of the time, Mr Wilton H. Welling:

There were present a dozen people, including Paul Harsh, Mark Yuri, and Mr Ferguson. I first witnessed a demonstration of this device three months ago. The cabinet containing the machine has been simplified and improved. It was quite apparent there was no possible faking of the power produced. The tuning-in device was improved and the time required to bring in the energy was shortened from five minutes to less than a minute. The operation was as simple as tuning in a well-equipped radio set. This was shown by a lady who was witnessing the demonstration for the first time operating the device as easily as Dr Moray himself, after she had seen him 'tune in' the energy. A pilot light on the cabinet first became illuminated. The switch was then moved, connecting a light rack with the current. Instantly thirty 50-watt lamps and five 100-watt lamps were brilliantly lighted. A regular Hot Point flat iron was then connected without dimming the lights in the least. The inventor asserted that the result would have been the same had one hundred lights been used in place of the thirty-five on the light rack. The lights and iron together were consuming more than four horsepower of electric energy. On account of the brilliancy of the light it was apparent that much more than the ordinary voltage was going into these lamps and the excessive heat developed in one spot made me feel that they would soon burn out, but they did not.

I confidently believe Dr Moray is on the threshold of perfecting one of the most amazing fundamental inventions of history.[2]

This kind of testimonial was not a rarity; many swore affidavits and notarized statements that what they had seen was real. Moray believed that this would be enough to convince a sceptical world of the device's reality.

Around this time, and despite some misgivings, Moray decided to seek the help of lawyers to secure the future of his device. He asked Robert L. Judd, of attorneys Bagley, Judd and Ray, to represent him. Judd asked if he could see the device working. Moray described the meeting in his own record of events: 'August 6 1925. Judd came down this evening. I let him see the whole device in operation. The largest instrument is about 6 inches high, circular in shape and about 8 inches in diameter. He seemed much impressed.'[3]

Judd decided to consult Dr Harvey Fletcher, a well-known and highly respected expert, then at Western Electric, with the aim of securing his technical backing for the device. When Judd returned, Moray learned that he was to be put through some hoops: 'Judd is back from the East. Dr Fletcher seems to have made a good many suggestions to him. Fletcher must have tried to tell Judd there is a nigger in the woodpile at least I guess as much from what Judd says. Judd has asked for another demonstration.'[4]

In October Moray gave Judd another demonstration:

> We went out on the roof of the coop [sic] which is 50 feet from the house and where we demonstrated about 100 feet from the house – the coop being 150 feet long . . . Then I wired up the machine right in front of Judd and started the device going. Judd timed me to see how long it would take for me to bring in the light. I was able to light a 100-watt . . . G.E. [General Electric] lamp to full capacity. I also heated a Hot Point electric flat iron which took 665 watts. Judd asked me to take off the antenna. The light went out. It did the same when the ground was taken off and came back when they were put back. We drove a new ground at a spot selected by him, made a quick change over to the new ground and the light burned dim; but became brighter and brighter as the new ground was driven deeper and deeper.
>
> Judd stayed about two and a half hours, all of which time we had the machine in operation. He wanted to know how long it would continue to operate. I told him if he wished to stay and watch it all night I would try and make him as comfortable as I could where he could watch it all night. He said his one great desire would be for Dr Harvey Fletcher . . . to see it. After Judd left I moved the device into the house and kept it in operation all that night and the next day and did so for three days and three nights. I then took the device apart as I did not care to have it go any longer.[5]

Moray here records his concerns over the machine's key component, the detector, and its reliability, a theme to which he returns a number of times: 'Everything going fine except the detector which is the bone of contention. It gives me considerable trouble and cannot be depended on as it is so easy to get out of order and sometimes takes hours to get back into operation again.'[6]

In November 1925 Moray played host for the first time to Dr Carl F. Eyring from the Brigham Young University in Provo, Utah. Dr Eyring was a well-respected electrical engineer, and came to Moray and Judd highly recommended:

> One day Judd bought Dr Eyring from the B.Y.U. Dr Fletcher had told Judd that if Dr Eyring had a chance to see the device, it would be as good as if Dr Fletcher were to see it himself. Dr Eyring can find no fault with the demonstration and can only say that it might be induction. That is foolish as the distance from all power lines is too great . . . They have made complete tests for batteries and looked for hidden wires, but it is the induction idea [that] is the funny bone of them all . . . [7]

In early December 1925 Moray, unaware of the tests he was yet to endure, reviewed his progress so far:

> Soon Christmas and the end of 1925. Seventeen years of effort and all these months of demonstrations. Every one I make they now promise will be the last one they will ask for. Have made more outward progress during 1925 than all the other years put together. All these years' efforts have led up to this year's success. Wish I could make certain experiments I would like to make, and get that detector where I want it. It's the big worry now.[8]

To test Dr Eyring's idea that somehow Moray's device was simply 'picking up' power from local power lines, Judd now suggested an 'out-of-town' test. So on the snowy afternoon of 21 December

1925, Moray took a trip with Judd and two other 'disinterested parties', a Mr Adams and another attorney, Mr Nebeker. Moray, referring to himself as 'the inventor', describes the event:

> Today Mr Judd, Mr Adams and Attorney Nebeker called at the inventor's laboratory in Attorney Nebeker's automobile. When the 'Radiant Energy' device was packed in the auto we drove away. The three above-mentioned gentlemen began then to discuss where they should go to make the test experiment. The inventor did not want to have any say in where the test should be made as he wanted the experiment made at a place selected by them and not him, or by his having anything to say about the location. As last the three mentioned decided to go up Emigration Canyon, as there are no power lines in that canyon.[9]

After they had driven about four miles up the canyon, the three witnesses chose a place to set up the equipment. Judd decided that he would have to stay in the car, as he had an injured foot. Nebeker and Adams set up the antenna and the ground while Moray got the device out of the car. He then connected the machine to the antenna and the ground:

> The switch on the device was opened and closed as in all former experiments time and time again, but no light appeared. The device was then 'tuned in' as in all the former experiments that Mr Judd had seen and then when the switch on the device was closed the lights came on. The 'antenna wire' was momentarily disconnected, the light went out but came back when the 'antenna' was again connected to the device. The same happened when the 'ground wire' was disconnected and again connected in the same way as described above. (All this with Attorney Judd hopping around on one foot, he having gotten out of the car

when tuning the device was started.) All three gentlemen were very well satisfied and pleased with what they saw. It was dusk when they left the canyon.[10]

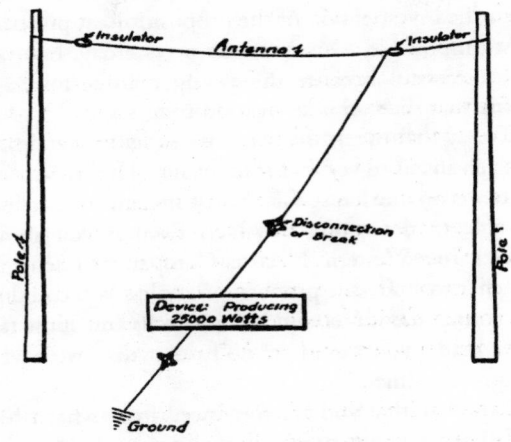

FIGURE 3.1 Antenna set-up employed by T.Henry Moray's Radiant Energy Device.

Following the test Judd wrote a highly favourable letter to Eyring, testifying to the machine's functioning away from the influence of power lines. In his notes Moray commented optimistically: 'Think such a demonstration ought to settle the question of induction and all other questions for ever . . .' He had no idea of the events that still awaited him. Indeed, on Christmas Day 1925, his notes simply read: 'I burned out my machine today.'[11]

On 6 February 1926 Eyring delivered his cautious verdict on the machine in a letter to Judd. He complained, in effect, that while he had been able to see the machine working, lighting lights and heating a flat iron, he had not been able to carry out tests:

I am sure, therefore, you realize that I have had no opportunity to make a scientific investigation of this apparatus, having seen it once in operation with no instruments at hand to make a study of it and having seen it once again in a torn-down and dilapidated condition. The lack of confidence and the apparent desire of secrecy on the part of the young man makes a scientific investigation of the proposition, at present at least, impossible. Our conference yesterday, however, was successful because the young man seems to be seeing that such an investigation is necessary.

To say that the instrument has no value would be as unscientific as to say that it has value. The truth of the matter is no one has so far made sufficient study of it to be able to determine this fact. Even if you should induce the Western Electric Company to send Dr Fletcher to study the proposition, unless you could get the young man to rebuild his apparatus and allow tests to be made, you would get no further than we have at the present time . . .

I am sure that you are convinced from what I have said that I am not prepared at this time to draw any definite conclusion as to the value of the device.[12]

By May 1926 Moray had rebuilt the device, and continued work on the improvement of its performance. Moray always claimed that he was afraid the secrets of his machine would be stolen. He was well aware that such a machine was a huge technological leap forward, and, if it were possible to develop it commercially, a hugely valuable commodity. He also felt that he had a responsibility to see it used for positive humanitarian purposes. He feared, though, that certain people might be willing to kill to know its secret. This meant that so long as he hung on to the technological secrets of the machine and, particularly, the detector valve he was more useful alive.

Moray's reticence in revealing every detail of the machine's workings to Eyring at first deterred Fletcher's further investigation of the device. Judd had made an offer to Fletcher, asking whether he would be interested in joining the corporation that was being formed around Moray's research. Yet it was not until September 1928 that Fletcher made his own investigations of the machine. He was impressed by the machine's ability to light three 100-watt light bulbs and a 575-watt flat iron, and described the demonstration as 'wonderful'. And yet he was still left none the wiser as to the means of the machine's operation. He did, however, suggest that 'an endurance test' should be organized to see how long the machine could continue to function practically.

On the morning of Monday, 1 October 1928, Judd arrived at Moray's home accompanied by two more scientists who were to play a key role in Moray's future – Dr Murray O. Hayes, an ex-vice president of the physics department at Brigham Young University, and E.C. Jensen, who wrote the following report of the test:

> The equipment, which was the same as I have seen on several previous demonstrations, including the one made for Dr Fletcher, was enclosed in two wooden boxes, which were in turn placed in a trunk having two holes bored in it to admit the connecting ground and antenna wire to the equipment and two additional holes of about one-half and three-quarter inch diameter respectively for ventilation and observation purposes.
>
> Dr Moray began tuning in at 7.49 a.m. and switched on the light at 7.59 a.m. Two globes were used, a master globe of 100 watts capacity and a pilot globe of 10 watts capacity; the purpose of the two lights being to ensure continuous burning of one at least, even though the other should fail. The trunk was closed and sealed immediately after tuning in and in the presence of Mr T.H. Moray, Dr Murray O. Hayes, Mr R.L. Judd and the writer. Railroad seals of the foolproof automatic locking type were used in sealing the trunk. They were applied on three different places and an accurate record of their numbers and locations was kept by the writer . . .

It was agreed that the three of us, not including the inventor, should visit the laboratory as frequently as we could conveniently do so to see if the lights were still burning and that the equipment had not been tampered with and to observe the brightness of lights and any other things pertinent to the test.[13]

Three days later, at around 11.00 a.m. on 4 October 1928, Moray telephoned Jensen to tell him that the lights had gone out. The reason? Tree surgeons had been topping two poplar trees near the laboratory, and when the branches hit the ground 'the tops shook the ground sufficiently to throw the detector out of adjustment and stop the lights'.[14] They agreed to meet in the evening to unseal the trunk, inspect the apparatus and decide on their next steps.

At 6.30 p.m. 4 October 1928, with Moray, Hayes and Jensen present, seals were inspected and found to be OK. Seals were then broken, the trunk lid raised, and the cover to the top box unscrewed and taken off and the detector only taken out. Mr Moray shook the detector gently and we all heard a rattling sound, which Mr Moray pronounced as the part of the detector jarred out of position when the trees fell. Mr Moray further stated that he thought he could adjust it quickly and started to do so immediately in the laboratory and in our presence. The detector was pronounced OK and ready for installation and further demonstration at 6.53 p.m.[15]

Once Moray had retuned the device it was sealed again under the supervision of the witnesses. The machine then ran for a further 83 hours and 34 minutes, a total (not including the break for the 'tree incident') of 157 hours and 55 minutes in a sealed environment. This was certainly enough to dispel any ideas the witnesses may have had that batteries, or any other kind of fraud, were involved. It also meant that they had a witnessed endurance test to talk to people about.

When Fletcher heard about the test he was still equivocal. Even though there had already been a second out-of-town test, some twenty-six miles from the nearest power line, Fletcher wanted further testing of the 'induction' theory. On 16 October he wrote to Judd:

> The experiments which you report only make the puzzle more difficult. There is only one further thing that I could suggest you might try while making such a test. If you could persuade the power company which is furnishing electrical power in Salt Lake City to turn off their power at the main switch for two or three seconds, the possibility of there being any induction from such sources would be eliminated provided the light in Mr Moray's laboratory continued burning. Of course it may be impossible to arrange for such a thing . . .[16]

For whatever reason it remained impossible, yet in order to satisfy himself and his colleagues at Western Electric, Fletcher was keen to bring Moray's device to his lab for a third-party inspection and test. Fletcher was keen to give the impression that this would not only help Moray's cause with funding, but also with the protection of his rights:

> Do you think there is any possibility that Mr Moray would consider coming to our laboratories and setting up his apparatus for a demonstration? We have access to one of the finest antennas in the United States . . . Also I could give you a better notion of what could be done regarding the protection of Mr Moray's secret.[17]

Following the receipt of this letter Moray and Judd spoke at length about the way forward for the machine. While Judd was keen to progress the commercialization of the machine with a large corporation such as Western Electric, Moray said he was deeply concerned that allowing such tests would simply open up the technology to theft. To some, though, Moray's reticence was taken to be a sign that he was definitely a fraud, afraid to be found out by a proper testing. It also marked him as a difficult character to deal with.

Fletcher, afraid to end up with scientific egg on his face, offered Moray a make-or-break deal: in order to secure patent protection with the help of Western Electric, Moray would need to deliver two similar devices, one which could be given to Eyring and another to a colleague – each with a set of instructions which they could work to. Once these disclosures had been made, he suggested, they would all be in a better position to decide whether Moray's work had merit. Fletcher ended his letter to Judd with a note of finality: 'I hope this will aid you in making your future plans to bring this matter to a successful conclusion or else bring to light some facts which will make you satisfied to drop the whole matter . . .'[18]

Unwilling to take the risk of full disclosure, for whatever reason, Moray's response to Western Electric's heavy hand was to take another route. Sympathetic to Moray's fears, Judd rejected Fletcher's requirements and pressed ahead towards what would, in 1931, become the Moray Products Company.

Meanwhile, Moray was continuing to give controlled demonstrations from his laboratory at home. On 16 March 1929 Mr T.J.Yates, an electrical and mechanical engineer, and a graduate of Cornell University, wrote a detailed report on the device, on which Moray had permitted him to carry out extensive testing. He made exhaustive checks to see whether there were any batteries, or any form of external power source which could be powering the device. He found none. This is his complete statement:

TO WHOM IT MAY CONCERN:
This is to certify that on the evening of 16 March 1929, in connection with Dr Wilkinson, of Cedar City, I

witnessed a demonstration at the laboratory of T. Henry Moray, Salt Lake City, Utah.

Dr Moray claims to have devised and invented an apparatus that will produce electrical energy without the use of a prime mover, and this is the apparatus demonstrated on the occasion above referred to.

The subjects of this article will be treated in the following order:

1. Description of Apparatus
2. Demonstration
3. Objections that I have heard
4. Tests
5. Conclusion

1. Description of Apparatus

The apparatus consists of an antenna specially balanced or aerial capacitor and a special ground wire. These are connected to the terminals of a switch. Two wooden boxes were placed on a table. On one of these boxes was a high-frequency transformer and in the other box were two sets of condensers, ten large condensers in one set and ten small condensers in the other set; two composition cylinders, each about 1⅛ inches in diameter and 4 inches long, each of these weighed about three or four ounces; and another box approximately hemispherical in shape about two inches in diameter and weighing about two ounces; and coils of wires and other equipment. These pieces of apparatus were connected by a number of wires by which the hook-up was connected.

Two of these wires were led out to the switch. One was attached to the blade of the switch and the other the jaw of the switch so that when the switch was open the antenna, lead-in, apparatus in the boxes, and ground wire, were all in series.

The other wires leading out of the box were connected to six 100 watt lamps connected in multiple during part of the demonstration, and to a flat iron during part of the demonstration.

2. Demonstration

During the demonstration the apparatus was connected in series as above described, except that a small switch connected in series with the coil was left open. Dr Moray energized and synchronized the device in three or four minutes; the lamps were lighted and remained bright as long as the circuit was left closed, which was about 60 minutes. He then connected an electric flat iron. In a short time the iron was hot. When the 'ground wire' was disconnected and then the lead-in was disconnected, the lights went out.

3. Objections that I have heard

i. That the power is obtained by a hidden wire from the electric lighting current.

ii. That the power is obtained from batteries.

4. Tests

Before and after the demonstration I closed the big switch which connects or shorts the antenna and ground and made other tests. If the antenna or lead-in were connected to the lighting circuit this would have produced a short circuit. I further tested by closing and opening the switch several times to see if any sparks appeared, but there were no sparks. I placed my wet finger between the blade and the jaws of the switch and could not feel any electricity. I touched my hand to both sides of the switch and the wall to check for ground but could not feel anything. We turned the table over and examined it carefully for hidden wires but found none. With the apparatus all connected as when operating the lights, the contacts with the switch were moved but produced no arcing. This indicates that the circuit was dead.

While the demonstration was being conducted and the lamps were receiving the energy through the apparatus the main switch that controls the lights in the building was opened. All lights on the house circuit went out but the light on the Radiant Energy circuit were not altered – were neither brighter nor dimmer at that time. Thus the lights could not have received their power from that source. The condensers were thoroughly tested. The terminals were shorted, the positive to the negative. If they had been batteries they would have showed a spark, but no sign of spark appeared. They were then tested by connecting them to the electric terminals. After thus being charged the large condensers gave a vigorous discharge, showing a brilliant strong arc and a loud snappy sound showing a sudden discharge as condensers are supposed to do and batteries never do.

The small condensers were less vigorous in discharging but the same snappy discharge of a condenser and not how a battery discharges. These tests proved positively that condensers and not batteries were in the cases supposed by some to contain batteries. Besides no batteries of such size could produce such power.

The boxes were completely emptied thus leaving no possible place for batteries to be stored. Besides the boxes were not large enough to hide batteries in. During the time that the lights were burning the connection with the big switch was moved along the switch and vigorous arcing occurred, thus proving that electrical energy was passing through this apparatus.

5. Conclusions

The electric lamps were receiving energy from some source and during the demonstration, which lasted for more than an hour, the lights were brilliant at all times,

just as bright at the last as at the first of the demonstration. The lights on demonstration were a different color and brighter and whiter than those on the house circuit. The electric energy that lighted the lamps and heated the flat iron was not received from the house circuit. One is therefore forced to the conclusion that the electric energy was received from some other source and difficult as it is to understand, with our present knowledge generation, no other conclusion can be drawn from the demonstration as above described than that the energy was received by and through the apparatus as claimed by Dr Moray.
     [Signed] T. J. Yates[19]

Another person who would play a large part in the unfolding story of Moray's attempts to bring his device to completion was Dr Murray O. Hayes, who would later become a director in the Moray Products Company. In late 1929 he wrote a testimonial letter to Mr Lovesy of the Utah Oil Refining Company. The letter seems to reveal the growing trust between Moray and Hayes:

> Dear Mr Lovesy:
> Pursuant to my promise to you at our recent discussion, I am writing to make record of the extent of my acquaintance with the construction and operation principles of the Moray device for utilizing cosmic energy. You are already aware that I have seen many demonstrations of what this mechanism will do and that I have seen the parts of which it is built. Recently Dr Moray has shown to me the wiring diagram of the assembly, and I am free to say that I can find no inconsistencies in it, or anything which does not appear to be logical and sound. While this hook-up appears to be very complicated, when looking at the machine, it is in reality very simple in essence, and based on reorganized laws of electricity, when all is explained.

There are many features which appear to be incidental, but they are in reality of basic importance.

He has also shown to me and explained the detector which he uses. In this he has applied a fundamental principle of electric circuit which, I believe, would not be noticed unless pointed out by him. This element of his device also, as above mentioned in respect to the circuit, has numerous features which appear incidental but are the heart of the matter and of first importance.

He connected his detector in a crystal set for receiving radio, in place of the crystal, and obtained better reception than with the Erla crystal, though the antenna was merely one of the bell type, in my own home. He also took a lump of lead treated according to the process which he has invented and used it in place of the crystal, and got wonderful reception of radio loud enough in fact, to operate an old fashioned horn speaker of the type put out of RCA about 1923.

I was recently present when an electrical engineer representing a foreign government was given an experimental demonstration of the energy machine. He at first said that amplification of radio waves accounted for what he saw, although it would be a real achievement to amplify such waves sufficiently to light six 100 watt lights at one time, and also to heat a flat iron of the standard 575-watt type; when he had seen the inside of the device he admitted that it could not have been what he had supposed. He remarked many times, 'It is very interesting.'

This machine has been operated in my presence so many times, under so many different conditions of weather and of season that I am positively convinced that it is what its inventor claims it to be, and that its commercial adaptation is feasible. I believe that Dr Moray has explained all to me without reservation, and

I am sure that this is a revolutionary and epoch-making invention.
Sincerely yours,
[Signed] Murray O. Hayes, Dr.[20]

Dr Hayes, on a separate sheet, also provided Lovesy with his scientific credentials:

Dr Murray O. Hayes, who makes the above statement, has Educational Record and qualifications as follows:
A. B. with major in physics under Dr Harvey Fletcher;
M.S. including graduate courses in physics and mathematics;
Ph.D. in geology;
Five years in examining corps, US Patent Office;
To take Bar examination soon;
Acting head of department of physics, Brigham Young University, 1922–23, vice Carl F. Eyring, who was finished work for doctorate.[21]

Problems with Patents . . .

With patenting in mind, it was decided that the era of demonstrations would have to stop. Not only had Moray become tired of the repeated experiments in front of witnesses, but they were not fully achieving his aim of 'proving' the validity of his technology. He also discovered that he might be jeopardizing the eventual patenting of his device under the US Patent Law of 'public use' section 4886, which works against patent applications which can be shown to be already in the public domain. Also, the demands of the new incorporation Moray Products Company seemed to be more businesslike than the situation that had worked up until 1931.

In preparation for filing his patent, Moray had been assured that he had a very good chance of success. Murray O. Hayes believed that he had established there were no clashes with any existing patents. However, when the first patent application for a radiant energy device – incorporating the germanium-based Moray Valve – was filed on 13 July 1931, it was rejected on two main grounds. The first said that the valve tubes could not work since they had no means of heating the cathode inside them.

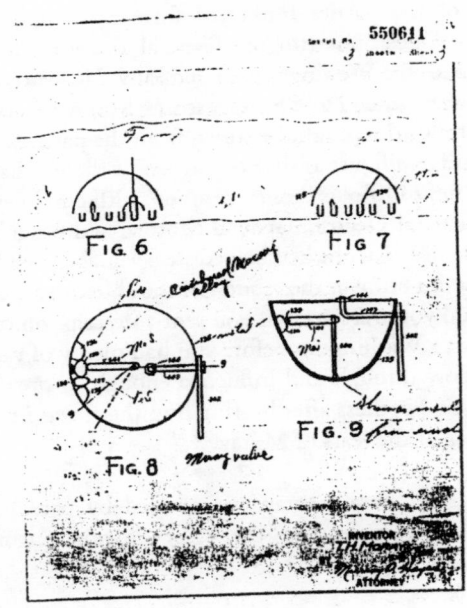

FIGURE 3.2 Image from T. Henry Moray's patent application No. 550611.

It was indeed true that they had no means of heating: they were in fact one of the first examples of 'cold cathode' technology. The second objection was much more basic, and more troubling for Moray's cause: 'No natural source of electricity wave energy is known to the examiner and proof of the existence of such is requested.'[22] In other words there was no way such a machine could work since radiant energy simply didn't exist.

Moray had always been concerned about the patenting maze, and his fears were further amplified when Hayes received a letter – purportedly from a John Y. Smith – recounting a problem he had encountered with the US Patent Office on a specific case:

> One of the parties interested formerly held a con-fidential position with the General Electric Co. and later with the Westinghouse Company. He nearly took my breath when I told him regarding Moray's fears that the proposition might be stolen from the patent office. He said it will just as sure as you sent it there. That the US Patent Office is 'honey combed' with employees of the General Electric, General Motors, and other large companies. That he had helped steal valuable data from the patent office at the request of the above companies. He said you were crazy if you sent a description of the device to Washington before you had plenty of money to follow through and influence enough to prevent a theft. So I confess after hearing him that I was in error scoffing at the fears of Moray.[23]

Yet at the same time Moray was advised by patent attorneys Alwine of Washington of the risks of not getting patent protection:

> Up to the time, and prior to the time you actually have on file all US and foreign patent applications which it is desired to file, and sufficient technical data to complete patent applications to obtain full coverage, any demonstrations which are not experimental could endanger and cause you to lose all your patent rights to your invention – see Sec. 4886 US patent law.[24]

At the time when the Moray Products Company was attempting

to get patent approval on the radiant energy device, Moray discovered that Murray O. Hayes, who was both a director of the company and a patent attorney, and two of the other directors of the company were effectively trying to steal from him. They had made an attempt to duplicate the technology from the details of the patent without Moray knowing; and they had started to take money from the company's funds without providing receipts or information, also without Moray's knowledge or approval.

Surprised and amazed by his collaborators' breach of trust, Moray had little option but to take them to court to save his invention, his status as its inventor and the finances of the company he saw himself as responsible for. A process was started which was to drain both his financial and creative resources over the next few years.

He might not have known what Hayes had been planning behind his back had it not been for a letter, written on 29 June 1932, that he received from W. H. Lovesy of the Utah Oil Refining Company:

> Murray O. Hayes . . . definitely advised me that he could make one of the machines himself from the information that had been given to him.
>
> Murray O. Hayes made these similar statements to me several times, and it may be from my determination in having him repeatedly make the declaration that he had been shown every detail of the invention that would give him the impression that I had a doubt about the invention.
>
> Personally, I have never had a doubt, but I thought the real detailed secrets of the invention were held only by yourself, and after my conference at New York with Harvey Fletcher and Carl Eyring, at the Bell Laboratories – having agreed with them I would endeavour to induce you to give the detail of your invention to Murray O. Hayes – I did, as I have stated, repeatedly ask Murray O. Hayes if he could duplicate

> your machine, and in every instance his answer was
> emphatic and to the effect that he could do so.[25]

Moray was eventually able to remove Hayes and the other directors from the company, but they had depleted the company's funds by thousands of dollars. Even when they had been officially and legally removed, they continued to try to take over the situation, even swearing a statement on oath that Moray should be 'excluded from access' to his own papers at the patent office. This stricture was eventually overturned by order of court and Moray's rights restored, but the company was by now crippled financially. After a further five years it folded.

It is interesting, and – some have suggested – perhaps more than coincidental, that Harvey Fletcher worked at the Bell Telephone Laboratories where a number of scientists were later to develop silicon-based semi-conductors. Moray's germanium-based semi-conductors were at the heart of the radiant energy machine, at a time when the concept of a semi-conductor was unknown to the scientific world.

Of Communism and Rural Electrification . . .

In the summer of 1938, and again in early 1939, Moray was invited to Washington DC to meet John M. Carmody of the Rural Electrification Administration, the organization responsible for bringing electricity to America's outlying farming communities. The organization made Moray an offer which it claimed would protect his patent interests and lead to the development of the technology. Moray, though, was uncomfortable that, despite the fact that the US Department of Justice would be assisting in the patenting process, he might be risking the patent protection that he still hoped to achieve independently. On top of this there was no offer of money except a $25 *per diem* payment for a few months' work.

In the end Moray decided to accept the offer in the hope

that at last it might lead to widescale acceptance of radiant energy. Moray was now a consulting engineer for a government agency. He started by building a new twenty-room laboratory, but it was not long before he started to have concerns about the motives of some of his associates. In February 1939 he wrote in his notes:

> I began to fear, from personal contact, that Washington had more radicals in it than I had the slightest idea of and it worried me. I expressed my fears to some of my associates in Salt Lake society upon my return from Washington . . . and later so informed a Dr Frazer whom the REA had called in as a scientific expert to consult with me on my work and as my bodyguard.[26]

As it turned out, Moray would need a bodyguard, but Felix Frazer would not necessarily be the best candidate. After some extensive experimentation, Frazer concluded to Moray: 'I have tested and tested until I am fully satisfied and feel there are no tests left to make . . .'[27] But he added, ominously: 'As long as you have the device I will want to run tests, so I wish you would destroy the damn thing so I cannot ask for more tests . . .'[28]

For a total of two months Moray allowed Frazer to inspect and test the device in his laboratory, with the assistance and suggestions of scientists from New York's Columbia University. Moray revealed to him details of three of the radiant energy tubes, and allowed him to make drawings, ostensibly for patent purposes, something he had done with only one other scientist, believed to be Hayes: 'I think that speaks for itself as I have only permitted one other scientific man to ever get that far into details of the construction during my entire work with this research.'[29]

At the same time that he hoped the REA could further his work, Moray became increasingly worried by its infiltration by communists and their 'daring plans'. Moray was even invited to meetings with Russian visitors, and saw his materials handed to them.

Even stranger and more worrying things started to happen. Moray became the object of death threats, and both he and his wife were shot at a number of times. The Morays decided to order a bulletproof car. Richard Moray, one of Moray's two sons, remembered later being driven around town when the car was hit by a hail of bullets fired from a mysterious black sedan. John E. Moray, the second son, says that his mother received a string of anonymous phone calls threatening their lives. In one she was told that her husband's life wasn't worth 'a plugged nickel', unless he co-operated with the caller's agents over the radiant energy machine. Moray's home and his laboratory were repeatedly broken into, but the machine was never stolen. The aim, it was presumed by the family, was to discover the machine's secrets using industrial espionage techniques rather than outright theft.

In a subsequent incident Moray was shot in the leg while working in the laboratory. Moray firmly believed that this was all part of a plot to get him to hand over the invention.

Things took a more bizarre turn following a crucial test to demonstrate the ability of the radiant energy current to pass through thick sheets of glass. Felix Frazer suddenly grabbed a hammer and smashed much of the machine into pieces before Moray could stop him. He left the stunned Moray with the words: 'Now I cannot ask for any more tests.' With his single destructive act, Frazer put Moray's efforts back many years. Components that had taken huge efforts to perfect were damaged beyond usefulness, and other key parts were totally destroyed.

When, in December 1941, House Representative Thomas Winter of Kansas demanded an investigation of the REA on the grounds that it was 'obstructing national defense as surely as a paid saboteur', Moray felt his suspicions confirmed. The federal agency had, Winter went on, 'fallen into the hands of a gang of communists . . . who do not hesitate to sabotage the national defence program in the interests of . . . their political theories'. It was clear to Moray that it was time to part with the REA, but, again, it was to prove a costly divorce which would starve his efforts of the funds he needed to pursue further research and the patent protection which he still believed he could secure.

Throughout the 1940s and '50s Moray continued to try, with the help of his sons Richard and John, to secure funding for his device. In 1959, Dr Robert Craig, a former deputy administrator at the REA who had not gone along with the 'radicals', wrote a letter of support for Moray's work:

> I have known Dr Moray now for about twenty years and have observed him single-handedly trying to get acceptance of some of his ideas and discoveries, particularly in the area of 'radiant energy'. Many of the now accepted areas in atomic and nuclear physics were outlined by Dr Moray as early as the middle '30s.
>
> At one time or another I have endeavoured to help him by bringing his work to the attention of people in the government without any great success. Of course, no longer do they dispute the basis of his work. However, to bring pure research to successful commercial application involves time and money, particularly the latter. While we can spend millions for missiles that are abortive and no one seems to mind, a few hundred thousand dollars available to this man would obviate, I believe, much of the need for missiles.[30]

The fact that Moray's progress seems to have died off in the 1940s and '50s may, of course, not simply be because of lack of funding. Even those who supported his work, including his family, have suggested clear technical reasons why the device failed to progress. In the fifth edition of Moray's *The Sea of Energy in Which the Earth Floats* – published in 1978 – Moray's sons come clean about the key problem that Moray faced:

> In 1942, shortly after World War II began for the United States, Henry Moray attempted to rebuild a

radiant energy device using the remaining bit of what was known as the 'Swedish stone'. This material, which was the heart of his original RE detector, he had never been able to duplicate, and the shortage of this material limited the amount of power he could draw. Consequently, in the larger unit he developed a second detector that forced him into extensive research involving nuclear materials and radioactive reactions.[31]

Later interviews with Moray revealed him attempting to source and use radioactive materials. Some say he was using uranium, or possibly radium, although others challenge this idea. Radioactive lead was also mentioned as a possible replacement material in the famous detector. Whatever it was, it's far from clear whether it ever proved a successful substitute.

In 1974 T. Henry Moray died, his mission to bring radiant energy to the world still a distant dream. After his death his sons John and Richard took up the radiant energy torch, attempting to raise further money to replicate their father's work.

In 1976 the US Air Force initiated a research contract with Cosray, the company formed by Moray and his sons to further radiant energy. The contract involved an attempt to either find or replicate the Swedish stone material. When they failed to locate any further sources, they attempted to devise an acceptable synthetic substitute. After many months of trying, they failed to produce anything with the necessary 'rectifying' qualities. During the research, the Air Force team was also thwarted by the fact that many of Moray's original designs, drawn on linen, had faded beyond comprehension. It was further observed that Moray's designs were often obscure:

> Presumably Dr Moray made his notes no more precise, or specific, simply because he always expected to have the financial opportunity to produce the device himself. His linen tracings were intended to support his own efforts, so he didn't make them as complete or

careful as he could have, had he intended them to be used by others.[32]

His sons John and Richard continue his work in relative secrecy. They still have possession of their father's laboratory notes, which they claim will be sufficient to help them develop the technology, so long as they can secure the millions of 'benign' dollars it would apparently take to get from where they are to having a workable, replicable unit. Others who believe the stories about the performance of the radiant energy machine wonder if the secrets of Moray's device died with him.

Did it Really Work?

So what are the possibilities? Did Moray's device really work? Or was he deluded – either partially or totally? Is it possible he was simply a fraudster, out to fleece investors and fool the academic community?

First the fraud theory. There are those who believe that Moray did not really have a working invention, that he somehow managed an illusion or magic trick to convince people into giving him financial backing. Others have stressed the scientific angle: that he was desperate to prove his radiant energy theory, and used a hoax machine to win people over to his theory. Yet while Moray was always keen to protect the technology contained within his detector, no one was ever able to find any batteries or power source in his device. Even Harvey Fletcher, writing in 1940, admitted that during his tests he was unable to find anything which would have powered the lights and iron that he saw working: 'I confess I was mystified because I could find no box or condenser which would have housed any dry batteries. Mr Moray permitted me to examine the apparatus and although I had only a short time there was no evidence that it was connected to any source of electrical power.'[33]

Suspicions about Moray were raised mostly because he

adamantly refused to reveal the secrets of his machine to those who wanted to duplicate it. Yet what motivation could a man have to carry out a practical hoax over a period of some thirty years or more and, equally, to expose himself to both physical danger, ridicule and financial ruin? What could he have gained by trying to fool anyone by the use of batteries, secret wires, etc.? The 'regular' answer is money. Yet in Moray's case there is little evidence that he ever benefited from his invention: in fact the opposite is true. He nearly ruined himself twice trying to pay off debts incurred by others involved in his machine. Indeed he was, by all accounts, not a businessman.

He had gone straight to the top of the scientific and public tree. He talked with the top scientists of his day, highly ranked politicians and administrators. This was no P.T. Barnum show. If he had been perpetrating a charlatan's hoax, he would, in the end, have been found out. This never happened: all that people ever said was that they didn't understand it, and that they wanted to see more details of its method. It's hard to imagine anyone embarking on Moray's path without having something he at least believed could work.

He never received patent status for the machine, a fact that meant Moray never had the protection of the law from anyone who might steal and duplicate the technology. Without this protection he remained vulnerable, perhaps fearful of those around him who might be able to help him. It is entirely possible that Moray's secret was never properly shared with anyone. There was the further problem – which Moray managed to keep secret – that he wasn't able to replicate the Swedish stone. If he knew, or believed that the stone was a non-renewable resource, then he had reason to keep the machine's detector design a secret.

Is it really possible that Moray could have deluded himself about the successful operation of his technology? It's hard to see how. He may have overclaimed for it publicly, saying that it was ready for commercialization before he had overcome problems with the detector, he may have been wrong about the theory behind its working but there seems little way that he could have deceived himself as to whether it produced useful power.

While some scientists, faced with the machine's apparent lack of normal power source, claimed it was working via electro-magnetic induction from power lines, there were two well-attested experiments carried out many miles from any sources of power, which should have been enough to put those claims to rest.

We may need to ask some more difficult questions: if the machine really worked, is it possible that the forces that came to bear on Moray were enough to stop a prototype that worked from being developed into a commercial device? We then face the possibility that other beneficial technologies may have been kept from us – either through deliberately malevolent or jealous action by individuals, by some form of organized conspiracy, or just by good old-fashioned 'cock-up'. Many people don't like to accept this kind of thinking. Despite the fact that damaging technologies have been created – germ warfare, nuclear weapons, toxic chemicals, it is still hard to accept that we might not live in the best possible world in which 'good always triumphs eventually'. 'Eventually' may include a good few failures and disappearances along the way.

It's certainly more comfortable, psychologically, to believe that Moray failed because he was wrong – either about his technology or his theory – or that he was a fraud. That way we don't have to face the possibility of either conspiracy or cock-up – either of which may involve us having to face a responsibility towards the emergence of such technologies.

Whatever the truth is, we still don't have a working radiant energy device.

Independent Researchers Take Up the Flame

In the last thirty years or so, T. Henry Moray's work has become the focus of many independent researchers, who believe that Moray held the key to the tapping of unlimited energy. While they haven't been given access to the information held by the Moray family, Moray's original patent applications and some other writings are in the public domain.

Bruce Perreault is an independent energy researcher, based in Concord, New Hampshire. By his own account, he would not claim to be a highly educated 'university type'. There are many, though, who believe that he may be the only person who has the insight and understanding to take Moray's work to a point where it can be developed into a reliable energy technology. Over the past five years he has earned an enthusiastic and respectful following among new energy researchers who like his self-deprecating and low-tech, low-bucks approach to inventing.

In a 1999 conference lecture Perreault described the inner workings of his small cylindrical device known as the Perreault Radiant Energy Valve: 'In a nutshell, polonium is deposited on a thin wire forming a cathode which emits electrons [electricity]. These electrons rush toward the cylinder's anode, thus generating electrical current.'[34] This is not, though, an atomic battery in any sense.

> The plated polonium heats the cathode wire dislodging millions more electrons than a cold cathode would in a conventional atomic cell. My unique tube generates the high voltage normally associated with atomic batteries; however, one of its unique characteristics is that it also converts the heat of the polonium to amperage. A little extra amperage goes a long way in increasing the wattage to high levels.[35]

Perreault's device, which he exhibited at two conferences during 1999, is clearly based on the work of T. Henry Moray. He describes how the devices work:

> The radiant energy power generation process artificially induces and controls nuclear energy . . . with a system that requires electronic circuits currently used in radio frequency applications.

Perreault valves, similar to Moray valves, utilize a pumping effect to siphon electrons from the earth to be stored in high-voltage capacitors. A second stage converts the high-voltage charge into usable power at any frequency. This innovative generator utilizes energy-releasing nuclear reactions that involve radioactive ores. The reactions involved do not generate toxic by-products as is normally associated with nuclear reactions.[36]

Perhaps controversially the device uses radioactive polonium, which most people regard as a hazardous substance.

Polonium releases more energy than any single element yet discovered. In fact, polonium is 5,000 times more powerful than radium. The energy released by its decay is so great that a capsule containing about half a gram reaches a temperature above 932 degrees. The problem with polonium is its rarity as a natural element; so scarce in fact that a ton of uranium ore contains only about 100 micrograms.[37]

Perreault claims to have solved this problem by extracting the gas that is generated by radioactive ores. This gas, he says, should decay to polonium in about three or four days. Perreault points out that polonium is a pure alpha emitter and that all its alpha radiation can be absorbed within one of his tubes and converted to electrical power. This, he says, makes it an attractive lightweight source of energy.

In August 2000 Perreault distributed an e-mail committing himself to the 'complete restoration' of T. Henry Moray's Radiant Energy Device. Whether it can be developed, either effectively or safely, into a commercial application, could be quite another question.

It's Nuclear Power Jim, But Not As We Know It . . .

Paul M. Brown of Boise, Idaho, has been in the nuclear power business since 1978 when he was still a college student. He has made a detailed study of T. Henry Moray's work, and has written perhaps the most comprehensive independent study of the Radiant Energy Device, entitled 'The Moray Energy Device: Operational Parameters, Design Criteria, and Considerations'. His main conclusion threw new light on how exactly the Radiant Energy Device might work: 'The novelty of the Moray Valve was in that it was a semi-conductor device predating the invention of the transistor. The Moray Valve also contained radium, making it a type of p-n [positive-negative] junction isotopic generator.'[38] He also identified what he considered to be another unique feature of the Moray tubes: 'The novelty of the tubes lies in the fact that they were not vacuum tubes at all. Rather, these composition cylinders were also predecessors to the transistor, only the junction is a gas rather than semi-conductor material.'[39]

The idea that the valve contained radium, and that a nuclear process was part of the circuit's working, was central to Brown's interest. With a Ph.D. in nuclear physics, Brown had become involved in new ways to generate useful electrical energy from genuinely safe nuclear processes. Through his own company, Nucell, Brown developed small nuclear batteries which worked by using the energy given off by radioactive strontium-90 – converting it directly into a continuous AC electrical current. It was claimed in 1988 that Brown's first prototype power cell produced 100,000 times as much energy per gram of strontium-90 than the most powerful nuclear battery yet in existence.

And yet in November 1991 Brown issued 'an open letter to all working in alternate energy' (see Appendix 4 for a full transcript), in which he gave his reasons for withdrawing from the energy scene:

Over the years I have heard many nightmare stories about people who developed something significant only to be persecuted, harassed, prosecuted, and even killed. I was sure that these stories were exaggerated or possibly the result of the inventor's own paranoia or such.

But, Brown explained, with increasing success he began to attract the wrong kind of attention:

I began to receive threats (i.e. 'We will bulldoze your house with your family in it'); securities fraud charges were then filed against my company and myself; then investigation by the Oregon Dept. Finance; then the tax man; then the Securities and Exchange Commission; my wife was assaulted; I lost control of my company; my home has been robbed three times and vandalized on four other occasions; twice now I have been accused of drug manufacturing; I lost my home; most recently my mother's car was pipe-bombed. With each hardship I strive harder toward successful development of the technologies under my endeavour. But it only seems to get worse . . .

My advice is to keep a low profile until you have completed your endeavour; be selective in choosing your business partners; protect yourself and your family; know that the nightmare stories are true.[40]

Despite his withdrawal in 1991, Brown's fighting spirit has continued to function. After a long legal case over his battery technology, he has finally secured credit on a patent (following an out-of-court settlement) by Bell Labs/Lucent Technologies for a 'Self-Powered Device' nuclear battery.

Most recently Brown has developed a technology which may offer the world not just a new energy source, but a solution to the huge problem of nuclear waste. His 'Photodeactivation of Nuclear Waste' technology has already been the subject of a development contract with a Russian ministry. Brown's company will build a prototype plant which will bombard highly radioactive elements with high-energy photon radiation in the form of X-rays produced by a linear accelerator.

This is not some pseudo-science: it is based on sound, textbook nuclear theory. It is well known that X-ray or gamma-ray bombardment of nuclei can induce nuclear decay. Brown's trick is to apply this to highly radioactive elements such as iodine-129 which normally has a half-life of 1,700,000,000 years. Brown claims that bombardment leads the iodine-129 to transmute into iodine-130, which has a half-life of only 12.4 hours, and which will naturally decay to xenon-130 – a safe, stable gas – plus an electron. Brown claims to have similar reactions for all the most dangerous radioactive isotopes found in radioactive waste. If this process can really be made to work efficiently, Brown will have made a major contribution to the planet's safety. What is even more remarkable is that the process also appears to produce large and usable amounts of heat energy which can be captured and used. The Russian 'portable' plant is expected to produce 10 megawatts – enough to power a thousand homes. It almost sounds too good to be true. We may know soon whether it is.

*

On 7 April 2002, to the great shock of many in the energy research field, Paul M. Brown was killed in a car crash. Although some observers have speculated about the involvement of other agencies in the accident, there is no evidence that the event was not just another random traffic crash.

The newly elected directors of his NASDAQ-quoted company – Nuclear Solutions – has promised to develop his technology through to commercial success.

CHAPTER FOUR

The N-machine – Michael Faraday's Mysterious Legacy

'If thinking about the homopolar generator causes someone to develop a concept to tap into a new energy source, all this work will have been worthwhile.'
Dr Gary L Johnson, Professor Emeritus, Department of Electrical and Computer Engineering, Kansas State University

'We live in a technological world. We tend to think all problems in the world can be solved through science and technology. If this were the case, we would have free energy now, and the world would be at peace . . . I have had to learn by direct experience certain realities of the world we live in and the consequences of introducing a possibly world-changing invention to mankind.'
Bruce DePalma, inventor of the N-machine

How could the homopolar generator – the very earliest electromagnetic machine designed by Michael Faraday in 1831 – turn out to be the free energy generator that so many people have been searching for?

Throughout the 1970s, '80s and '90s a range of researchers, inventors, scientific celebrities and investors became convinced that Faraday's invention was indeed the Holy Grail, and that we were on the brink of a revolution in both theory and technology. In about 1977 a scientist named Bruce DePalma redesigned and repackaged the homopolar generator as the N-machine: the machine with 'N' – or 'any number of' – uses. For a number of years a wave of excitement and some substantial investment carried the N-research along at a pretty pace. But where did it lead? After thirty years of major claims and controversial results, some scientists say we are no closer to having a fully functional, free energy N-machine than we were in 1831. So what happened? Did everyone fall for a mass delusion, or is there still one more key that will unlock the secret of the N-machine?

Faraday's Breakthrough

It was the work of a few influential and brilliant scientists in the early nineteenth century that laid the foundations for our modern world of electrical and electronic codependence. It started in 1800 with Italian Count Alessandro Volta's invention of the 'voltaic pile', the world's first battery. This meant that, for the first time, the world had a reliable source of constantly flowing electrical current. This led to a great deal of experimentation with electrical circuits, and in 1819 the Danish scientist Hans Christian Oersted discovered that electrical current moving within a wire caused a magnetic effect on the environment around the wire. He found this out by studying the effects of placing a live cable close to a magnetic compass, and so recorded the world's first evidence of an 'electromagnetic' effect.

Following this key work, Frenchman André Marie Ampère noted that the strength of the magnetic field around a wire was related to two chief factors: the amount of current running through the wire, and the distance from the wire. From these observations he was able to formulate the relationship of these variables in Ampère's law. He also discovered that by winding wire into a coil it was possible to increase the strength of the magnetic effect in the wire.

Perhaps the most important discovery of all, though, was Michael Faraday's formulation, in 1831, of the laws of electromagnetic induction. Faraday, the most brilliant scientist of his generation, was able to determine that by moving a wire within a magnetic field it was possible to induce a current in the wire. This discovery and the subsequent development of laws (by both Faraday and James Clerk Maxwell) that relate magnetism, current and force is responsible for all the electric motors, generators – and thus heating, lighting and electrical supply – that the world now depends on for its civilization.

Within months of these discoveries, Faraday had invented the very first electric motor, which used the electromagnetic principle to turn an electric current into rotational motive power. This first machine became known as the Faraday Disk Motor (accurately known as the 'two-piece' homopolar motor), and consists of a metal disk made to rotate between the two poles of a fixed magnet when an electric current is applied at the axle and the periphery simultaneously.

The motor works in reverse as a generator: when the disk is turned, a DC voltage can be extracted via an electric circuit applied at the axle and the periphery. This was achieved, in Faraday's case, by the use of sliding metal contacts.

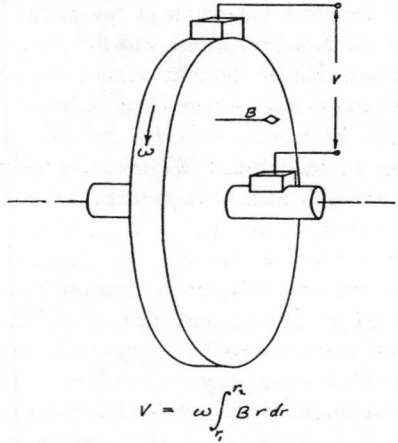

$$V = \omega \int_{r_1}^{r_2} B\, r\, dr$$

FIGURE 4.1 Faraday disk dynamo.

The detailed notes which documented his experimental discoveries were only made public 100 years later. Their release was announced via the *New York Times* on 20 June 1931:

> The thoughts and emotions of Faraday as he worked on his inventions, which brought into being the modern era of electricity, were revealed for the first time this afternoon before an audience of a hundred physicists and chemists gathered at Cornell University. Sir William Bragg, British scientist and Nobel Prize winner, read to them extracts from Faraday's diary, which has never been published . . .
>
> Sir William revealed at the opening that 29 August 1931, 100 years from the data entered by Faraday in his diary reporting his first successful experiment on the relation of electricity and magnetism, which was in effect the first dynamo, is to be celebrated as the centenary of the dynamo. He said that on date unknown the diary would be published in full in six volumes.
>
> 'The diary which Faraday kept day by day,' said Sir William, 'contained his ideas as to the progress of his experiments, what he thought of them, and what he expected to do next. Its interest lies in the revelation of the thoughts of the man who changed the complexion of our entire civilization. We see him feel his way slowly toward an idea we now expect . . . an entry student to know.[1]

Over the first 100 years since its discovery, electromagnetic induction had become the cornerstone of electrical energy.

Some four months after the original triumph, though – on 26 December 1831 – Faraday recorded his observation of a strange electrical anomaly. In both his laboratory notebook and his own diary Faraday described how he fixed a cylindrical magnet and a circular copper conductor together. He then rotated them about an axle and measured the voltage in the circuit formed between electrical sliding contacts on both the axle and the periphery of the wheel. Since there is no relative motion between the magnet and the conductor disk he expected that there would be no voltage produced in the circuit. What Faraday observed, though, was that there was just as much voltage as if the copper conductor disk were static in relation to the moving magnet. The one-piece homopolar generator – a 'one-piece' because the magnets and disk rotate as one unit – had been born. To this day the anomaly has never been completely, satisfactorily explained.

Faraday first published these results in 1832, in the *Philosophical Transactions of the Royal Society*.

> Another point which I endeavoured to ascertain, was, whether it was essential or not that the moving part of the wire would, in cutting the magnetic curves, pass into positions of greater or lesser magnetic force; or whether, always intersecting curves of equal magnetic intensity, the mere motion was sufficient for the production of current. That the latter is true has been proved already in several of the experiments . . . To prove the point with an ordinary magnet, a copper disc was cemented upon the end of a cylinder magnet . . . rotated together. The galvanometer needle moved as in former cases . . . Hence, rotating the magnet caused no difference in the results; for a rotatory and a stationary magnet produce the same effect upon the moving copper.[2]

Faraday was the first scientist to put forward the idea of 'lines of force' to demonstrate magnetism. But what actually happens to the magnetic field and its lines of force when it is rotated? In conventional terms there should be no voltage 'induced' unless there is some form of cutting of the lines of force – the flux lines. Yet in the one-piece homopolar generator voltage could be produced with no apparent cutting of the flux lines. Faraday had started a puzzle that still occupies and mystifies physicists today. Is it really correct that a rotating magnet can have a static magnetic field?

It was not long before Faraday put forward the startling idea that the earth itself was a homopolar generator: its magnetic iron core co-rotated with the conducting mass of the planet. He postulated that there should be a huge voltage difference to be tapped between one of the poles (the axle) and the equator (the perimeter). He even recorded experiments in which he went out to rivers and streams to attempt to measure voltages across them. He failed to detect any effect, although he did not fully realize that he was also a part of the homopolar generator, and thus not relative to it. He remained convinced of his theory though, and viewed certain atmospheric effects – such as the aurora borealis – as the result of the earth's role as a unipolar (one-poled) generator.

Tesla Takes an Interest

Even the great Nikola Tesla was mystified by the strangeness of Faraday's discoveries, and wrote a key paper 'Notes on a Unipolar Dynamo', which was published in the *Electrical Engineer* of 2 September 1891. In the paper he wrote about the Faraday disk motor/generator's potential as an energy source:

> It is characteristic of fundamental discoveries, of great achievements of intellect, that they retain an undiminished power upon the imagination of the thinker. The memorable experiment of Faraday with the disc rotating between the two poles of a magnet, which has borne such magnificent fruit, has long passed into everyday experience; yet there are certain features about this embryo of the present dynamos and motors which even today appear to us striking, and are worthy of the most careful study . . . It would appear that the output of such a machine should, for the same weight, be

much greater than that of any other machine in which
the armature current tends to demagnetize the field.[3]

In this paper Tesla points towards anomalies that were not to be
addressed until much later in the twentieth century. In any
normal electric generator – such as a dynamo – there is a drag
from the magnetic field on the turning force being applied. This
is Sir Isaac Newton's 'equal and opposite' reactive force applied to
the sphere of rotation. In a motor, this effect is called back emf
(back electro-magnetic force) or back torque, and is defined by
what is called Lenz's law.

In a homopolar generator, though, the situation appears to
be different: since the conductor and the magnet are rotating
together it seems possible that there will be no drag – or reactive
'back torque' – between them. A generator without back torque
is, to any free energy researcher, a truly wonderful idea. For
without the equal and opposite back torque, it becomes possible,
in theory, to 'get around Newton' and have a machine that can
produce more output than input.

Despite its apparently anomalous behaviour, the homopolar generator remained a neglected area of significant research
as a possible energy source until the late 1960s. True, it was being
developed as a niche device for high-current, low-voltage
applications such as welding and some weapons applications, but
only a few energy researchers had thought it worthy of serious
consideration as a new source of power. Also, none had bothered
to look deeply into the issue of whether it really was producing
back torque or not. Indeed, such measurements proved difficult
to carry out in practice, and for most scientists there seemed little
reason to look at it. Yet it is precisely the difficulty in measuring
the mysterious back torque that has, to a large extent, fuelled and
maintained the controversy that has surrounded the homopolar
generator for the past thirty years.

To those who became convinced that Faraday's machine
truly does escape the tyranny of back torque, the potential to
produce free energy was intoxicating. But are they right, or have

they fallen into a delusion, a trap set by the universe to catch unwary idealists? The rest of this chapter investigates the attempts to transform Michael Faraday's homopolar generator into the N-machine: the machine of the twentieth century with N number of applications and uses.

The Birth of Bruce DePalma's N-machine

While Brian DePalma was busy developing his career as a famous film director, his brother Bruce was starting to create significant controversy in the field of physics. After graduating from Massachusetts Institute of Technology (MIT) in 1958 from the school of electrical engineering, Bruce – who bore more than a slight resemblance to the young Marlon Brando – took up a career as a research physicist at Harvard University in 1961. He later returned to MIT as a member of the teaching faculty, but left during the 1970s to pursue his own, more controversial ideas, which he fervently believed would transform the mainstream understanding of physics.

DePalma started to attract a reputation for unexpected results when he carried out a range of unorthodox experiments involving gyroscopes, pendulums and ball bearings. He had already become fascinated by the effects of spin on matter, and particularly on how spin may affect the inertial and gravitational properties of objects – indeed his home had become a virtual shrine to spin: gyroscopes hung from the ceiling, and a record turntable carried a pot filled with growing grass.

One of these experiments involved what he started to call 'the force machine', which was a combination of two counter-rotating gyroscopes with axles parallel and rotors co-planar (in the same plane).

The original force machine was constructed in 1971. The total weight of the apparatus was 276 lbs. The 'active' mass at the rim of the flywheels was 10 lbs. The assembly was suspended from a spring scale and the gyroscopes driven counter-rotating at 7600 r.p.m. Under these conditions the support cylinder was driven at 4 r.p.s. to precess the gyros. A consistent set of experiments repeatably showed 4–6 lbs. of weight loss.

To put it simply, DePalma believed that he had found a way to induce anti-gravitational effects. Later he put his own spin on some of the other results he had achieved: 'Simply stated, you can drop a rotating object and find that it falls faster and consequently hits harder . . . than a non-rotating object . . . And you can collide a rotating object and find it collides harder.'[4]

This is already pretty hard for 'dyed-in-the-wool' Newtonians to take, but DePalma went further: 'These collisions and droppings are taking energy out of space in some way that at that time we didn't understand. There is energy in space that flows through everything and gives objects mass and inertia.'[5]

His particular imaginative leap was to hypothesize that the secret to liberating vast amounts of 'space' energy was spin. So when, in about 1977, he rediscovered the writings of Faraday on the homopolar generator, he believed that here might lie the very gyroscopic device that would liberate the energy of the vacuum. For DePalma, the idea that the machine might not be producing back torque was a sure sign that some other key mechanism was at work. Within a short time he had renamed the Faraday generator the 'N-machine' and claimed it as his own: 'Electrical loading of an N generator produces an internal torque between the conducting electrical disk and the attached ring magnets. However, since they are firmly cemented together this torque cannot escape from the machine and load the drive motor or engine.'[6]

In a further report he developed this idea: 'The absence of rotational drag when power is withdrawn from the machine validates the hypothesis of direct conversion of inertial energy to electrical energy through separation of the energy aspects in a rotating disk which is magnetized to convert the inertial polarization into the positive and negative poles of electricity.'[7]

DePalma had convinced himself that this was the machine
that would change the world. It was now only a case of building
one that demonstrated what he already felt was true. In 1977 he
made contact with a Californian spiritual community called
Sunburst, based near Santa Barbara in California. They were
interested in DePalma's design ideas, and felt that they might
offer a solution to the global energy crisis. The community
decided to commit funds and resources to help DePalma build
the first prototype generator – the Sunburst N-machine.

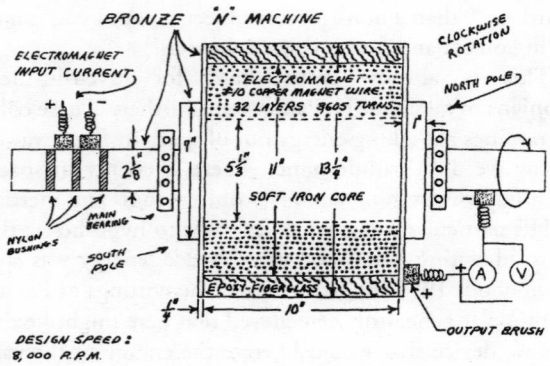

FIGURE 4.2 Sunburst N-Machine designed by Bruce DePalma.

As a development of Faraday's original designs, DePalma had
decided to replace the conventional magnets with an electro-
magnetic coil. This was made up of 3605 turns of copper wire
wrapped around a soft iron core. It was activated via a set of
brushes on the axle on the machine's main axle. The conductor
plates in contact with the electromagnet were thin (¼ inch) circular
bronze plates of some 13½ inches diameter. The power was taken
from the machine via a second set of high-resistance carbon
brushes – one contacting the bronze axle, and the other close to the
perimeter of the bronze conductor plate.

During 1980 DePalma conducted tests on the Sunburst N-machine and finally released his results in an unpublished report. In the tests, the N-machine generator was driven by a 3-phase AC 40 horsepower motor. The belt driving the machine was made sufficiently long for DePalma to believe that there would be no interaction between the magnetic fields of the motor and those of the N-machine. He was obviously keen that his results vindicated not only his theories but also the $25,000 investment on behalf of the Sunburst community. He was not to be disappointed.

Questions of Measurement

The table below shows the results that were obtained. They require some careful analysis, as they involved the measuring of a difficult set-up: an AC motor driving a DC generator with an electromagnet in place of a permanent magnet.

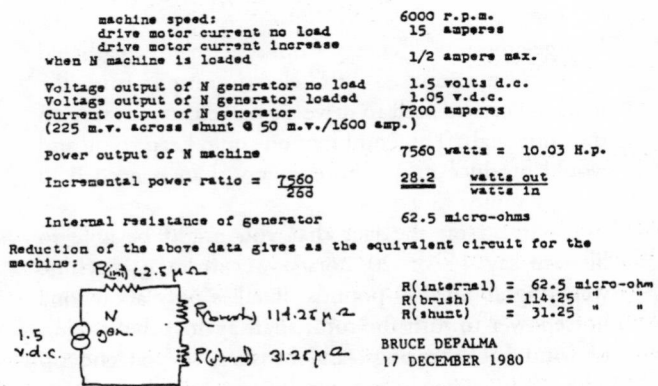

PERFORMANCE OF THE SUNBURST HOMOPOLAR GENERATOR

machine speed:	6000 r.p.m.
drive motor current no load	15 amperes
drive motor current increase when N machine is loaded	1/2 ampere max.
Voltage output of N generator no load	1.5 volts d.c.
Voltage output of N generator loaded	1.05 v.d.c.
Current output of N generator (225 m.v. across shunt @ 50 m.v./1600 amp.)	7200 amperes
Power output of N machine	7560 watts = 10.03 H.p.
Incremental power ratio = 7560/268	28.2 watts out/watts in
Internal resistance of generator	62.5 micro-ohms

Reduction of the above data gives as the equivalent circuit for the machine:

R(internal) = 62.5 micro-ohm
R(brush)   = 114.25 " "
R(shunt)   = 31.25 " "

BRUCE DePALMA
17 DECEMBER 1980

FIGURE 4.3 Bruce DePalma's results data from Sunburst machine, 1980.

They claim to show that for a constant rotational speed of 6000 r.p.m in the N-machine, an output power of 7560 watts required only an increase of 268 watts in the input motor, as compared with the power required to overcome losses (friction, windage in coils, etc.) in the N-machine with the output switch open (with no load).

In simple terms DePalma is saying that for an extra 268 watts of input the machine goes from only just overcoming its losses (and producing no output) to generating over 7 kW of output. If this were true, it would mean that the output power was 28.2 times the (incremental) input power needed to produce it, or even more simply: that the machine was working with an efficiency of 2820 per cent.

That indeed was the bottom line that DePalma now felt able, and willing, to quote: 28.2 times over-unity. As far as DePalma was concerned he had proved his point: the theory that the N-machine could extract energy from the very fabric of space had been correct and it had been demonstrated. He was elated. He believed that his work was about to herald a new age of energy technology. When he was interviewed in 1980 in the *News-Press* of Santa Barbara, there was no holding back:

> If large amounts of energy from space can be gathered with this machine . . . the electric output from the machine can be used to drive a small electric motor on the same shaft. This combination could keep going and would produce much more energy than is needed to run the motor.
>
> It's based on the fact that you might be able to liberate say 15 or 20 horsepower from a machine weighing about 200 pounds. It takes only about one horsepower to turn the rotor shaft against the friction of wind [sic], bearings, and brushes, so you end up with 19 horsepower left over to run your house, car, community or hospital.[8]

As soon as word started to leak out there was, understandably, tremendous interest in what DePalma was claiming. In the alter-

native energy world he soon drew a
replicate his work. The race was
energy effect, then it should be po
demonstrate the world's first self-susta...
Following his reported successes, DePalm...
contributions from a well-known eye spe...
Raiford, and a Mormon family called the Tann...
really needed to get big money was a high-credibili...
verification of his achievements. In this department th...
not going so smoothly.

The Road to Independent Validation

During 1980 DePalma agreed to allow Tim Wilhelm of the Stelle
Group in Illinois to witness testing of an earlier demonstration
model of the N-machine prototype. The Stelle Group was a group
of like-minded people keen to investigate and develop new, 'clean'
energy sources 'from the abundance of field forces that permeate
the universe' – what some would call zero-point energy (see
Chapter 9). The group had an interest in the success of the
machine. Wilhelm, with information provided directly by
DePalma, built up his own test model (using permanent magnets
rather than an electromagnet) to see whether the N-machine really
did produce no back torque, and thus contravene Lenz's law.

What Wilhelm's report concluded, though, was not what
DePalma wanted to hear:

> At this point in time, my best conclusion regarding our
> test results is this: That a one-piece homopolar
> generator, of the type and configuration illustrated in
> this report, *does* exhibit back-torque when electrically
> loaded, per Lenz's law, and thus cannot be considered
> as a viable device for tapping free energy from space and
> converting it to a useful form.[9]

not fully deter Wilhelm. He was still open to the
ty that DePalma had made an important breakthrough
gniting interest in the homopolar generator, and that there
still some potential for the machine to form a new energy
urce. Above all, perhaps, he did not want to be the one to spoil
DePalma's free energy party.

By the time of a major new energy conference in Hanover,
Germany, in November 1980, a number of further research
projects to replicate the Sunburst results had already started in
earnest. Perhaps the two most important and influential were
those led by Tom Valone and by Adam Trombly. Tom Valone,
aged twenty-nine at the time, had visited the Sunburst community, had met DePalma separately and subsequently arranged
with the State University of New York at Buffalo Physics
Department to build an N-machine for his Masters degree. Adam
Trombly – a Masters degree holder in physics and astronomy –
was partnered in his venture by physicist Joseph Kahn. DePalma
appeared far from competitive with these other builders: after all,
their success would only provide further vindication for his work.
He went out of his way to give them his backing: 'Trombly and
Kahn are two of the brightest young physicists in America today
. . . their work is of the very highest quality.'[10]

He provided them all with answers to their questions, and
with any other information which he felt might help. It appeared
to be a time of great mutual collaboration. Typically there were
discussions about optimum configurations and specifications for
the machines and their testing equipment, after which the
experimenters would then follow their own paths.

Valone's approach, which proceeded with limited resources,
was based on using heated liquid solder to provide low-friction,
low-loss brushes. His focus was on establishing the truth of the
mystery over the machine's back torque. He was also keen to
explore the idea that the anomalies of the machine could only be
explained by an appeal to Einstein's relativity.

The Trombly design was to be a much more expensive and
ambitious affair: he had managed to secure some $100,000 of

research funding through his own company, the ACME Energy Research Company. Far from being something from a *Bugs Bunny* cartoon, ACME was short for 'Acyclic Closed Magnetic Experiment' and was a commercially focused operation. Within a few short months the company had filed a patent for a revised design of the N-machine – a 'closed path' design which encased the whole machine in a steel shell, in an effort to contain more of the magnetic field and so increase efficiency.

A Giant Leap for Mankind?

With the help of contacts from Tom Valone, DePalma now attracted the interest of Edgar Mitchell, the sixth man to walk on the moon. Mitchell, at that time an influential character in financial and political circles, visited DePalma in his California garage. He was shown the development work on the self-sustaining generator, and was soon convinced of the research value of the work. He added his weight to the fundraising efforts needed to get the machine to the next step, preparing a research specification for the verification work that was needed to confirm DePalma's credentials. The work was to cost around $270,000 over a period of a few months, and would involve independent testing by Dr D.C. White of the well-respected MIT Energy Lab. The bill was to be paid by a private company called Dart Industries.

When the results came back, the project was brought into crisis: Dr White's report of 3 September 1981 was far from complimentary:

> DePalma's problem stems from his very sloppy measurement of power into the drive motor. Careful instrumentation would show that the input drive power goes up when current is drawn from the homopolar machine. You will recall that I noticed in his film that the ammeter in the drive motor circuit jumped [increased] when he drew power from the

homopolar generator. At the time there was no way to
fully verify that result at the time of the visit.[11]

The report was a bitter blow, and soon had Mitchell and Dart
Industries running for the woods. Before all the fall-out landed,
however, DePalma had signed a new research contract with the
good Dr Morgan Raiford, which would allow him to continue
development on trying to create a self-sustaining N-machine.

By this time Adam Trombly had applied for an international patent for his 'closed-path' version of the Faraday
generator (PCT No. WO-82/02126), which had already been
featured in an article in *Satellite News* of February 1981.

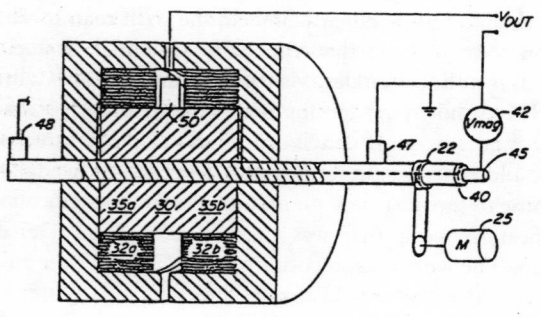

FIGURE 4.4 Diagram from Adam Trombly's PCT Patent Application.

The article, which also featured the work of DePalma,
included some bold claims. DePalma talked of his machine
producing 'almost no drag'. Trombly was confident of producing
'50 kW of AC electrical power'. The article concluded with a
more than upbeat summary of both machines' abilities: 'The
power-in/power-out ratio for the ACME generator is not as high
as the DePalma machine, but it still puts out about 3 to 4 times
more electrical power than it takes to run the device. DePalma is
building a bigger machine – a 250 kW version with a 2-ft
diameter rotor.'[12]

What actually happened during the building and testing of Adam Trombly's N-machine is still far from clear. Conditions of extreme secrecy were in operation around the company's headquarters in San Rafael, California. As far as is known, the completed machine was only ever seen by Trombly and Kahn (and, possibly, DePalma). In tandem with their patent applications, they had embarked on some very sophisticated developments to their contact brushes: these were to be made of a combination of sodium and potassium, in an effort to reduce losses.

Their international patent applications (which only involved the submission of design specifications) were rejected by the US patent office twice: the first time, according to Trombly, for the reason that the machine 'could not possibly work'; the second time they were turned down because their revised brush design represented 'prior art' and was not novel. Shortly after the second patent refusal the Office of Naval Intelligence became involved and declared Trombly's brush design 'classified'. This meant that he could not talk about the design without first informing the office of Naval Intelligence.

Having a Breakdown . . .

At this point the story took a strange turn, when Trombly announced the dramatic results of his and Kahn's experimental work. There was good news and there was bad news. During testing in 1982, he claimed, the machine had reached an efficiency close to 250 per cent when disaster struck: the machine experienced a 'parasitic uniaxle breakdown'. In other words it destroyed itself: even its iron core had turned to dust. It's still not fully known how the inventors, or the investors, reacted. It *is* known, however, that Adam Trombly had bought a $10,000 DC-to-AC inverter shortly before the self-destruct. Evidently he had hoped that he would soon be 'closing the loop' and would be needing the inverter to power practical appliances. It was not to be, though. The ACME machine would never be rebuilt, and Adam Trombly has since pursued research in seismology and other environmental sciences.

Meanwhile Tom Valone continued to try to establish the exact nature of the back torque in his version of the machine:

> During 1982 and 1983, my one-piece HG [homopolar generator] was put through a series of experiments to test for back torque . . . The measurements of input power versus output power, which in most cases was below unity, the most direct experience of back torque was the deceleration time. When power was cut from the HG, it always decelerated at least 10 per cent sooner with a closed circuit than with an open circuit. My average measurement of the back torque was 0.17 N-m [Newton Metres] which was within classical limits.[13]

So Valone's measurements quite clearly showed that there was indeed some back torque being generated in the N-machine. Valone was always keen to be scrupulous about the potential for error in measurements on the machine – something he'd spoken about publicly. Whether or not this was taken to be a slur on his work, DePalma wrote to Valone in December 1983 and threatened to start a verbal attack on his work if he did not start to mention him as the inventor of the N-machine. At the same time DePalma, who was apparently not having marked success in developing the self-sustaining machine he desired, started to change his ideas about how best to make the N-machine produce power. This threw some of those who were trying to replicate his work – including Valone – into a state of confusion:

> This new concept . . . actually decreases the voltage and decreases the power output (as evident to those who have experienced this phenomena of reversed field through the disk). After losing over 80 per cent of the

> theoretical voltage due to filed reversal, I spent a whole
> summer redesigning my homopolar generator.[14]

Even if DePalma was losing the support of those in America, he
was starting to attract adherents from further afield. In India, a
nuclear engineer named Paramahamsa Tewari had built his own
homopolar generator, which he had named the Space Power
Generator. He claimed that it was providing over-unity performance, and was up to 400 per cent efficient. His own reading
of the literature on DePalma's machine led him to believe that it
had been 'most accurately' measured as 760 per cent. Tewari's
work had the virtue of being funded by the Indian government,
under his work at the Kaiga Power Project where he was the chief
engineer.

In Japan an engineer and inventor named Shiuji Inomata
was also carrying out N-machine research. He was confident that
the N-machine was truly groundbreaking. In a later letter to
Valone, he laid out his beliefs about the machine: 'The N-
machine functioning is in conflict with the present, physical laws.
And we need a new paradigm of science.'[15]

These international developments brought DePalma's
work a new credibility at a time when belief in the technology in
the United States was starting to waver.

High-Level Support

Controversy over the machine was brought to life again, however,
when perhaps the most important independent test report on
DePalma's work was first publicly presented to the Society for
Scientific Exploration on 21 June 1986. Its author was Robert
Kincheloe, Emeritus Professor of Electrical Engineering at the
well-respected Stanford University. In many ways it was strange
that a scientist with Kincheloe's reputation to maintain should –
after so many doubts had been expressed – accept an invitation to
test the machine at all. It appears, though, that curiosity had got

the better of him: 'Being intrigued by DePalma's claims, the author accepted the offer by Mr Norman Paulsen, founder of the Sunburst community, to conduct tests on the generator which had not been used since the tests by DePalma.'

First the bad news: in the paper, Kincheloe revisited the test results produced by DePalma six years earlier in 1980. He first criticized the machine itself: 'From the standpoint of prior art, DePalma's design of the Sunburst generator is inefficient and not suitable for power generation.' He went on to criticize DePalma's methodology, his experimental assumptions and the way that the inventor had approached the task of measuring his own machine. His conclusion was pretty damning: 'It is the opinion of this author that some of DePalma's numerical results are questionable.'

There was, however, some good news: Kincheloe's own tests on the machine seemed to produce some promising conclusions:

> While it did not perform as claimed, repeatable data showed anomalous results that did not seem to conform to traditional theory. In particular, under certain assumptions about internally generated output voltage the increase in input power when power was extracted from the generator over that measured due to frictional losses with the generator unexcited seems to be about 26 per cent of the maximum computed output power.

To put it more simply: under certain conditions, when the machine was connected to a load and generated power, Kincheloe was saying that it produced four times the power that it took to run it.

> We are . . . faced with the apparent result that the output power obtained when the generator magnet is energized greatly exceeds the increase in drive motor

power over that required to supply friction losses with
the magnet not energized, which is certainly anomalous
in terms of conventional theory.

While Kincheloe accepted that this could be due to poor
experimental method, he proposed that it was at least worthy of
further study: 'While DePalma's measurement technique was
flawed and his numbers overly optimistic, his basic premise has
not been disproved.'[16]

This was clearly a great support to DePalma's cause, and
gave him renewed faith and credibility with which to garner more
public acceptance for his work. But if he thought it would be
enough to convince the world he was to be disappointed. Between
1986 and 1993 the DePalma Institute continued to publish
papers and documents, in an effort to convince people of the
importance of his work. Since there was no self-sustaining
generator to show, most observers could not take the work
seriously – they figured that if DePalma could not turn a real over-
unity effect into a working over-unity machine, there must be
something wrong somewhere.

DePalma claimed that it would be too dangerous – from a
personal security point of view – to 'close the loop'. When asked
by journalist Jeane Manning why he hadn't made a self-sustaining
machine, he replied: 'Because I would get my head blown off.'[17]

He maintained that he had been threatened by someone
with high-up connections in the US government. In one of his
Institute's papers, published in 1995, he developed the theme:

> Once I had demonstrated the reality of direct
> extraction of electrical energy in a small model N-
> machine, I thought commercial development would be
> obvious and easy. That was seventeen years ago. We
> live in a technological world. We tend to think all
> problems in the world can be solved through science
> and technology. If this were the case, we would have
> free energy now, and the world would be at peace. The

details of my experiences with the N-machines I have built and demonstrated have been published elsewhere. Through it all I have had to learn by direct experience certain realities of the world we live in and the consequences of introducing a possibly world-changing invention to mankind.

Einstein showed us power was in the existence of all things, and nowhere is that more true than in the works and activities of the élite groups who attempt to control society. The nature of these groups and their power has come to light in the studies of the Tri-lateral Commission, the CFR, the World Bank, and Dope Inc. Power and energy, the generation and control thereof, is the number-one business in the world, more powerful than guns and drugs, food and property.

One of my first discoveries, after having graduated from university, was that science and scientists in general were controlled in their activities by managers and political influences originating from individuals with no intrinsic knowledge of science. The feeling was that if there was a job to be done, a specification could be generated, money could be offered and technical people would step forward. If there were first-rate scientists who felt the job was immoral or impossible, then there were legions of second and third raters who would step forward and take the money. This ensured the control of science and scientists could be maintained by money. In this world nothing was impossible and all things could be done. As soon as a scientist would step forward and challenge the rationality, viability, or morality of a given program, he could be stopped through excommunication.[18]

In 1992 DePalma left the United States and landed first in Australia, before eventually settling in New Zealand with his partner Andrew Mount. He managed to engage an investor there, and was able to build another N-machine – the Mark II Quadropole – based on permanent magnets. It failed to produce any positive results. DePalma died in 1998 following a short illness.

It's a remarkable testament to the genius of Michael Faraday that his discoveries of 1831 are still proving important and controversial today. The homopolar generator has now developed a niche role as a commercially efficient way of generating low-voltage, high-current power for the specific needs of certain industrial sectors. For some, though, it is the promise of free energy that still holds a seemingly endless fascination. We may not yet have heard the last of the N-machine.

CHAPTER FIVE

A Secret in the Swiss Mountains –
Paul Baumann and the
Thesta-Distatica

'The fact that all essential functions of Methernitha are fulfilled without
any external force, driven solely through inner conviction which causes
everybody to help and take care of the other – this is, for me, the most
astonishing effect which is produced by this form of living together. It
seems to be a miracle.'
                    Anonymous member of the Methernitha community

Is it likely that a small Christian community living in an isolated
valley high in the Swiss Alps is the home to the world's only
known example of a self-sustaining, energy-producing free energy
generator? Is it possible that it was developed by an ex-
watchmaker named Paul Baumann who, by most accounts, has
had little formal scientific training? Is it credible that the Christian
community – named Methernitha – has refused to make
prototype devices available since it believes that mankind is not
ready for such a technology?

The story of the Methernitha community and its electrical
generating machine called the Thesta-Distatica reads like a bizarre
modern folk tale. In the late 1950s a small group of Swiss citizens

came together to establish a new community based on Christian ideals and a concern for the environment. They bought land high in the Emmenthal valley, close to the village of Linden, near Bern. They quickly set about building new homes and workshops to supplement the existing collection of prefabricated structures. They established a small business making office furniture to support their needs, and started to live out their idealistic vision. This vision – which appears to have remained intact over thirty years – was of an independent community, free of alcohol, nicotine and drugs, and dedicated to the ideal of mutual sharing of help and resources – following a simple maxim of 'all for one and one for all'.

From the beginning it was also very important that they remained free of dependencies on outside resources. They intended to be self-sufficient in a number of ways. They soon started to establish independent means of meeting their energy requirements. Water pumping by windmills, solar water-heating panels and electricity supplied by wind generators all appeared during the early years of the community. This fulfilled a strong part of their Utopian ethos: to be in 'balance' with nature. Their technological ambitions did not stop there, however. Throughout the 1960s and '70s one member of their founding group – ex-watchmaker Paul Baumann – sought an even more exalted scientific Holy Grail: an electrical generator that derived all its power from the electrostatic energy available in the atmosphere.

In 1978, after many years' research – about which there are still a considerable number of mysteries – the first working prototype of the machine was revealed within the community and christened the Thesta-Distatica. This first machine was relatively small with a single rotating wheel of about 4–5 inches diameter, a number of charge-collecting 'antennae' positioned on and around the disk, a series of magnets and coils, a pair of glass Leyden jars, and wires leading here and there. From its design it was clear to all who saw it that it was well-thought out, as well as being beautifully finished.

In operation it was simple: once the wheel was rotated it continued to turn, stabilizing at around 60 r.p.m. It needed nothing further to sustain it: in theory, and bearings permitting, it could run for ever. To accomplish this new feat it extracted electrostatic energy from the Swiss mountain air, separated this into positive and negative charge, and then transformed this polarity into a true electrodynamic motive force – in other words: electrical power.

This prototype Thesta-Distatica wasn't simply a perpetual motion machine, though. It could do more work than simply keep itself going. It was a true generator. Even when a reasonable electrical load was taken from it, the machine's wheel still continued to turn at normal speed. The prototype apparently produced a few hundred useful watts that could be used to light bulbs and run small motors. If any school science teacher had seen the device he or she would have quickly realized that a good number of the machine's parts resembled a device known as a Wimshurst generator, a British invention of the early 1900s that was used for many years in school laboratories to produce high-voltage sparks.

Under conditions of relative secrecy, further prototypes were built throughout the late 1970s and early 1980s. They were gradually scaled up: the rotating wheels measuring as much as 18 inches on the largest machine, which was able to produce 3kW of power. Most machines now contained two contra-rotating wheels, which were simply turned – by hand – in opposite directions to start the machines. The prototypes worked better in low humidity: if the atmosphere was too high in water vapour, the electrostatic energy could diffuse too easily from the machine's charge collection system.

A way of turning electrostatic energy into electrodynamic usable power – it sounded almost ridiculously simple when put into words. If this were true, one might think, they had done what every scientist, government, environmentalist had dreamed of.

Paul Baumann, a quietly spoken, unassuming man, together with the community's team of scientists, had apparently

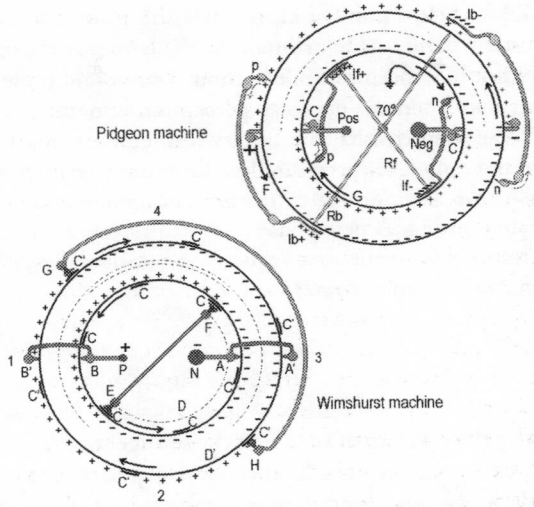

Pidgeon machine

Wimshurst machine

FIGURE 5.1 Diagrammatic image of the Wimshurst and Pidgeon Generators by Paul Potter.

achieved what others would not even dare to believe possible. At the same time, Baumann, together with the community's council, had decided that they would not yet make the secrets of their technology publicly available. There were secrets here, they realized, that could be used for good and bad. This was to put them on a collision path with any conventional scientists who believed in the sharing of knowledge. The community also decided that it did not wish to patent what they had done: as part of their fiercely independent ethos, they shunned virtually all bureaucratic institutions, including Swiss banks and patenting authorities.

They did not feel though – at this point – that they had anything to lose by showing the world the results of their endeavours. Paul Baumann was confident that showing the machines would not reveal how they worked. He knew that what he had done would be almost impossible to replicate: the technology held a number of secrets which most observers would find utterly baffling. He maintained his claim that the technology would not have been possible without a profound understanding and an acute, perhaps mystical, perception of nature.

The Methernitha community had set itself on a road which would not only test the credibility of those they met, but would – by their own account – test their faith in human nature, and find it sorely wanting. A new phase in the story was about to start as they responded to the first requests to see the Thesta-Distatica. Would the wise men come?

First Reports

When the first information about the strange story of the Thesta-Distatica started to appear, there was a polarized reaction. So incredible was the Methernitha community's claim that most 'reputable' scientists wouldn't even go near it, for fear of being tarnished with the weirdness of it all. After all, it was apparently a perpetual motion machine – something that simply must be a fraud. Instead they would wait for Methernitha to reveal their methods through peer-reviewed journals, or via patents.

There were, predictably, the more unorthodox researchers who were beyond the ridicule of the mainstream. Dr Hans Nieper of the German Association of Gravity Field Energy and his scientific colleagues inspected the machines five times during the community's period of openness between 1982 and 1985, and were stunned by the machine's performance:

> Members of the GAGFE (German Association of Gravity Field Energy) have inspected the Swiss system on five different occasions from 1984 to the present. There are two small units and this presently described larger unit (below) located in a commune near Bern, Switzerland. This machine and the two smaller units have been running, on and off since 1982.

The larger machine produces 3 to 4 kW at 230 volts DC, and apparently extracts energy from the gravity stressing field, and there is no primary propulsion of any kind.[1]

Nieper's description of the machine was surprisingly detailed:

The converter runs continuously by itself, with only rotating wear parts being the two ball bearings at the centre of the two discs.

The M-L [Methernitha-Linden] converter is functionally constructed, completely symmetrical with the two discs made of acrylic plastic, a light metal lattice, insulated copper wires, a secret crystal-diode rectifier, and gold-plated electrical connections. Everything is hand-made with the finest craftsmanship, with an elegant beauty. The operating principle has been known for a long time, and these machines have been developed over a twenty-year time span.

In [the] electrostatic generators, the air molecules between the two acrylic discs which closely counter-rotate, side by side, become electrically activated by friction. This causes the discs to be continually charged, until a flashover equalizes them. To limit the electrical voltage to a desired amount, the positive charged particles on one of the counter-rotating discs and the negative-charged particles on the other disc are extracted by means of separately adjustable lattice-electrodes, and are fed into a Leyden jar which collects the energy. The speed of the discs, on which a fan-like structure of 50 lattice electrodes is etched out, is 60 r.p.m. (It is obvious that this discrete ratio of lattice/segments and speed will produce a 50 hertz, pulsed DC output.) This speed is synchronized by magnetic impulses.

The unit is hand-started by revolving the two discs

in opposite directions, until the converter was charged up to such a degree that it synchronized itself and continued to rotate smoothly and noiselessly, without any input source of power. A centrally mounted disc of about 4 inches in diameter was glimmering in all the colours of the rainbow. After only a few seconds the Leyden jars were ready for operation, so that 300 volts DC, with a current of 10 amperes, could be extracted at the terminals, and this could be done continuously for hours, or for years, without any wear!

To demonstrate the power available, connections were made to both, alternately, a high-power incandescent lamp and a heating element, each of which was rated at 380 volt service. The brilliant light from the lamp was blinding . . . The heating element became so hot, after a few seconds, that it could not be touched.

This experience was certainly a look into the future for all of us, and the start of a new era. It became evident for everybody who saw this converter functioning, that the teachings of orthodox science must undergo a complete revision in order to be taken seriously.[2]

This report, along with some basic black-and-white photographs, was soon being circulated and avidly consumed by those with an interest in new energy production technologies. It was soon clear to many, however, that although the machine appeared to use relatively conventional components, it was going to be extremely difficult to understand how it could possibly work. Nevertheless, the replications started . . .

Of the number of independent researchers who have attempted to copy the Methernitha machine, only a few, such as Albert Hauser, a Dane, have benefited from a detailed visit to view the Methernitha machine. On 14 February 1986, Hauser had a four-hour session with Paul Baumann and the machines, during which he was able to examine the technology in some detail. Following the meeting he was able to publish detailed plan

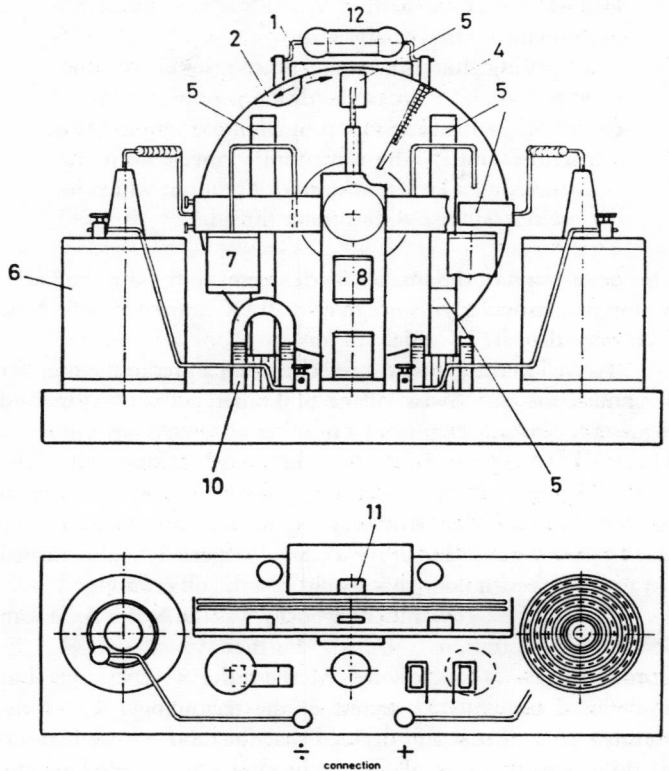

FIGURE 5.2 Detail from Albert Hauser's design drawings for an 'Influence Converter' of '3–5Kw 300V DC', based on the Thesta-Distatica.

drawings, which have since formed the basis of many attempts to replicate the machine. As well as the larger machine they witnessed the smaller machine being started up:

> Also they started a smaller machine which was running for two hours. We tested the machine with only measuring instruments. It means to say that we didn't

load the machine with any resistance. I think the performance is maybe 200 watt.

Surprising, but this model wasn't so heavy, only approx. 1 kg. The size of the disk was only approx. 12 cm, and the construction was much more simple. (Few 'capacitors' only.) The self-running mechanism was constructed of a little traditional DC motor, which for the use was winded with thinner thread.[3]

This description of the smaller model seems to fit with the initial prototype, particularly its use of a small DC motor to power the disks once they are in initial motion.

As well as the genuine researchers and a predicable number of cranks, the tiny Swiss village of Linden received visits and requests for information from a number of foreign governments. The Soviet Academy of Science requested information. The French Ministry of Defence wanted to know all about it. National agencies took the view that they would not be forgiven if they failed to carry out a due diligence test – especially if this turned out to be the technology that would end the oil economy.

One of these government agencies was the North American Space Administration (NASA). Further to a visit by its representatives, NASA offered Methernitha a very large, but undisclosed sum for the secrets of the technology. The community's council met and decided that they did not want to do anything which might allow the machines to be used in any military or other non-humanitarian beneficial use.

In 1986 the community decided to close the public doors on the technology and develop further working prototypes in private – moving their research facility to another secret location. As self-professed guardians of the technology they announced that they would not allow its public dissemination and distribution until the rest of humanity had proved that it could treat such a technology with the responsibility that the community required. At first people outside the community thought that they would eventually relent – especially as news of global warming and climate disruption was beginning to make a big impact on the world stage. Despite protests from the technology's supporters, and the understandable scepticism from its detractors, the situation remained at an impasse.

The interest in the machines from specialist researchers and more official agencies did not relent and the community found themselves overwhelmed with requests. While they were always generally polite to such advances, they found that the running of their community was becoming more and more difficult. Viktor Bosshard, a member of the community's council, was appointed to deal with all the public requests, and, in general, to turn them down.

By this point in the story many observers felt that if the Methernitha members really had achieved all this, and if the machines really worked relatively safely (as they claimed), then it was absolutely ridiculous that a so-called Christian community would not release something to the world that could have so many environmental and social benefits – particularly in developing countries where there is a huge need for independent power generators that can run in remote places. Wasn't this more dog-in-the-manger than Christ in the manger?

Methernitha's Public Display

Then, in 1989, at a major free energy conference held in Einsiedeln, Switzerland, the Methernitha community surprised the world by showing a video not just about the Thesta-Distatica but also about the community and its ethos. The narration gave a strong Christian message about the evils of war and the history of mankind's inhumanity to man:

> Instead of utilizing the achievements of science and technology for the benefit and preservation of all forms of life, they are abused carelessly, irresponsibly, in order to destroy and to kill – and thus turn them into a curse

upon mankind. To change all this the evolution of a
new technology is not enough – even if it were the most
ecological and ingenious. To change this present status
one has to go much deeper down: to the root cause of
all this evil. And this is man's way of thinking, his state
of mind.[4]

The video also impressed upon its audience the story of Galileo,
and of the time it took for his discoveries about the sun's centrality
to be accepted. (The Roman Catholic church only made their
official acceptance of Galileo's correctness in the 1980s.) The
message was that technology has never made people good.

The response at the conference amongst those trying to
develop new energy technologies was predictable: we need new
technologies if we are to avoid the problems of global warming
and climate change. This has to be a risk worth taking, even if
there are ways in which the technology will be employed for other
purposes. These arguments were not, though, about to change
Methernitha's mind.

The Strange Case of Dr Marinov

It was at this conference that I first met Dr Stefan Marinov,
perhaps the Thesta-Distatica's greatest scientific ally. Originally
born in Bulgaria, Marinov was a physicist who had eventually
settled in Graz, Austria, where he was a professor of physics at the
University of Graz. He had a reputation for being unorthodox, a
maverick, someone who enjoyed challenging the status quo. He
had made contact with the Methernitha community in the early
1980s and had been convinced by their technology. They had
given him some privileged access to the machines, although he
had never been able to replicate the technology himself. Nevertheless he believed wholeheartedly in its reality and importance.

On a number of occasions he had tried, and in most cases
failed, to place full-page advertisements in *Nature* – science's most

prestigious, peer-reviewed journal – challenging some aspect of scientific dogma which he believed to be incorrect. A scientific feud developed between Dr Marinov and *Nature*'s then editor John Maddox, which rumbled on for many years.

When I asked Maddox about Marinov he let me know that he viewed Marinov as a crazy maverick. Marinov, on the other hand, saw Maddox's position as that of a fascist dictator – able to guide the soul of orthodox science from within his prestigious journal. One of the advertisements that Marinov tried to place featured the Thesta-Distatica, stating that it was the world's first practical self-sustaining electricity generator. Maddox refused to include the advertisement, and – as he had done so many times before – returned Dr Marinov's cheque.

As we were having dinner together, Dr Marinov was talking animatedly, and with extraordinary quickness of mind, about physics, food and Methernitha. To my slight shock, he suddenly started to unbutton his shirt. Fortunately he stopped after two buttons, and pulled out a silver pendant: on it was the word Methernitha. Marinov was a member of the community.

Given the fact that we were both drinking beer, I took it that his dedication to the ascetic precepts of the community was less important than the fact he now had direct access to Paul Baumann, the main inventor, Luzi Cathomen, the chief engineer, and the machines themselves. He told me that he had ceaselessly tried to get the community's council to make the Thesta-Distatica publicly available, but he was always frustrated. In every meeting of the community's council he would be the lone voice that believed the machine should be released immediately. Having seen the machines over a period of time – illuminating light bulbs, running motors and so on – he was totally convinced of the fact that they worked, and that they could easily be commercialized, if only the community would allow it.

While he was unable to replicate the machine independently, Marinov continued his own passionate campaign on behalf of the Thesta-Distatica, even writing to political leaders in many countries. He had persuaded his friend and scientific colleague Andrei Sakharov, the Russian Nobel Prize winner for physics, to visit the Methernitha community. Sakharov's visit, which was to be accompanied by Russian television, had been fully arranged, when Sakharov died quite suddenly.

Visiting Methernitha

It was very soon after my meeting with Marinov that I first visited the Methernitha community. My visit was hosted by Viktor Bosshard, the English-speaking face of Methernitha, who, over the space of two days, showed me around the community and answered most of my questions about the community and its achievements.

He also told me the story of traumatic events which might have brought some groups to an end, but which appeared to have made Methernitha even stronger. In the late 1960s (before the invention of the Thesta-Distatica) the community was infiltrated by a small group of destructive individuals, who spread discontent and conflict. In efforts to rid the community of these people, Paul Baumann – one of the key members of the community – was arrested and ended up being sentenced to prison for a number of years.

While serving his sentence, Baumann, who was not a highly technical man, started to work on a new form of energy generator. With the help of the community's more technical members, the machine was perfected inside the prison in 1978, where, Bosshard told me, it was first run. Baumann's solitary experience had, it seems, liberated some intuition about how energy could be captured from the atmosphere. His language about the technology he had created was not scientific: he described various parts of the machine using natural terms like clouds, lightning and ground. Perhaps the most interesting description of the device was that it was not a machine but an 'organism'. Nevertheless, this erstwhile Swiss 'peasant' seemed to have had succeeded in developing a technology which had eluded the best minds and resources of mainstream science. No wonder they didn't believe him.

Since the first machine was built the community has made as many as a dozen prototype generators of different sizes and wattages. Despite accounts to the contrary, they have never been used to power any parts of the community's normal power needs. This has been left to their wind, solar and woodburning power, as well as, in some cases, a conventional grid connection.

While the smallest machines would fit into a biscuit tin and produce only a few hundred watts or so, the community is now building a machine – some two and a half metres high – which is claimed to be capable of producing 30 kW, and which they are intending to use to power the community's health centre. Bosshard implied that the operation of the machine may even have positive health benefits. This may be connected to the idea that the machine is believed to create a beneficial, negatively ionized field around it. It is also said by some observers that it appears to cool the atmosphere around it. This, again, is a signature of negative ionization.

Some reports have since said that the community has not been able to make the 30 kW 'Elephant' machine work – that the principle cannot be scaled up this far. Methernitha do not claim to have the large machine working yet. It has certainly cost them a lot of time and money to get as far as they have with this machine.

Since my visit in 1989, and despite their general closed-door policy on the technology, I discovered they have in fact continued to allow limited access to a very small number of scientists whom they believed they could trust. Some have been able simply to view demonstrations, while others have been permitted to make measurements, examine the components, and, of course, check for hidden wires and other power sources.

By allowing in the scientists they were surely giving the secret away, you might think. But if, in say 1960, an organization had been able to demonstrate a modern computer of today, and had shown the contents to a moderately skilled scientist of the time, would that scientist have been able to build his or her own computer? Even if that person were given a good few hours to look at it? He might have been able to confirm that it worked, but it might have taken many, many years to fathom out the basic technologies which had been developed to create such a machine. Perhaps that is how it is with the Thesta-Distatica.

Paul Baumann has, though, given some clues. In the early 1990s he started to make public something called the Linden Experiment – a kind of proof of concept which he claims gives a large clue to the operation of the machine. It involves inducing a resonance (of some 80–140 megahertz) in a coil around a horseshoe-shaped magnet. He then places between the legs of the magnet a block formed of repeated layers of copper, plexiglass and aluminium. According to those who have witnessed this experiment Baumann is able to put a multimeter across the plates in the block which shows a voltage of around 700 volts. This should *not* be possible! No one has yet found an acceptable explanation for this phenomenon, which could be the key to the whole machine.

Today, the members of the Methernitha community see themselves as survivors carrying on a pioneering tradition. Despite the attentions of different parties, they seem to have remained very much the same. Their simple website (which has had only 1300 visitors by the turn of the millennium) describes some of their aims, and some of their achievements, but also speaks of the philosophy behind their ability to survive more than thirty years as an independent community.

> Methernitha is something outstanding. The evolution
> of human society has always forged ahead via groups
> and individuals who ventured to live a life beyond
> everything considered to be the norm, groups and
> individuals who lived unlike the majority of mankind.
> To human society these groups and individuals appear
> to pose a threat. The human society resists these groups

> by pillorying them. Half-truth and untruth are used to
> describe them as a sect. This is not only discriminating,
> but also very seldom true. Like all prejudices: no one
> seems to know the reality. The ignorance and the
> readiness to condemn are used by certain groups to
> their own advantage.[5]

This extract gives the impression of a group of idealists who have
suffered from outside prejudice and discrimination. And yet
today the local mayor of Linden seems totally supportive of this
independent group:

> The Community of Methernitha makes no bad
> impressions at all within our rural commune; we have
> good relations . . . Their products are of high quality
> and are partly globally well known. There are no walls
> between Methernitha inhabitants and the village. The
> inhabitants – roughly 120 people, including children –
> have their own free opinion and philosophy and also
> have their personal freedom and freedom of action
> which they never try to impose on other people.[6]

This sunny description fails to tell very much of the community's
real history. Only very recently has their website even mentioned
the fact that they have developed what many people in this closely
guarded field regard as the most highly sophisticated, thoroughly
developed and most practical example of a free energy generator
presently in existence.

An Appalling Tragedy

A bizarre twist to the whole Methernitha story came on 15 July
1997 when news of Dr Stefan Marinov's death filtered over the
Internet. After a series of setbacks in his own research, and the
continued rejection of his ideas by mainstream science, Dr Stefan

Marinov unexpectedly committed suicide by deliberately falling from the university building in Graz where he worked. Everything had been planned very carefully and deliberately: messages were left for his wife and children. He left many notes detailing his final wishes, as well as a scientific testament. His short suicide note, however, summed up the reasons for his decision:

> After having walked so many years on the thorny way of truth, I became tired. My books and papers are my scientific testament.
>
> I hope that soon the absolute [Newtonian] space-time concepts, which I restored by numerous experiments and by simple mathematical theory, will be accepted by the scientific community as those corresponding to physical reality.
>
> I hope the perpetual motion machines, of which I constructed many prototypes without closing the energetic circuits, will successfully be built by other people.
>
> And if my achievements in space-time physics, in electrodynamics and in the domain of the violation of the laws of conservation will be silenced also after my death, by leaving this world, I can only repeat the eternal words: *feci quod potui*.
> Graz, Austria, 15 July 1997
> Stefan Marinov

Feci quod potui – I did what I could.[7]

His scientific colleagues were distraught. Dr Robert W. Bass wrote:

> I was appalled by word of Marinov's suicide. For a professed Christian (about which he and I had corresponded) this is like saying, OK, Lucifer, you win! I give up!

> Marinov, in my opinion, was a real genius in the sense that he well understood all of the classical theoretical physics in great detail (sufficient detail to argue that historically some wrong turnings had been taken, and that Maxwell's equations as we normally see them can be readily disproved by a large number of table-top Faraday/Ampère experiments) and yet Marinov was an exceedingly good experimentalist who invented and had built and tested a large number of *very* complicated electro-mechanical & hydro-electromagnetic devices and systems.[8]

Another colleague, Erwin Schneeberger was equally startled: 'For all his friends, Stefan's decision is absolutely unbelievable. He was a powerful, enthusiastic physicist with a bright smile on his face until the last time I had seen him.'[9]

Marinov's death seemed to leave no one in the scientific community to act as bridge between Methernitha and the world.

A New Openness?

In July 1999, though, the Methernitha community appeared to take a bold step in opening up their technology to the world. They invited a group of around thirty Swiss technicians and engineers to visit them for a demonstration of their technology. Hans Holzherr, a Swiss engineer, wrote a report of the event in answer to some questions posed by a German researcher:

> To your questions:
> Q: Have you seen live a machine with a load? If so, what load?
> A: I am referring in the following to the model with the 50-cm diameter disks. This machine was already running when the visitors stepped into the room, and was not halted during the whole time – we were there

for about 1½ hours. As a first load a 1000-watt lamp was connected for approximately ten seconds, whose brightness did *not* diminish – the corresponding sequence on the Thesta-Distatica film is just an effect of the camera aperture's automatic adjusting to the sudden brightness![10]

This is an important point – on the community's own video (described by Hans Holzherr as a film), the light level does appear to dim almost as soon as the electric light 'load' is applied. It makes complete sense that this is an effect due to the camera's automatic exposure system.

A: The second load was a U-shaped heating element, and Mr Baumann handed it to me. It became so hot within one second that I had to put it down immediately! What was particularly impressive was that while he pulled back one of the contact wires (that was with the lamp, I believe), a 1-cm-long arc appeared between the output electrode and the connecting wire for approximately one second. The apparatus was under a plexiglass hood. Near the base it had two holes which Baumann used to insert the contact wires to touch the output electrodes.

Q: How do you think the wattage is produced?
A: Good question! I'd love to know the answer, too!
Q: Did the disks slow down when a load was placed across the output electrodes?
A: I did notice that (nobody else did), but of course you tend to turn your look to where the action is (the lamp etc.) The disks turned with 15 r.p.m, which is quite slow. The spin rate was regulated magnetically.
Q: What general impression did you have?
A: It was really impressive! One can hardly believe it, with this slow rotation. In any case, this cannot be explained in terms of bare electrostatics in the sense of the Wimshurst machine. The perforated sheets seem to

have a key function . . . Beside the pick-up and the drive electrodes there are a number of small plexiglass blocks with glued-on perforated sheets, whose function is unknown.

Q: Did the machine run the whole time? i.e. 1½ hours?

A: Yes.

Q: Could you imagine that in the base of the machine batteries of the flat cheque-card type are hidden, or would these be depleted too soon to account for the power produced during that 1½ hour period?

A: Unfortunately, I cannot judge that. If one considers that the Methernitha community gains neither money nor fame from the machine, and that they are so media-shy and otherwise restrictive I find the thought of a simple battery trick pretty absurd . . . (Of course a sceptic might argue that they are media-shy *because* it's a battery trick . . .)

Q: Could you touch the machine? Is the base of the device empty or is there something in it, or is it built from massive wood?

A: It was forbidden to touch the 50-cm machine, let alone lift it up. Therefore I cannot say anything about the base other than that it appeared solid. But one could touch the smaller type models, e.g. the small models with the 12-cm disks. One could lift them and examine them – while the disks kept turning. The whole atmosphere was rather loose – surprisingly. In this regard, being a group of over thirty persons was an advantage: the two Methernitha people (Viktor Bosshard and Paul Baumann) couldn't watch our fingers all the time! The earliest model is, by the way, the only one whose disks are propelled by an electric motor, which is driven by a capacitor which in turn is continuously recharged.

Q: I see, the plastic cover was for HV [high-voltage] security?

A: Also, I think it is a dust shield. The machine is really beautiful . . .

Q: In former reports it was stated that it ran with 50 r.p.m!?

A: I have read that, too. With this demo, however, the speed was approximately just 15 r.p.m. There are a number of plexiglass blocks with glued-on perforated sheet. Their function is unknown.

Q: Very strange. Are these 'special antennas'?

A: I don't know. Some have perforated sheets glued on two opposite sides, so they could be condensers; others have only one perforated sheet which is bent over an edge of the plexiglass block, so it covers two adjacent sides. After my visit I made a diagram of the 'principle experiment'.

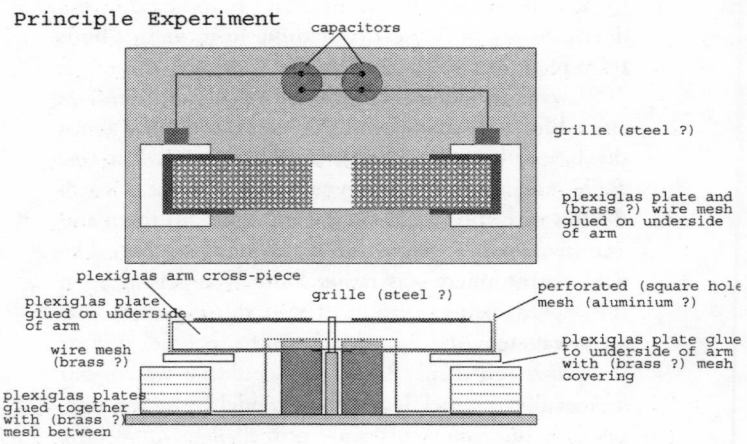

FIGURE 5.3   An interpretation of the 'Principle Experiment' by British researcher Paul Potter.

Q: Was that another device, or was that just a briefly modified existing machine?!

A: Another device? Baumann's comment: this is how it all started!

Q: Recently we got to know a person who had copied the 50-cm machine based on the Thesta-Distatica literature. However, this model does not function [is not self-running].

A: Yes. A pure Wimshurst machine will probably not even run itself, if one does not know the Methernitha secrets. I saw a photo from this copied device, and at first sight it looked like the original, including the horseshoe magnets.

Q: Apparently, Mr Baumann and Mr Bosshard were in a pretty informative mood that day?!

A: Yes. You could say that. Unfortunately, I had difficulties to understand Baumann because he spoke softly and fast, and provided explanations in non-scientific terms. However, it's very interesting that he answered my question [whether] the source of the Thesta-Distatica was radium chloride with a definite *no*. Also, they said, there exists no other Thesta-Distatica machine elsewhere. Nelson Camus [a free energy researcher] had told a different story: that he had encountered a similar community in South America which was in touch with Methernitha and which also possessed a Thesta-Distatica. According to Camus, the apparatus functions with radium chloride-doped condensers.[11]

There has been some speculation that the Thesta-Distatica contains a radioactive source, which is key to its working. Paul Baumann and the rest of the Methernitha team continue to deny this claim. It would seem unlikely that a community professedly committed to clean energy and a clean environment would get involved in using radioactive elements or compounds, but nevertheless the rumours persist. For some researchers it is the only explanation for the efficient capture of electrons on the machines' antennae. Paul Baumann says that a key secret lies in another direction: with the Linden experiment that Hans Holzherr described:

Q: Did Methernitha have no problem to show you the 'principle set-up' of your diagram?

A: Obviously not. They probably trust in the fact that not all secrets are *visible* on the machine. E.g. it looks like the molecular orientation of all plexiglass plates must be the same. And then the material plays a role.

Q: Don't they object against anybody copying the machine? Or do they think that one cannot understand the whole system quickly enough in such a demo?

A: No and yes. And they are probably darn right! It is hard to grasp!

Q: Could you see the small machines with a load, too? How much watts could these deliver? Approx. 300 watts? Those are more simply built, right?

A: With the 12-cm original model, Baumann got a voltage of 130 volts. He connected a load to it, which consisted of two small lamps and a resistor. Values unknown. After that, two visitors were asked to short-circuit the apparatus via their bodies, which gave them an electric shock! Interestingly enough, the digital voltmeter showed only briefly 130 volts, and then stopped working. All following measurements, also on the 50-cm machine, were made with an analogue meter. The smaller Thesta-Distaticas are simpler. Each one is built a bit differently. One has only one disk. Several, including a 1-m model under construction, have 'sector wires' instead of 'sector foils', which are sort of 'woven' into the disk, changing side three times.

Q: Were there bifilary coils inside the Leyden bottles (jars)?

> A: You could not see inside them. In the large capacitors there are twenty layers of perforated sheet, Baumann said. One just cannot see inside!
>
> Q: And there is a crystal diode somewhere?
>
> A: Yes. It's probably the object at the top. Baumann mentioned that also. On the original model it seemed to me to consist only of a rough coil around one central straight wire, with a total of four leads. With the 50-cm apparatus I tried my best, but could only make out two supply wires, so the structure was not very clear, maybe also a rough spiral around something (tube made from perforated sheet?). Perhaps there was also a tube around everything (my memory has faded), but I could not detect a crystal. I remember that it was hard to see inside. Regarding visibility in general, I noticed that a thin layer (which might be a lead) between two plexiglass plates is hardly noticeable at all, because of the total light reflection.[12]

While these kind of descriptions are useful to those attempting to 'reverse engineer' the machine, there is a still very little information from scientists claiming to understand *how* it actually works. Researchers Nelson Camus and J.L. Naudin both claim that the radioactive aspect is key to its functioning, but there is no first-hand evidence to support this idea. Yet Paul Potter, an independent British researcher who has looked seriously at the Methernitha machine over the last ten years, believes he has isolated the way that the machine could work. In an unpublished article, 'The Back-engineered Thesta-Distatica', he has attempted to pin down and describe all aspects of the machine:

> Obviously, the electronics are in two parts: one – the electrostatic generator and its particular technologies of how to direct what charged where; and two – the very unique auxiliary electromagnetic circuit of inductances, capacitances and rectification that mobilizes

that 'static' electricity. To understand how they convert static energy into an electromotive force you would do well to go back to the earliest years of radio. From the pages of spark radio news soon appreciate just how important isolation circuits and valve rectifiers were, and moreover, how difficult it proved to engineer them.[13]

Where Potter's understanding departs from that of some other researchers is in suggesting that the main power output does not come from the two contra-rotating disks alone:

There is, I believe, a far more important power generator, the electron cascade generator, and the Methernitha has two of them, held inside the two horseshoe magnets, and providing the circuits to the magnets are made to oscillate at the right frequency at high enough voltage then these metallized-perspex laminated blocks can enmass a much larger amount of electricity than is put into them . . .

The electron cascade or avalanche effect is where the air molecules are accelerated to the device at such a high velocity that they collide with other molecules and atoms in the air to liberate new electrons which in turn also collide and liberate even more 'free electrons' from other air molecules, all of which become accelerated by the electric field and an avalanche of electron multiplication as it progresses throughout the whole immediate environment. It's a chain reaction, it happens in a more ferocious way in lightning strikes. And, as in this case, the environment actually becomes part of the circuit because the process is actually negatively-ionizing the air surrounding the machines, and that is why those who have seen these new generators when working say the air around about them is cool and fresh.

Full Circuit

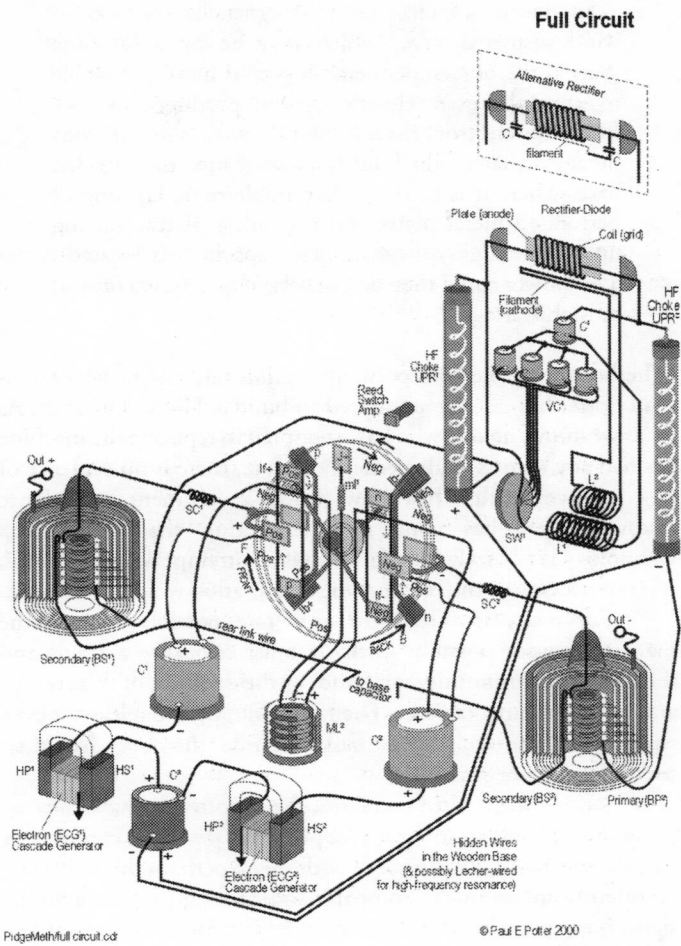

FIGURE 5.4 Exploded diagram of Methernitha's Thesta-Distatica by Paul Potter.

In view of the fact that its designers have chosen to wind insulated wire (which may be by a fine art) around the horseshoe metal, it would be very possible to draw the extra electric current produced directly from the electron cascade blocks, with suitable connections that might lead downward into the wooden base (where it is believed that an alternate layering of perforated metal plates and insulating plates, making up a large high-voltage storage capacitor, is located). This power could then be discharged as a pulsed output of high wattage.[14]

Whether this is the correct interpretation remains to be seen, as Paul Potter has not yet attempted to build a Thesta-Distatica. As far as we know, no one who has attempted to replicate the machine has had any success at all; certainly to date, there is no evidence of any positive results. Just how much government or defence research effort has gone into replicating the Methernitha technology is not fully known. Even if an attempt were successful, it is not necessarily the case that the information would be released.

For many this leads to only one possible answer: the machine cannot possibly work. It must either be a fraud and therefore the community is a fraud, or the delusion of this strange and possibly demented sect. Their unwillingness to release or even share the technology is a mask to hide the fact that their technology is not real.

If it is a fraud, then there must be a motive: perhaps they are using the machine to try to attract people to join their community and to share their worldly goods with them; perhaps they will soon be offering shares in the company and cashing in. There are no signs, however, that they are using the machine to actively attract people. Their website does not even mention its existence. They seem to spend a fair amount of time trying to put people off the scent, stressing that they have no intention of making it any more public than it currently is. Viktor Bosshard gives the appearance of being someone who would rather trade verses from the Bible than shares in any company. The members of the co-operative appear to be quiet, Bible-loving folk, keen to be left alone.

What could this religious group of people have to gain from over twenty years of pretence? Money? There was some good evidence that they'd already turned down some significant offers, and they certainly didn't seem to be selling. Indeed they seemed to be saying that they might all go to their graves with the secret intact, rather than release it to a God-ignoring world. Was it all a hoax designed to bring credit to their faith – a kind of modern, scientific miracle? A demonstration of proof not only of God's existence, but of his special love for his dedicated followers?

The only other possible explanation is that Paul Baumann is self-deluded about the workings of his machine. This is entirely tenable in most free-energy claims. Hundreds of researchers have caught themselves out by a combination of wishful thinking and incorrect or poor measurement techniques. In some cases they have compounded the problem by believing the error, promoting it and even raising money on it, before having to face the reality that they were wrong. By this time, for many, it's too late to admit they're wrong: in these cases the inventor may end up going to his grave with the denial still intact.

Yet where the Methernitha machines are more conclusive than virtually all other over-unity devices is that they don't just rely on measurement techniques: they appear to be self-sustaining. They appear to have closed the loop, to be running themselves *and* supplying usable energy.

And there can be no self-delusion in this case. It's either sustaining the motion of its counter-rotating disks, or it's not. If it's not, Baumann must be secretly helping with an outside source of energy like a battery, in which case he knows about it and it's fraud.

For many scientists, concerned about the impact of such a technology, coming as it does from a non-university, under-educated inventor, the possibility of the technology's reality as a solution to the energy crisis would be very embarrassing. It would really be much 'neater' if it were found to be a fraud or a delusion.

That would be a nice simple answer, which would let us all go home to 'normality'. All the tension induced by the Thesta-Distatica would no longer exist. We could relax.

If the technology is not a fraud, we cannot simply say we have a solution to the energy crisis. In fact the issue is more complicated: we have what could be the best, most effective self-sustaining energy-generating technology on the planet *and* we are told we can't have it. That's really frustrating! That's like being told you can be perfectly happy, peaceful and content, if only you can change your whole life right now. And perhaps, ironically, that's the point they're trying to make. Perhaps if we did all change and treat the planet as it deserved to be treated we wouldn't even need these machines. Perhaps the machines are some bizarre irrelevance to make us think about our 'Godless' ways . . .

Having visited the community, stayed with them, and talked extensively with them about their lives and the development of the Thesta-Distatica, I can only say that I found them genuine and sincere. They were unpretentious to the point of dullness. They seemed a very down-to-earth and hard-working group of people, who were as serious about their work in the furniture factory and in the market garden as they were about their faith. Regular prayer meetings were held, and the meetings of the community's council – which makes all the major decisions affecting the community – were always prefaced by prayers.

They said that all the development work was being carried out at another secret location. I have, though, seen Methernitha's own video footage of the machine functioning which formed part of the community's video about itself. At that time they were not showing outsiders any of the machines. I have also spoken to scientists who are more adept at spotting trickery and fraud than I am, who have personally examined the Thesta-Distatica and been convinced of its ability to produce energy from the atmosphere alone.

Here the search for the scientific truth is, in a strange way, reduced to a matter of belief. Either I believe what these, apparently genuine, Bible-reading people were saying, or I am accusing them of lying.

The suspicious, sceptical arguments didn't seem to square with the people I talked to. When I met them, my personal truth about the Thesta-Distatica's reality as the world's only true self-sustaining 'closed-loop' free-energy machine was reduced not to a set of energy measurements, or an independently carried out, third-party laboratory investigation, but to my own judgement of these people's character. It's not science, I know, but it's the only conclusion I can offer.

Today Paul Baumann and the Methernitha community continue their work on larger generators, apparently waiting for the time when humanity proves itself to be more than simply human.

CHAPTER SIX

The Life and Premature Death

of Cold Fusion

'Rumours of my death have been greatly exaggerated.'
                                        Mark Twain

'One of the greatest scandals in the history of science.'
Sir Arthur C. Clarke, June 1998, *Science*, talking about the ignoring
                                        of cold fusion.

Most people remember cold fusion as a strange announcement that was made in 1989 by two scientists, Professor Martin Fleischmann and Professor Stanley Pons, from University of Utah. The conventional story runs like this: they thought they'd achieved nuclear fusion in a glass of water and discovered the solution to the world's energy problem. After a few experiments by some other experts it was revealed that they'd made a mistake – even though the 'misguided pair' couldn't admit it – and everyone went back to the normality of a globally warmed world without the hope of a solution to our energy crisis.

Cold fusion entered the history books as a bad joke about bad science. Journalists, politicians and patent offices would never again get caught out, and everyone would be wiser next time a maverick scientist or two tried a similar trick . . .

Was that really the end of the story, though? And was it the true story? If so, why are laboratories in at least eight countries still spending millions on cold fusion research? And if cold fusion is impossible, how can it be that there are hundreds of documented experiments which demonstrate that cold fusion effects are real. How can it be that there is continually stronger evidence that a small group of scientists have already gone a long way towards a viable, commercial power source? Is it possible that parts of the scientific establishment acted to stamp out a technology which promised so much?

Here we look at the real story of cold fusion's premature demise, at the evidence for a cover-up and at the research that shows cold fusion wasn't bunk after all. We analyse some of the hundreds of experiments that demonstrate the reality of the cold fusion phenomenon, and hear from some of the many scientists who are still firmly convinced that it offers hope of a new energy technology for the twenty-first century and beyond.

What is Nuclear Fusion?

Not many miles from the dreaming spires of Oxford University is a machine called the Joint European Torus (JET). It is some 40 feet high and 60 feet in diameter, weighs 2700 tonnes and plays host to some of the hottest temperatures ever witnessed on planet earth. It is structured like the mould for a giant doughnut – a hollow ring-shaped vessel, surrounded by massive magnets, both conventional and electric. Energized by the machine's massive magnetic and electric fields, deuterium and tritium gases in the reaction vessel – which are the machine's fuel – can reach around 300 million degrees Celsius, many times hotter than the centre of the sun. Under these conditions electrons are stripped from their atoms, leaving the nucleii free to crash into each other and 'fuse', forming new helium atoms and giving off large releases of neutrons and heat.

This fusion reaction is the same mechanism by which stars, including our sun, generate their huge energy outputs. It has been known since Einstein's discovery of mass-energy equivalence (better known by its formula $E=mc^2$) that if it were possible to fuse hydrogen isotopes, then enormous amounts of energy could be liberated for our use. In theory it would be possible to fulfil one person's lifetime energy requirement by fusing only 15 grammes of tritium (hydrogen-3) and 10 grammes of deuterium (hydrogen-2). In this way fusion could be significantly more efficient and, some say, potentially safer than the nuclear fission process we currently employ in nuclear power plants.

In typical fission plants heavy, unstable isotopes of elements such as uranium are encouraged to undergo fission, or splitting, into isotopes of lighter elements such as strontium and caesium. While this process releases large amounts of heat, it also leaves unstable radioactive elements which remain active and dangerous for many years.

The challenge for the designers of fusion reactors is to engineer the process to yield more energy than is required to run it – an over-unity efficiency. Sadly, the highest level of efficiency ever achieved in a fusion reactor – at the JET reactor – is still only around 60 per cent, an event which lasted less than a second.

Since it was first built in the early 1980s, JET's fifteen European sponsor countries have put around £700 million into the project. In the US, where these hot fusion reactors are usually called Tokamaks, they have been even more fabulously expensive to build and run. Since 1950 some $15 billion of US government money have been spent on this Holy Grail of 'big science'. What is even more disappointing for the US taxpayer is that the US Department of Energy recently estimated that successful hot fusion is around five decades away, and they can still not guarantee that it will ever work reliably. The joke that dogs hot fusion is that it is the energy source of the future . . . and always will be. The expenditure has also been criticized because some scientists believe that even if a hot fusion reactor were to work, it would not be any more environmentally benign than other forms of nuclear power. It would have to generate its heat by slamming deadly neutron radiation into a surrounding container of a molten material such as liquid lithium, irradiating the entire machine with deadly radiation, and, eventually, damaging the reactor's structure. One of hot fusion's critics, Professor Lawrence Lidsky – who was an associate director of MIT's Plasma Fusion Center (PFC) for some time – has described the hot fusion project in less than glowing terms. In a 1983 article for MIT's *Technology Review*, he claimed that:

> Even if the fusion program produces a reactor, no one will want it . . . Long touted as an inexhaustible energy source for the next century, fusion as it is now being developed will almost certainly be too expensive and unreliable for commercial use . . . The scientific goal of the fusion program turns out to be an engineering nightmare . . . a fusion reactor might well produce only one-tenth as much power as a fission reactor of the same size.[1]

Lidsky's position did nothing to dampen the funding for MIT's hot fusion program, though, which still attracts tens of millions of dollars each year. With this kind of big science and big money at the heart of fusion research, perhaps it wasn't surprising that there were scientists who were wary, even suspicious, of Pons and Fleischmann with their beakerful of 'heavy' water . . .

The Real Story of Cold Fusion

Professor Martin Fleischmann and Professor Stanley Pons announced the birth of cold fusion to the world in Salt Lake City, Utah, at a news conference on 23 March 1989. Many spectators immediately believed they were witnessing the arrival of a new saviour: huge amounts of excess energy from a bottle of heavy water containing two metal electrodes – one of platinum and one of palladium. In exaltation, cold fusion's new parents were immediately celebrated for the extraordinarily happy event. Before the saviour could be confirmed as such, of course, rigorous tests would need to be performed.

Using the limited information available from Fleischmann and Pons's 'preliminary paper', the world's most respected laboratories attempted to repeat their experiments. They were looking for the 'tell-tale signs' of fusion reactions – a combination of 'excess heat' – output levels as much as ten times the input levels – and neutrons, tiny particles emitted from the nucleii of hydrogen atoms. The early, university-based Internet hummed with exchanges of method and theory.

Initially groups were divided about the results they were getting. A number of laboratories around the world came back with positive evidence: Professor Noburo Koyama of Tokyo University reported large amounts of heat and gamma radiation; in Italy Francesco Scaramuzzi, using a different approach, produced huge amounts of neutrons, but a tiny amount of heat; at Stanford University, Robert Huggins said he had obtained excess heat from his cell; John Bockris's team at Texas A&M University claimed to witness high levels of the signatures of nuclear fusion: neutrons released from the heavy water, tritium – the heaviest form of hydrogen – and helium, the new element formed in the fusion reaction. Researchers at Case Western Reserve University reported excess heat and tritium generation in their electrochemical cells.

Others said they were getting nothing – no heat, no neutrons, no helium. Yale University and the Brookhaven National Laboratory jointly reported no nuclear products. Harwell in the UK – part of the UK Atomic Energy Authority which oversees the nearby JET reactor – also said that it could not see any positive results.

While newspapers, governments and many scientists were eager for a quick and easy answer to the viability of the new saviour, what quickly became clear – even to cold fusion's adherents – was that these experiments were not as simple as at first thought. There were questions about the specific qualities of the materials involved, particularly the palladium, and the heat and power measurements required to produce accurate and reliable data were also proving intensely difficult to pin down.

What also became clear was that although Pons and Fleischmann were utterly confident of their measurements of large amounts of heat, they were not claiming that they understood how to control the process, or that they knew how to make it more reliable. Fleischmann even said that it could take as long as twenty-five years before the process could be fully commercialized. For those looking for definite answers, however, this was not what they wanted to hear.

In most conventional hot fusion projects – under what's known as the Rutherford model – physicists aim to 'fuse' deuterium ('heavy' hydrogen comprising one neutron and one proton in the nucleus) and tritium (hydrogen-3 with two neutrons and one proton in the nucleus). In this model the two atoms fuse to form a helium-4 nucleus plus a high energy neutron. Pons and Fleischmann had quite a different fusion reaction in their electrolytic cells: they thought that they were bringing together deuterium nucleii under such a force that they were fusing together. From the conventional standpoint this reaction between two deuterium nucleii has three possible outcomes: about half the reactions lead to helium-3 (two protons and a neutron) plus a high energy neutron; the other half result in

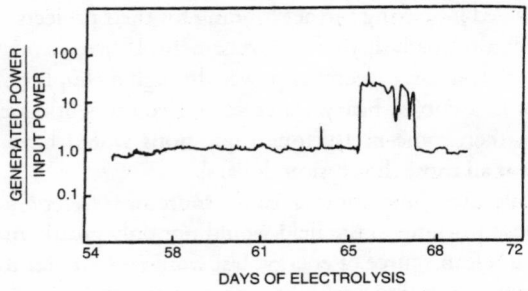

FIGURE 6.1 A 'power burst' of excess heat described in the first Pons/Fleischmann paper following the initial Utah annoucement in March 1989. The burst continues from day 65 to day 68. For about 48 hours the ratio of generated power to input power is around 20.

tritium (two neutrons and a proton) plus a high energy proton; in rare cases – around one in ten million cases – the reaction yields helium-4 (two protons and two neutrons) plus a high-energy gamma ray. The hot fusion camp were quite adamant about their expectations: if this really was fusion then Pons and Fleischmann should be getting these productions along with their heathelium-3 and a neutron. But where was the evidence?

In questioning the Pons–Fleischmann experiment, some sceptical scientists put their objection quite bluntly: 'Why aren't you dead?' If it really was fusion in the normal sense, then the neutron radiation from the process should have killed them. Pons and Fleischmann had themselves expected that the reaction would probably produce the same nuclear products, even though they had not tested for either helium-3 or helium-4. They believed they had detected both tritium and neutrons, although they eventually had to retract their claim for neutrons amidst fierce recriminations from their sceptical critics that they had manipulated data.

The second cause for pressure on Pons and Fleischmann was the predictable reaction that hot fusion scientists – who had been the beneficiaries of much government funding over the years – felt understandably threatened. Many of them were, at this time, involved in seeking further funding for their projects. There was the definite possibility of embarrassment. If two chemists had been able to run some electrical power through a couple of metal electrodes in a cup of heavy water and solve the world's energy problems, then some pretty tough questions would have to be asked about all those 'hot fusion dollars'.

While everyone wants a clean source of energy for the world, those working in the field would not only greatly prefer it to be 'their' clean source of energy, but would also prefer to keep their jobs and scientific credibility intact. Pons and Fleischmann were threatening the reputations, livelihoods, not to mention the egos, of a lot of prominent people. With presidents, prime ministers and governments from all over the world wanting to know whether this thing was real, there was pressure to come to a

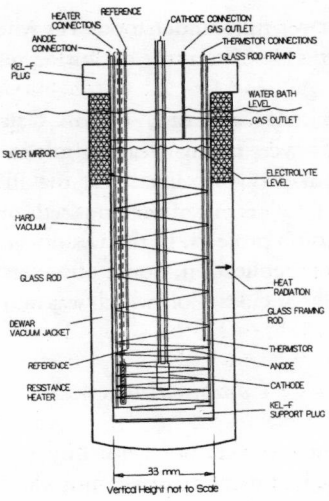

FIGURE 6.2 Schematic diagram of a Pons/Fleischmann cell. (The height is foreshortened.)

quick and final answer: did it work, or was it all a load of hooey?

As Robin McKie of the *Sunday Times* put it on 16 April 1989:

> Clearly something very peculiar is happening. Either previous fusion researchers have been guilty of squandering billions of pounds trying to recreate the power of the sun in huge expensive machines when a couple of metal tubes and a beaker could do the job much better – or one of the greatest hypes in history has just been perpetrated.

It is interesting that the choice even had to be put in this way: someone is guilty and someone has to pay the price. There are, of course, a number of other possibilities – one being Fleischmann's original claim that what they had witnessed was a 'hitherto unknown process' which was quite distinct from the hot fusion reaction, and not yet fully understood. Yet when it came to the judgement over this issue it was the hot fusion researchers who got to decide . . .

In the US, MIT's Plasma Fusion Center and its own Tokamak reactor – were taking a leading role in the assessment of the Pons–Fleischmann work. Each year the PFC would receive tens of millions of dollars out of the hundreds of millions that are awarded to hot fusion projects. In the UK it was Harwell that was attempting the key replication. Some observers said it was a bit like asking the folks at Coca-Cola which was best – Pepsi or Coke?

Complications . . .

Pons and Fleischmann were not helped by a number of further complicating factors. Firstly they were not physicists. They were, in fact, electrochemists. Albeit that Fleischmann was probably the most highly respected electrochemist in the world at this time, it was still a transgression of the rule that nuclear fusion belonged to the physicists.

The second complicating factor that did not endear them to their peers was that they had announced their 'preliminary' result at a news conference, instead of through the normal channels of peer-reviewed journals such as *Nature* and *Science*. The reasons behind this were not simple either. Pons and Fleischmann, who had been funding this research out of their own money – about $100,000 of it – had discovered that another scientist, Dr Steve Jones of Brigham Young University (also in Utah), was about to make an announcement of his own, claiming the production of neutrons from a similar 'palladium in heavy water' electro-chemical reaction. When Pons and Fleischmann told their own University of Utah what the situation was, they were told that they would have to initiate patent protection and announce their results quickly, before Jones made his announcement. This was not what Pons and Fleischmann wanted to do: knowing the controversial nature of their results, they would much rather have gone for a low-key, drip-by-drip information feed. It was not to be. Despite his protests, Fleischmann was put up before the world's press and a university press release was issued which read: 'Breakthrough process has potential to provide inexhaustible source of energy.'

Fleischmann was questioned about the announcement on the UK's BBC Radio 4 in 1997 (For a full transcript, see Appendix 6). The interview with presenter John Humphrys went as follows:

Martin Fleischmann: I knew it would go bad . . .

John Humphrys: And it did go bad.

Martin Fleischmann: Yes. I knew it was not a sensible thing to do.

John Humphrys: And the result of that was that it exposed, I suppose, apart from anything else, all the jealousies that operate in the scientific world.

Martin Fleischmann: Well, there were plenty of jealousies. It was a singularly unfortunate time to make this announcement. It was the fiftieth anniversary of the discovery of nuclear fission. And the hot fusion brigade were just gearing themselves up to ask for a lot more money. For the next step in the research in [to] hot fusion. So it was a singularly unfortunate time for two chemists to make such an announcement. That was certainly true, and of course, if we had not been put into that situation in March 1989 – if we could have delayed, even until December 1989 – we would then have published the full paper rather than the preliminary paper. And my recommendation was that this should be let out at the lowest possible level.

John Humphrys: Without a great fuss, you mean?

Martin Fleischmann: Yes. In fact, I wanted to have it published in the *Annals of Utah Science*, of which I believe they only print seven copies.

John Humphrys: Not a best-seller, exactly.

> Martin Fleischmann: Not a best-seller. I wanted to
> really let it out in a really very minor way.[2]

Could it really be that professional jealousies and fears of
embarrassment would be enough to motivate scientists to kill off
what promised to be major technological breakthrough? It seems
almost unthinkable. Fleischmann himself believes that there were
also forces inside the US Department of Energy – led by its
director Admiral Watkins – that were extremely unhappy with
the idea that such a potentially useful military technology could
be developed by chemists in ordinary university laboratories.

May, June and July Are the Strangest Months

What was perhaps the first of the 'killer blows' to cold fusion's
reputation occurred on 1 May 1989. A front-page article
appeared in the *Boston Herald* with the headline: 'MIT
BOMBSHELL KNOCKS FUSION "BREAKTHROUGH" COLD'. The
article, written by a young journalist named Nick Tate, was the
result of an interview with the director of MIT's Plasma Fusion
Center, Professor Ronald R. Parker. In the piece Parker, who was
intimately involved in gaining funding for MIT's hot fusion
project, described the work of Pons and Fleischmann as 'scientific
schlock' and 'maybe fraud'. He claimed that the results were just
not true' and added: 'Everything I've been able to track down has
been bogus.' He also criticized University of Utah's attempt to
attract $25 million of funding from the US Congress to set up a
fusion centre to commercialize the technology, describing the
actions as an attempt to 'fleece' the government. The article had a
huge impact, despite the fact that Parker subsequent denied that
he had actually said the key words. His 'analysis' of Pons and
Fleischmann's work was to prove immensely influential in the
weeks, months and years that followed. The battle for the soul of
fusion was now in full swing – and it would no longer be fought
out in the world's laboratories. The battleground had shifted to

the corridors of scientific and political power.

The very next day, 2 May, at a meeting of the American Physical Society in Baltimore, Maryland, Parker, together with other 'sceptical' scientists from Caltech and other universities, rounded on the work of Pons and Fleischmann, claiming that they had found flaws in their original neutron data. At this stage MIT had not completed any of their own experiments in an attempt to replicate the original work, nor had they taken into consideration any positive data coming from other sources.

A week later in Los Angeles, Pons and Fleischmann retracted their neutron analysis but stood firm on their excess heat data. While the pair acknowledged that their neutron data was open to some questioning, they were adamant that their energy production data was consistent and accurate – they had seen massive amounts of energy over a period of months. Speaking in 1997, Fleischmann emphasized just how far they had got: 'It is important to recall that we had by that time reached specific rates of energy production roughly equal to those in gas-cooled fission reactors.'[3] While he knew that controlling and scaling up this reaction was a task that would take tens of years, he was standing firm on the importance of the breakthrough. The assumption behind the attack was important, though. The sceptics' approach was that if they could prove that there were no significant levels of neutrons, then the reaction could not be fusion, and the whole experiment would be flawed.

A further ten days later, on 18 May, the influential, but already sceptical journal *Nature* published more of MIT's criticisms of Pons and Fleischmann's work. At this point there were suggestions from some quarters that John Maddox, the editor of *Nature*, was upset at being left out of the process by the original news conference. Maddox maintained that his scepticism was purely a response to what he regarded as poorly conducted science.

On 15 June Harwell, unable to replicate any of the results – despite some consultation with Fleischmann – stopped work on cold fusion research, and went back to its hot fusion work.

Fleischmann, however remains critical of Harwell's methods and analysis: 'The apparatus used at Harwell was deficient in many regards. You have to design the experiment and then you have to analyse the results. And this is . . . this problem of analysing the results is where most of the failures in science take place.'[4]

Not only were there questions about the materials available to Harwell (a factor that has been found to be absolutely critical to success); other scientists have questioned the analysis methods applied by Harwell. Dr Harold Aspden of the University of Southampton was especially critical:

> To test whether the Fleischmann–Pons cell could produce excess heat Harwell put in a calorimeter which was controlled expressly to be at a uniform temperature. If temperature gradient is needed to trigger the effect leading to the action which stimulates cold fusion, then precluding that temperature gradient from existing is bound to get you nowhere.
>
> Harwell as good as killed the goose that laid the golden eggs and then declared that it could not lay any eggs![5]

Nevertheless, the press regarded Harwell's failure to get any positive results as terminal. Jane Bird, writing in the *Sunday Times* of 7 May 1989, had already commented on Harwell's initial negative results: 'Harwell's findings will be greeted with relief by scientists working on conventional fusion. Had cold fusion succeeded, forty years and £12 billion would have been wasted.'

Despite this, further positive results continued to flow in. On 26 June researchers at the Los Alamos National Laboratory announced that they had found tritium in their cold fusion experiment. The very same day, though, scientists at MIT's Plasma Fusion Center held a 'Wake for Cold Fusion', in spite of the fact that they had yet to complete any analysis of their own replication experiments – the Phase II Calorimetry experiments.

In late June the Utah State Fusion Energy Advisory Council

– loyal to their local university and the commercial potential of its discovery – released the first monies of a $5 million fund to further cold fusion research. Yet on 12 July a panel of the US Department of Energy – strongly influenced by the work of Harwell, Caltech and MIT – announced that it could find no evidence to support the setting up of a research centre for cold fusion. There would be no public dollars for cold fusion research, no open-minded funding to discover what was really going on in this mysterious new process. National scientific support for cold fusion in the US was now dead.

The final nail in the coffin for the public perception of cold fusion came with the publication of MIT's analysis of its own experiments, which showed that no generation of heat had occurred in their Phase II Calorimetry experiments. Yet it would be another eighteen months before the real story behind their results emerged – and accusations would be made (albeit too late) that they had manipulated their data to hide positive evidence of excess heat.

Despite all the positive experimental evidence to the contrary, 99.9 per cent of the public believed that cold fusion was not real. There is no doubt that the subject is a discredited field. The negative results of experiments at Harwell and MIT have seen to that. But is anyone really suggesting that these experiments were deliberately made to fail, or that the data was manipulated in some way?

Was there a 'Heavy Watergate'?

Perhaps the most severe critic of the events of 1989 is Eugene Mallove, an MIT graduate with three degrees in Engineering (one from Harvard) and now the editor of *Infinite Energy* magazine. At the time of the cold fusion announcement Mallove was in a privileged position: he was the chief science writer in the MIT's press office, and was party to nearly all the information that was put out by the Plasma Fusion Center. Over a number of weeks and months Mallove became utterly convinced that there was a deliberate campaign to discredit the work of Pons and Fleischmann, and to make sure that cold fusion research was able neither to embarrass the hot fusion camp nor to divert any of its regular budget (at least $200 million per annum in the United States) away from hot fusion.

> The actions of certain MIT staff members in 1989 were a major influence on the news media, on other scientists, and on the funding support for cold fusion. This is a matter of record. Though a small group of open-minded, involved faculty staff, and alumni pursued and continue to pursue cold fusion, MIT as a whole did, indeed, acquire the deserved reputation as a 'bastion of skepticism' on cold fusion. Sad to say, it was initially only a handful of MIT staff and faculty who gave MIT this reputation. They inappropriately drove many others – on campus and off – to dismiss the claims from Utah in 1989 and the research that has followed.
>
> As the record shows, the first assault against the truth in 1989 was press manipulation by faculty members at MIT's Plasma Fusion Center. They did not believe the Utah work at all. They suspected that Pons and Fleischmann were engaged in a 'scam', and they were concerned that if the public were to have a too open-minded attitude toward the prospect of cold fusion as an energy solution, funding for their beleaguered thermonuclear program would be endangered – even more so than its perennial brushes with budgetary extinction.[6]

Mallove, who had once been proud of his relationship with MIT, resigned from their press office in 1991 over what he believed was a hugely important scientific scandal. But what's the evidence for such an inflammatory claim?

When the *Boston Herald* ran its 1 May article headlined 'MIT BOMBSHELL KNOCKS FUSION "BREAKTHROUGH" COLD', the article's influence went around the world. It also went deep into the US Department of Energy, where its influence would be most clearly felt. Yet on the night before the newspaper article was published Professor Parker had rung Eugene Mallove at his home to orchestrate the issuing of a press release which would deny Parker's use of the terms 'scientific schlock' and 'maybe fraud' to describe Pons and Fleischmann's work. Mallove immediately issued the press release to the wire services, quoting Parker's denial. What made the next day's headlines, however, were the words 'schlock' and 'fraud'. Even MIT's president, Paul Gray, was drawn into the fray, backing Parker's position. Later that day Parker issued his own statement: 'Let me just say quite clearly for everybody, that I am not, have not, and, uh, really seriously doubt whether I ever will accuse Professors Pons and Fleischmann of fraud . . .'[7]

Journalist Nick Tate, the author of the article, was more than surprised by this: 'Not only were the concerns about possible misinterpretation and fraud and "scientific schlock" repeated to me more than one time during the course of our interview, but I also had them on tape.'[8]

At this time, though, Tate decided not to go public with the contents of his tape. It was not until July 1990 that he rang Eugene Mallove and played him the recording of the interview from 28 April 1989 involving Parker, Tate and another MIT anti-cold fusioneer Professor Richard Ballinger:

> Tate: Let me ask you, just back up a step. You're talking about – I presume you're talking about traditional scientific controls and traditional scientific methods that have not been observed in this particular situation.
> Parker: This is sci— I'll give you a quote: this is scientific schlock, OK.

A few paragraphs later, Parker goes even further:

> Parker: You can use the data in two ways, to show that
> they falsely interpreted it, but also that there weren't
> neutrons at the level they claimed.
> Tate: So at best it's misinterpretation and at worst it's
> – as you were saying . . .
> Parker: It's fraud.[9]

Some two years later the *Boston Herald* reporter acknowledged the
impact the article's contents may have had:

> The MIT analysis debunked the Utah claims, and in
> [the] interview with the *Herald*, Parker – who wrote the
> report with Dr Richard Petrasso – said the chemists
> [Pons and Fleischmann] misinterpreted their [own]
> results. He also called it possibly fraudulent 'scientific
> schlock'. Some say those comments set the tone for the
> national criticism of the Utah work that followed.[10]

The other piece of evidence that is key to Mallove's case against
the MIT's Plasma Fusion Center, is the data from the one single
experiment which had the most impact on the future progress of
cold fusion research. It was entitled, in typically complex
language, 'Measurement and Analysis of Neutron and Gamma-
Ray Emission Rates, Other Fusion Products, and Power in
Electrochemical Cells Having Pd Cathodes'. It became better
known by the abbreviated 'Phase II Calorimetry Study', and was
first published in MIT's own *Journal of Fusion Energy*. The results
of this experiment were used around the world, in *Nature* and
Science, by the US Department of Energy as the key reference in
its final funding rejection, and later by the US Patent Office, to
justify the rejection of further cold fusion technologies.

On 19 January 1991 Mallove made an extraordinary
discovery about the experiment. Sorting through some of the
massive amounts of information that had hit his desk during the

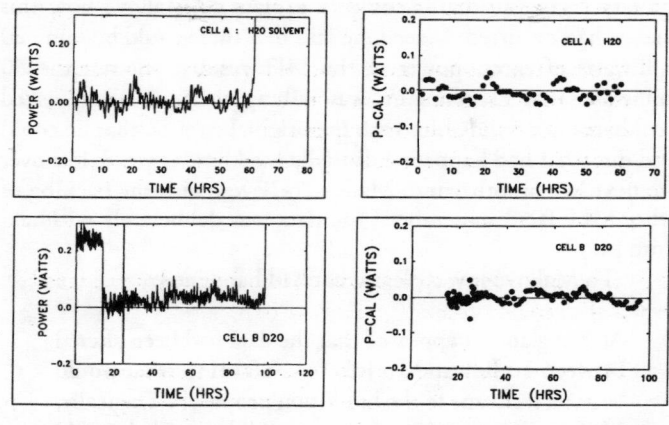

Calorimetry data from 10 July 1989 draft.   Calorimetry data from 13 July 1989 draft.

FIGURE 6.3 The two graphs on the left from the unpublished draft report show the control experiment CELL A using ordinary water (H_2O) and CELL B showing the Deuterium Oxide (D_2O). CELL B shows evidence of consistent excess heat (beyond electrical input power) while CELL A shows no such evidence. The two graphs on the right from the published report, which use dots to represent an average power over each hour, no longer show any excess heat in CELL B. The data appears to have been shifted down. MIT say that this 'compensation' was to allow for 'loss of solvent', a rationale that Mallove and others dispute.

events of 1989, he discovered two sets of draft data from the original Phase II Calorimetry Experiments. Both were visual graphs referring to the same experiment, but one was dated 10 July, the other 13 July. Both had been supplied by the PFC team during the rush to publish the paper.

Mallove was appalled and shocked: while the 13 July data – the data that was eventually published – displayed no excess heat, the 10 July data appeared to show continuous amounts of excess heat for the majority of the 100-hour test period.

He first challenged Dr Stanley Luckhardt, who had carried out the actual experiments on the cells. In a lunch meeting on 25

January 1991 Luckhardt couldn't explain to Mallove how this change had occurred. Indeed, he said that there could be some 20 milliwatts of excess power in the MIT results, but not the 80 milliwatts that Fleischmann was talking about. Mallove asked Luckhardt to provide him with the original data, so that he could find out what had happened. Initially Luckhardt agreed, but over the next five months, and, Mallove believes, with the backing of other MIT faculty members, the data was deliberately withheld from him.

To Mallove it was clear what had happened:

> At first glance it appeared that the data had been altered between 10 July and 13 July to conform to what would be most welcome to the hot fusion people . . . Tragically, MIT as an institution was not to fulfil the role it could have played in bringing cold fusion technology to the world. Quite the contrary: thanks to various false information coming from the hot fusion lab at MIT, the high-profile reputation of MIT was used to legitimize the view that cold fusion is bunk. It was said that the PFC calorimetry results disproved cold fusion – showed no excess heat. This is far from correct . . .
>
> The truth about the calorimetry experiment performed at MIT in 1989 under D.o.E. contract funding . . . is stark and unambiguous. Its purported 'negative' result was used to influence the US Department of Energy's rushed 1989 report against cold fusion.[11]

On 7 June 1991, disgusted with the actions of MIT's hot fusion experts, Mallove tendered his resignation in a seventeen-page letter. Two months later he wrote a formal request to the president of MIT for an investigation of scientific misconduct by a number of the PFC staff. Despite many months of wrangling with the authorities at MIT, his requests were denied. President Vest at MIT, having consulted with others, and having commissioned an internal assessment as to whether a formal enquiry should be put in place, supported the view that no one had done anything wrong. There had been no manipulation, either of data, or the media. End of story. Looking back, ten years after the event, Mallove is still as bitter about what happened as he was then:

> The energy and environmental future of the world hung in the balance – and the MIT PFC people failed us. They preferred to get rid of a scientific claim in which they did not believe, and which threatened their federally funded program, by playing politics with the media, trivializing their experiments, and ultimately foisting on the world highly flawed data – some would say fraudulently represented data – from a calorimetry experiment ostensibly performed to determine scientific truth.[12]

A set of events had been initiated which led to the conventional wisdom that cold fusion was, and still is, scientific bunk. Pons and Fleischmann, suddenly demoted from avatars to heretics, continued to claim that their new gnosis defied all denial: they had seen it, measured it. Given its potential importance it must surely be worth an open-minded analysis? After all, they also had the significant support of some other laboratories who had produced a variety of positive results. 'Not enough', said the orthodoxy. 'Until all can produce the same evidence, it cannot be true.' And lo, the orthodoxy prevailed: no more papers on cold fusion would henceforth be published in 'reputable' journals; no more serious funding would support it; and no more patents would be considered which claimed such impossible ideas.

To this day Mallove continues to support cold fusion research through his magazine *Infinite Energy*, which is itself supported by Sir Arthur C. Clarke. It is possibly the only organ that reports on all experiments carried out in the low-energy nuclear reaction field. Despite what Mallove perceives as the good news of this whole field – a growing list of positive results, an increased understanding of the problems inherent in the experiments, the development of strategies to commercialize successful technologies – scientists researching in this area are well aware that they work in a discredited field.

Why Haven't We Heard Anything Positive Since 1989?

The popular wisdom that cold fusion was bunk, a hoax and 'bad science' has prevailed since the middle of 1989, reinforced by a variety of books, jokes and magazine articles. The press now sees the subject as so comic, so archetypally ridiculous, that cold fusion now struggles to generate all but the most damning coverage.

The general public has been left with the image of cold fusion as a laughable mistake – an example of how scientists working alone in dark laboratories can become unhinged, self-deluded and self-deceived. After all, the lay person might think, it can't be that difficult to work out what's happening with a couple of pieces of metal in a jar of water. And, the logic says, if it works, it must be simple to recreate, simple to scale up, simple to prototype and commercialize. The fact that you can't buy a cold fusion power plant from the local shop must be proof that the whole thing was a mistake.

Think again, because cold fusion isn't what everyone expected.

In the years since the first announcement, an extraordinary story has unfolded, almost totally behind closed doors. The battle for cold fusion's life has been played out by researchers all over the world, reporting on thousands of experiments, based on hundreds of thousands of hours of running experimental cells.

What these researchers have discovered is that there is no one simple answer to the question 'What actually happens when you put different types, sizes and thicknesses of palladium and platinum electrodes in a jar of deuterium oxide [heavy water], and run an electric current through it?' Hal Fox, editor of *New Energy*

News, has been involved in assessing the 3000 papers generated by cold fusion experiments since 23 March 1989. He reports that: 'The initial Pons–Fleischmann effect has been replicated and/or improved as reported in over 600 papers from over 200 laboratories in 30 countries.'[13]

Apart from the original 'positive' results from 1989 quoted above, here are summaries of some of the key results which have been reported during the 1990s.

In August 1994 Stanford Research International (SRI) (a commercial spin-off from Stanford University) and the Electric Power Research Institute published a paper which confirmed the original claims of Fleischmann, Pons and Hawkins (another early cold fusion researcher) – namely the production of excess heat at levels too large to be explained by a normal chemical transformation. They also confirmed small but definite evidence for nuclear reactions occurring at forty orders of magnitude larger than expected.

One month earlier, in July 1994, Miles, Bush and Lagowski of the Naval Air Warfare Center (Weapons Division) at China

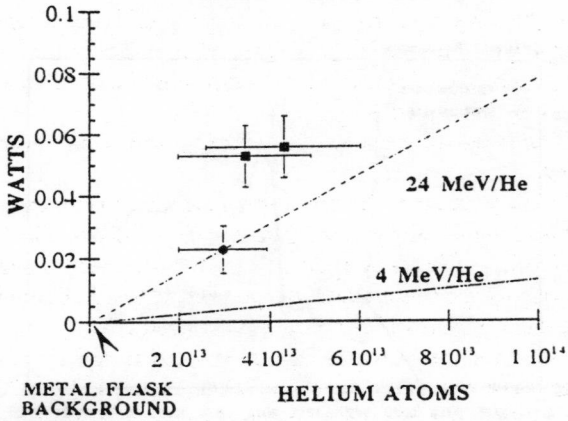

FIGURE 6.4 Miles reported the presence of helium atoms and showed that their number roughly correlated with the excess power generation in a Pons/Fleischmann type cell.

Lake, California confirmed the production of levels of helium-4 commensurate with a nuclear fusion reaction. In the same experiments they also confirmed evidence of excess power and some 'anomalous' radiation.

In September 1996 they followed this with a more detailed paper, 'Anomalous Effects in Deuterated Systems', in which 30 out of 33 experiments showed a correlation between excess heat and excess production of helium. 'Our results provide compelling evidence that the anomalous effects in deuterated systems are real . . . It is highly unlikely that our heat and helium correlations could be due to random errors . . . our best experiments produced up to 30 per cent excess heat, 0.52 watts of excess power.'[14]

At Texas A&M University in 1992, John O'M. Bockris and others published evidence of massive amounts of tritium production in their fusion cells' palladium electrode. (Bockris had undergone an investigation following claims by a journalist that one of the researchers had 'spiked' one of his 1989 cells with tritium to provide a positive result. No evidence to support this allegation had ever been brought forward.)

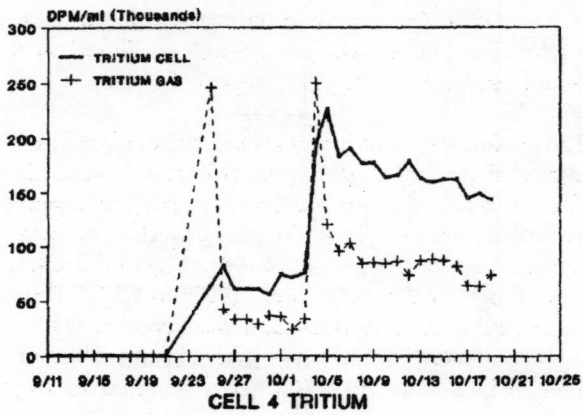

FIGURE 6.5 Bockris reported (Lin et al) tritium activity levels from their cell 4.

In 1991 the National Cold Fusion Institute, set up with $5 million of Utah state money in 1989, published evidence of highly significant tritium production inside their palladium cathodes: 'Only nuclear reactions, whose nature is as yet unknown, could have produced the observed tritium.'

In September 1993 Shell Research of France described:

Excess energy production, well above the background and in amounts of the same order of magnitude as the input energy, has been measured . . . This excess energy production is stable over long periods (several weeks) and is observed with both hydrogen and deuterium. Only extremely low levels of neutrons and tritium have been detected, many orders of magnitude below what would be expected from the excess energy production measured. On the contrary, copious emission of low-energy radiation (likely to be beta-rays) have been observed.[15]

In October 1996 a group from Tsinghua University in China announced the results of a long-term study of deuterium/palladium systems. In a comparison study between cells containing deuterium and those containing ordinary 'light' water, the team found significantly different 'outputs':

The preliminary result has shown that the calorimetric feature of the D/Pd [deuterium/palladium] system is distinct from that of its twin H/Pd [hydrogen/palladium] system. The difference between these twin systems can be attributed to the excess heat of the order of watts per cubic centimeter of palladium . . . We have observed this excess heat for more than five months . . . It is about 1,000 eV [electron volts] for each palladium atom, which it is very difficult to attribute to any chemical resource.

At Osaka University in Japan Professors Arata and Zhang announced in 1997 that they found significant and important support for a fusion reaction:

> Significantly large amounts of helium . . . were detected from deuterated palladium samples that had produced large amounts of anomalous excess energy (200-500 MJ/cm^3) [megajoules per cubic centimetre] during cold fusion experiments (~5000 hrs). The helium was released from samples after the observation of excess energy . . .[16]

These are just a sample of some of the experiments that have been carried out since 1989 which demonstrate either excess heat, helium generation, tritium generation or any combination of these (although, interestingly, few claim neutron emissions). It remains as true now as it did in 1989 that conventional theory predicts none of these things from a low-energy process. Nevertheless the research work has generated a great deal of new theory. Indeed there are now believed to be some thirty separate theories to explain the processes involved in 'low energy nuclear reactions' as they have become known.

Scott Chubb of the Naval Research Laboratory, a cold fusion researcher, believes that the very name may have led to its demise:

> A . . . lesson of CF [cold fusion] is the importance of language. From the beginning, incorrect language has plagued CF. The results have been catastrophic. The problems began when the Brigham Young University public relations department coined the expression 'cold fusion', and Pons and Fleischmann [PF] decided to use the same name. This almost killed the field because many scientists assumed from the name cold fusion that PF had discovered a colder version of conventional fusion, while, at an early stage, it was obvious that this

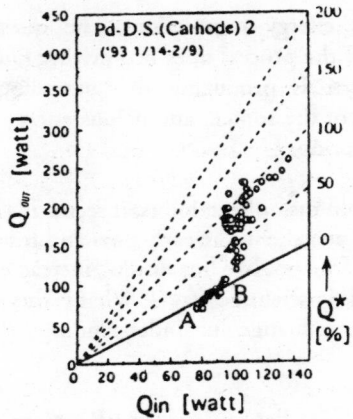

FIGURE 6.6 Arata showed power output as a function of input power. At 125 watts of input power, there was approximately 250 watts of output power – giving an output to input ratio of 2.

simply was not true. We now know that PF discovered a new form of room temperature nuclear reaction, in which no high-energy particles are released . . .[17]

Edmund Storms worked at the Los Alamos National Laboratory for thirty-four years, before retiring to pursue the cold fusion field more directly. He comments:

> The field, which is conventionally called 'cold fusion', has grown and now should be called 'chemically assisted nuclear reactions' or 'low-energy nuclear reactions' . . . The claims are supported by a wide range of anomalous behaviours involving nuclear reactions and energy production . . .
>
> Some scientists require neutron emission to be observed before they will accept the claim for a fusion reaction. Significant neutron emission (in a Pons–Fleischmann cell) is not observed during

anomalous energy production. The question then becomes, if the process does not involve conventional fusion, what is producing the anomalous energy? Regardless of the source, anomalous energy is a claim worth exploring.[18]

Whatever the cold fusion reaction is, it seems it's not the same as hot fusion. The mistake in the early days and months was to say, 'It can't be real if it's not like hot fusion', instead of saying – in an open-minded, truly scientific way – 'What is this reaction? Could it be new? Could it change our understanding?'

The Reproducibility Problem

One thing that has plagued progress in the cold fusion field is that the reactions involved are not fully reliable, consistent or reproducible on demand. Under some conditions certain nuclear products are created, while in others they are not. The amounts of excess heat generated are not consistent either, and the mechanism by which it is produced is a long way from being understood, let alone made fully controllable. This was one of the original points that Fleischmann and Pons had tried to make clear to their critics. In the rush for a swift answer, and an answer that pleased the hot fusioneers, it was much simpler to explain 'failed' experiments with the simple idea that the whole thing didn't work.

As the years have gone by, these shortcomings have been diminished through the minute analysis of all the variables involved in these experiments. Different types of palladium have been analysed, and some experimenters, such as Melvin Miles of the Naval Weapons Center at China Lake, California, have found that they can now achieve significant power output in as many as 80 per cent of their experiments.

It has become absolutely clear that excess heat from these cells still offers the real hope of a new energy source. Michael H.

McKubre, of Stanford Research International, is highly confident: 'The evidence, in my view, for the appearance of an anomalous unaccounted excess heat in the deuterium-palladium system is essentially overwhelming. There is something there. It's larger by more than one order of magnitude, in some cases by more than two orders of magnitude.'[19]

Asked recently about the potential for commercialization he was optimistic:

> We have to increase the effect, in scientific terms, intensively rather than extensively. We have to make the effect a larger fraction of the input. Then we'll scale it up and make the devices much bigger and more practical . . . So we need something that the average politician, the average banker, or the average person can understand the significance of, and I think we're pretty close.[20]

As far as the future goes, it's likely to be a long and rocky path to get more reliable, consistent and reproducible results. The variables that are involved in the experiments are far from fully understood. One researcher has likened the status of the technology to that of semi-conductors in the 1950s.

Despite the positive results it has become patently clear that even if cold fusion technologies (or low-energy nuclear reaction technologies) have a future, the experiments involved are considerably more complex and hard to replicate than anyone had, at first, imagined. Contributing editor of *Infinite Energy* magazine Jed Rothwell is sanguine:

> We want a simple and cheap experiment that anyone can do. But this may be inherently impossible. After all, there is no simple, cheap way to reproduce a Pentium processor, the alloy used in a jet engine fan blade, or the Sistine Chapel. Many objects are inherently difficult to reproduce, including a surprising number that are widely used and vital to modern lifestyles. Micro-

processors, laser printers, catalytic converters, long-life NiCad batteries and other high-tech products require expert attention, automated production lines, billion-dollar factories, clean rooms, and precision and purity that would have seemed impossible a generation ago. Yet these difficulties have not prevented widespread use and continuing price reduction.[21]

John O'M. Bockris, as a Professor of Chemistry at Texas A&M University in 1989, was one of the first whose laboratories replicated the original Pons–Fleischmann experiment. While he acknowledges the difficulties in reproducing such experiments reliably, he is still very bullish about the future of this field as the energy technology of the future:

> The discovery of low-energy nuclear reactions is on a par with the discovery of nuclear fission by Hahn and Meitner in 1939. It may be that we have the nuclear power source we need. But whether this will be in five or fifty years, a great deal will depend on the dying off of the old physicists, and their replacement by a group willing to face the facts.[22]

Hal Fox, who edits *New Energy News*, is just as clear about the significance of the original discovery:

> [In summary], the discovery of cold fusion, although vigorously attacked (especially by hot fusion lobbyists), marked the beginning of a series of discoveries of low-energy nuclear reactions. Pons and Fleischmann deserve a Nobel Prize. The nuclear reactions are complex and not, as yet, fully explained.[23]

Without funding, though, it is hard to see how this new technology can really thrive, given the amount of further research that still seems to be required to take it forward. The funding of current cold fusion research has, particularly in America, become something of a dark issue. While the mainstream research establishments officially dismiss cold fusion as a scientific mistake, there are some researchers who claim that the same labs that testified against Pons and Fleischmann are still deeply involved in the research.

On 20 October 1998, BBC Radio 4 *Today* programme carried a report on the current status of cold fusion research. In the programme, Dr Michael H. McKubre, electrochemist at SRI, confirmed that his laboratory had already spent $7 million on cold fusion research: 'We have an informal collaboration of four or five major research institutions in the United States, for example. The sponsors of these institutions may not want their involvement to be known.'[24]

Despite everything that has been thrown at it, cold fusion, it seems, is far from dead.

CHAPTER SEVEN

Cold Fusion Comes of Age

'A new scientific truth does not triumph by convincing its opponents and making them see the light, but rather because its opponents die, and a new generation grows up that is familiar with it.'

Max Planck, *A Scientific Autobiography*, 1949

'It [cold fusion] could be the end of the fossil fuel age; the end of oil and coal. And the end, incidentally, of many of our worries about global pollution and global warming.'

Sir Arthur C. Clarke, 'Cold Fusion: Fire from Water' video, 1999

There's no denying that even some of cold fusion's most ardent supporters are frustrated and disappointed by the technology's rate of progress. The slow pace of this work has inevitably contributed to the almost global perception that this area of science is discredited and quite without scientific or practical merit.

This view would be to deny the progress that has been made – both experimentally and theoretically – some of which has been examined in the previous chapter. Over ten years on from the original announcement it's perhaps easier to assess where the field has really got to, who its chief protagonists now are, and who the experimenters are who are most likely to make the next theoretical and practical breakthroughs.

Dr James Patterson of Sarasota, Florida, is the kind of man who likes to tinker. Born in 1922, and retired some years back, he still has the active mind of an experienced chemical engineer and a prodigious inventor. He's often to be found in his private lab, wrestling with a new engineering problem, where a sign announces: 'Hours Subject to Change During Fishing Season.' Before he retired he worked for prestigious organizations such as Dow Chemical, Fairchild Semiconductors, Lockheed and the Atomic Energy Commission, and during this time he brought forward some key innovations in a number of fields, filing over a hundred patents carrying his name. Perhaps the most important were his co-development of liquid chromatography, an important laboratory measuring technique, and the design and development of a technology for analysing DNA. Since 1990, however, he has become much more famous as the inventor of the Patterson Power Cell™, the only cold fusion device that comes with at least eleven US patents attached.

The silver-haired, kindly-faced Patterson is, perhaps, a little surprised with all the attention he's been receiving over the past years since he announced to the world that he had discovered a new source of energy. At the energy industry's Power-Gen '95 conference held in Anaheim, California, he amazed delegates with a liquid-filled, glass-walled cell that appeared to produce 1000 watts of heat output from only 1 watt of electrical input. 'Feel the Heat', his banner read – and indeed it felt as hot as a hair dryer. While not everyone liked the way Patterson had set up his measurement devices, few could deny that the energy effect appeared impressive.

Within a year Patterson's new company Clean Energy Technologies Inc. (CETI) had secured research relationships with the University of Missouri, the University of Illinois and Kansas City Power & Light. In a May 1995 scientific paper investigating the Patterson Power Cell, research scientist Dennis Cravens's conclusion was positive, without being ecstatic:

> The system does appear to be worth further study. Nothing discovered during the evaluation of the cell is inconsistent with the production of excess heat within the cell assembly provided that there is a positive

temperature rate coefficient . . . The high power ratios at the low current levels need to be revisited using measurements with tighter error bounds. However, regardless of the cause, the system does give repeatable results at substantial levels. If, as expected, the power levels persist with tighter experimental bounds in the low current levels, then the system should have important practical and commercial applications.'[1]

Cravens became a member of the CETI team, and began to promote the technology publicly. Then things seemed to get even better: communications giant Motorola made an offer to buy CETI for $15 million (so long as the technology worked). So what would you do? Patterson, together with his co-director and grandson, 28-year-old Jim Reding – an ex-Merrill Lynch banker – decided to stay independent: 'We're better off in the long run,' Reding would later tell a reporter.[2] Not everyone agreed.

In January 1996 an article appeared in the *Wall Street Journal* with the title: 'A Bottle Rekindles Scientific Debate About the Possibility of Cold Fusion.' The article, by Jerry E. Bishop – the same journalist who broke the original Utah story in 1989, was balanced and questioning. After talking about the demonstration at Anaheim, Bishop quoted Dr Birnbaum at the University of Illinois: 'Though the cold-fusion claims are "atrocious" science, the Patterson-cell people may have stumbled on something else. If so, I hope they are successful and make a lot of money. If not, this ought to be exposed as flimflam.'[3]

On 29 May 1997 a director from the Energy Assessments Division of the American Department of Energy and a number of colleagues visited CETI's facility in Sarasota. The tour was plainly successful, as the D.o.E. followed up with a letter:

We are putting together names etc. of other D.o.E. and US government organizations that may have an interest in your technology or may be able to assist you in obtaining funding, guidance or other types of support

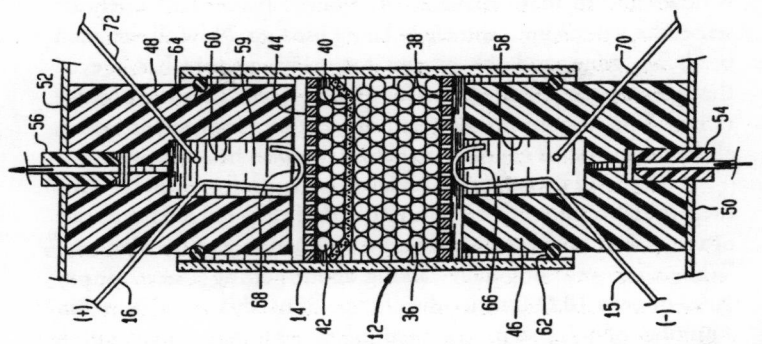

FIGURE 7.1 Image of Patterson Power Cell from US Patent No. 5,494,559.

as you bring your invention to market. Best of luck on
the development of what looks to be a most promising
innovation in energy production.[4]

If convincing the energy establishment was a key to unlocking the
door to public acceptance, then CETI seemed to have taken a
giant step forward.

A Technical Hitch With the Magic Beans

But that was 1997, and very little has been heard since then. So
what went wrong? The blunt, and rather disappointing, answer is
that they're having problems with the technology. Their process
involves running an electric current through a pair of platinum
electrodes in a cell containing ordinary light (not heavy) water
(H_2O) and some 'proprietary' beads made of copper covered,
plastic coated with three further layers of metal: nickel, palladium
and more nickel. For the first two years they had a batch of these
beads that 'produced robust effects consistently'. These beads were

originally considered to be catalysts for the process, although there is now concern that, unlike a real catalyst in the strict scientific sense, the palladium is somehow being used up. Now all the good beads are gone, and the process for creating more has – even though it's been patented – so far refused to yield further positive results. The story seems sadly reminiscent of a fairy tale in which all the magic beans get used up before the wish has come true.

The CETI team have also faced criticism for 'overclaiming' their initial results. It's certainly true that they reduced the scale of the claims for over-unity energy production as time went on. While they were originally talking about getting a heat output 1000 or even 10,000 times the energy input, this was reduced in a number of quick steps to something closer to ten or five or even just two or three times. Quite a difference, and a difference that's made a lot of people highly nervous about their original experimental work.

They've also faced the inevitable questions over theory: what the hell do they think is producing energy in a flask of ordinary water? Originally they were happy to be seen as part of cold fusion research, but being taken seriously by investors when you're working in a discredited field is difficult. In a press statement entitled 'It's Not Cold Fusion', released in 1996, the CETI team were keen to distance themselves from any taint of the cold fusion brush:

'The technology of Clean Energy Technologies Inc. is not cold fusion. We have been certain all along that the reaction is not a deuterium-deuterium reaction as previously proposed by Pons, Fleischmann and Jones of Utah,' stated James A. Patterson, Ph.D. CETI technology has received numerous patents from the US Patent Office as well as foreign countries. The technology has been reproduced by not only CETI scientists but also by independent scientists in respected research facilities and universities around the world. The technology is the evolution of over forty-five years of patented technology

by Dr Patterson and other CETI scientists. 'We scientists
believe that it is a low-energy nuclear reaction induced by
a proton or deuteron that occurs without the harmful
radioactive byproducts such as gamma radiation ... [It's]
new nuclear physics,' stated James A. Patterson, Ph.D.[5]

Nevertheless they faced the same kind of scepticism: 'MIT
Physics Professor Herman Fesbach appeared on ABC *Nightline*
on 11 June 1997. Admitting that he knew nothing about
the Patterson Power Cell™ he told viewers that he could
"categorically" state that there were no nuclear reactions
occurring within it.'[6]

Patents on Power

Despite its development difficulties, one of the strangest aspects
of the Patterson Power Cell™ is its collection of US patents. Dr
James Patterson is unique in US scientific history in being the
only man who has been granted so many (eleven at the last count)
patents for a cold fusion cell. The number of the key patent is
5,494,559 and it is dated 27 February 1996, following its initial
filing on 8 June 1995. It is innocently entitled 'System for
Electrolysis'. (This was followed by an amended version No.
5,607,563 and a further patent entitled 'System and Method for
Electrolysis and Heating of Water' and numbered 5,616,219,
along with some ancillary patents for other aspects of the
technology.)

There have been some allegations against the US Patent and
Trademark Office that, following the initial Pons–Fleischmann
débâcle, all claims for cold-fusion-related patents were to be
considered on a par with perpetual motion machines and
automatically thrown out. This is a claim that the Patent Office
strenuously denies, and it has had to defend itself in a number of
legal cases against accusations of this bias. Indeed, in its official
mandate it is not permitted to reject a patent on the basis of it

being a specific kind of technology. Their criteria for acceptance or rejection of any patent are actually relatively limited and specific. The three statutes of the US Code state that to qualify for a patent an invention must: 1) have utility (i.e. be useful); 2) be novel (i.e. not done before or found in 'prior art'); and 3) be non-obvious (in other words, even if partially found in the prior art, still not an obvious combination of two or more previous inventions). All inventions should also be 'fully disclosed' as to how they work – something which is not by any means always clear.

In one test case Mitchell R. Swartz tried to patent a Pons–Fleischmann-type cell on 27 June 1989 and was rejected. When he made an appeal (which was not heard until about three years afterwards) the Patents and Trademark Office Board found against him, referring to a number of reports and assessments from the time of the original announcement which had failed to find any evidence for cold fusion's existence:

> The Board found, based on the references of record, that skilled workers viewed the initial Fleischmann and Pons report with deep skepticism because they had been unable to reproduce the cold fusion phenomenon despite repeated attempts. Based on these references, the Board found that the relevant scientific community had a well-founded doubt that the phenomenon of cold fusion existed, and a view that cold fusion was incredible and inoperative. The board also concluded that cold fusion processes were not reproducible.[7]

Swartz's appeal continues at higher levels.

So how had Patterson managed to slip under the net to receive his patent for an energy-producing electrolysis cell? The answer is probably a mixture of luck and cunning: Patterson, who was over seventy at the time, fell under a US patenting law which favours older applicants, and gives them a fast track to rejection or acceptance. It could be construed that the fast track provides a less rigorous examination of the application. Patterson has implied – a little jokingly – that they took kindly to an older person. He also omitted to use terms such as 'cold fusion', even though he made passing mention to Pons and Fleischmann. Whatever the truth, the Patent Office has never indicated that it has made a mistake. It is, of course, always true that a patent is no indication that any technology works, and that the prime function of a patent is to protect the interests (financial and commercial) of the applicant. Nevertheless Patterson still stands alone with his patents. Whether they prove to be of any real value remains to be seen.

Best Case Scenario?

To avoid the risks that they see in the US patent system, some American researchers have gone further afield and applied through the international patent system, which awards patents under the Patent Co-operation Treaty (PCT). In November 1997 a new international patent application for the 'Coproduction of Energy and Helium from D_2' (WO 97/43768) appeared with the name of New Hampshire resident Dr Leslie C. Case. It described a new reaction called catalytic fusion, which Case had been working on for over six years after studying the work of a Japanese cold fusion researcher at NTT labs in Japan called Yamaguchi. Case was very impressed: 'He had obtained an 800 degrees C-plus exotherm [exothermic reaction] with, he thought, big bursts of neutrons. So I went to see him – actually in Tokyo at his laboratory – and looked at his equipment. Beautiful stuff! Very careful work. Clearly he had obtained a result which was very, very definite.'[8]

Case, who is an experienced chemical engineer with four degrees from MIT to his name, lost his wife to cancer in 1987, and, having recently built a new house with its own geothermal heat pump, decided to pursue his energy research with a new zeal. He travelled to Eastern Europe to find a 'good-value' lab capable of dealing with potential neutron radiation. At Charles University in Prague (which has a relationship with the European CERN particle accelerator) they opened their arms wide. He soon got to work with his apparatus, fashioned partly from some ex-military weapons parts. Right from the beginning Case's approach was different from the crowd's: he based his technology not on electrolysis of a liquid, but on the loading of his electrodes with deuterium gas at a mild pressure and an elevated temperature. After a year or two of trial and error with a number of types of catalyst for the reaction, Case started to see results:

> All of a sudden we started seeing temperature differences in one or two of the samples . . . And I can remember very clearly, one day it was, I think 1.2 or 2.1 degrees Celsius above the background in a particular catalyst sample. The physicist who was working with me was amazed, because as far as physicists are concerned, 1 or 2 degrees Celsius might as well be a million degrees, because it's clearly an effect and we were measuring it immediately versus an adjacent blank.[9]

Having found a suitable range of catalysts for his process he started to refine things even further. By 1999 he had an experiment running in which his deuterium cell was running 35 degrees Celsius hotter than a control cell running standard hydrogen. Not just for short bursts either: his cells were running like this for as long as two months.

The work at Charles University had proved one thing to Case: there were no neutrons coming from his system. What he later discovered was that he was getting high levels of helium-4 (a benign and safe element): instead of the normal 5.2 parts per million (p.p.m.) in air, he had an independent report from Oak Ridge National Laboratory telling him that he had over 90 p.p.m. in his cell. Once he'd satisfied himself it wasn't coming from contamination, Case now had a pretty clear picture of what might be happening in the cell: a classic fusion reaction, but not the one that the early critics of cold fusion had expected. This was another scientifically valid, and safe, reaction resulting from the fusion of two deuteron (heavy hydrogen-2) atoms: deuteron plus deuteron becomes helium-4 plus heat. Safe helium and useful heat. For Case it was a good result.

Following the initial information release via the patent, he revealed how the process worked in more detail the following April at the 1998 seventh International Conference on Cold Fusion, held in Vancouver, Canada. Soon after the conference the Case cell was independently tested by Eugene Mallove of *Infinite Energy* magazine and the New Energy Research labs. Mallove was impressed:

> I think this may be nearly the perfect embodiment of the original Pons–Fleischmann idea. It is very clear to me that this is like the heat-after-death phenomenon that so many have reported coming from cold fusion cells: heat production with no input power after the reaction is triggered . . .
>
> Case has confirmed helium-4 production in the reaction by sending samples to Oak Ridge National Laboratory. There should have been more of these tests to be even more certain of the result, but I am satisfied that Case is likely to have helium-4 production. It is at such a level – 100 p.p.m. [parts per million], which is way over the 6 p.p.m. in the air – that there is no way it could be from 'contamination'. If the Oak Ridge tests were valid, I think he has nailed it. This is the reaction: D+D [deuterium plus deuterium] going to helium-4, plus gorgeous, clean, excess heat.
>
> If replication holds up, it may be impossible for anyone to deny his process.[10]

Then Michael McKubre of Stanford University's commercial offshoot SRI became involved and started to see whether he could independently confirm Case's findings. From previous experience McKubre knew that 'replicability' – the ability to isolate variables in order to make experiments repeatable – was the key issue.

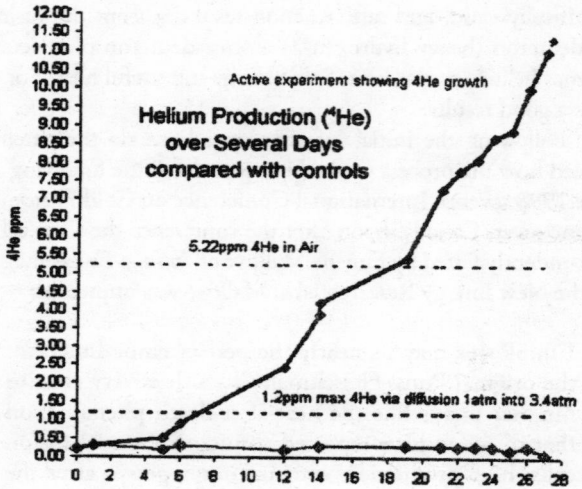

FIGURE 7.2 Les Case's experiment showed generation of helium-4 at eleven parts per million in 28 days – double the level in air.

Despite some of these general difficulties, McKubre has had good results with the Case gas cell. In heat terms he is getting between 5 per cent and 30 per cent excess energy with an error tolerance of only plus or minus 2 per cent. This is not yet enough to overcome potential losses in the system and to use the output to power the input (McKubre thinks he'll need 200 per cent excess to do that), but his prognosis is positive:

> The Case technology is attractive for several reasons. It's simply deuterium gas and carbon catalyst – commercial catalyst – something that can be obtained in 55-gallon drums, and the vagaries of the manufacturing process have already been mastered. So that if the Case process works to produce heat by a nuclear process, then it's something that can be very easily scaled up . . .

In Case's experiment, you have a gas, at easily accessible temperature, modest pressure in a sealed vessel. This is an experiment which many people can do and facilities exist to perform the experiment and understand its sensitivity to the various parameters.[11]

One of McKubre's priorities is establishing beyond all doubt that the reaction in these cells is nuclear. He sees no reason why this kind of low temperature reaction should follow the hot fusion model, and is open-minded about what will finally be discovered about the full complexity of the nuclear reactions. Having satisfied himself of some of the reactions involved, it's still a long, long journey to turn his results into a 'truth universally acknowledged'. McKubre wants to see younger engineers come into the low-energy nuclear reaction (LENR) field, to guard against his worst fear: 'As our average age increases with each ICCF [International Conference on Cold Fusion], as the rate of progress isn't as fast as it could be, we will just die before we understand this. Our critics will succeed not for any good reason but because we have lost the capacity to stand up at a microphone and speak.'[12]

Meanwhile Les Case, always the engineer, is keen to move towards heat generation on a larger scale. Yet while the basic reaction looks promising, there may be a fly in the ointment for a commercial strategy involving large amounts of palladium. While some of the processes we've looked at actually use up palladium, large-scale manufacture of cells would inevitably cause an increased demand for the metal, which is already one of the most expensive materials in the world. Annual supply is relatively limited, and has, in the past been drawn on by catalytic converters for cars and some other specialist requirements. A commercial strategy for a cell that included palladium could well be doomed to failure, and if no substitute can be found this could be a significant barrier to progress. Case has already addressed this issue, and while he has yet to find an experimental answer he believes he has the right approach:

If you were to use palladium catalysts of the type that's now in sight to build a 100-megawatt plant as a small commercial-sized power plant, you'd need something like 5 per cent of the world's palladium supply in one power plant. You can't build very many power plants a year without severely impacting the palladium market. So there will have to be a change of the catalyst . . .

There will have to be a way to use titanium or nickel or some other metal – a non-platinum group metal as the catalyst – as one scales up and goes commercial. That may take some years but that clearly is the way for the future.[13]

However, Michael McKubre believes that before Case can move that far ahead, there are still some replicability issues to address.

The Replicability Problem Solved in Japan?

As part of his overall theoretical progress, McKubre has examined the work of two highly reputable scientific professors based in Japan, named Yoshiaki Arata and Yue-Chang Zhang, for whom replicability does not seem to have been a problem. In a series of repeated (and potentially repeatable) experiments, they have demonstrated anomalous production of heat as well as elevated levels of helium-4. They have also, surprisingly, reported higher than expected levels of helium-3, a further sign that a nuclear reaction of some kind is occurring. Up to now, though, there has been no testing for another potential signature of fusion: neutron production.

The main problem of Arata and Zhang's work is that, while their own data show their results to be highly consistent over long periods of operating cells, it has not been yet replicated by any other laboratory. Since 1998 they have collaborated with Michael McKubre at SRI, but even he admits that there are problems in trying to recreate their experiments. In late 1999 he described the problems:

> The difficulty with Arata and Zhang's experiment is that it's only been performed by them and only in their laboratory. What we're attempting to do here is to produce their same results with their apparatus and their help.
>
> One of the difficulties with Arata's experiment is that it requires many, many months to produce a result, and quite literally we're not very experienced with Arata's methods, so we've had some difficulty getting his experiment set up and operational. Certainly it's caused me to have an increased level of respect for Arata and Zhang's technical competence. They are very, very good scientists.[14]

Such is the level of respect that Professor Yoshiaki Arata commands at Osaka University that he even has a building named after him. A university booklet takes some forty pages to list his academic and scientific accomplishments. He is the only physicist in Japan ever to have been awarded the Emperor's medal. As early as 1958 Arata was involved in Japan's hot fusion power programme, and it was around this time that he formed a working relationship with Professor Yue-Chang Zhang of the Welding Institute. They were both inspired by the Pons–Fleischmann announcement in 1989 to pursue cold fusion, and started their work with electrolytic cells. After many years of hard and careful work it seems possible that they may have laid the groundwork evidence for the existence of nuclear reactions at low temperatures. Michael McKubre at SRI is now convinced that these reactions, together with Les Case's work, are the way forward:

> Yes, we have amassed a great deal of evidence of heat and new nucleus production in deuterated (and even non-deuterated) metal systems, both in the electrolytic

and gas phases. It has often been said that this evidence in particular instances or generally is 'overwhelming'. Well, neither the scientific or public communities have been overwhelmed, and it is we who are at risk of being submerged. For a proof we need evidence that is easily understood, unarguable, and absolutely solid. To obtain this proof we at SRI are pursuing closely the experiments of Professors Arata and Zhang in the electrolytic system, and Les Case in the gas phase.[15]

The fact that the laboratory is continuing to receive funding is further proof that despite popular prejudice there are organizations – some believed to be military – who are willing to look seriously at the results.

Storms in New Mexico

Dr Edmund Storms is tall and bearded, with an almost biblical, Mosaic presence. His New Mexico home is only thirty-five miles from the Los Alamos National Laboratory where he worked for thirty-four years as a research scientist, focusing on high temperature chemistry in the nuclear power field. In 1989, though, his attention was suddenly taken up with the Los Alamos laboratory's response to the Pons–Fleischmann announcement. Very quickly he had begun his own experiments:

Chemists were actually speaking to physicists. Everyone got involved. We met once a week, more than 100 people. There must have been fifty attempts to reproduce the effect . . .

I put the cell into the calorimeter and it went through a few weeks doing essentially nothing. Then all of a sudden it just took off. It just started making significant heat. I was as surprised as anyone, let me tell you. You know, you sit there in front of the apparatus forever, and think, 'This is all so much nonsense. This isn't really real.' This waiting goes on for weeks, maybe months.

Then all of a sudden the readout device shows the cell has started taking off. And you say, 'Oh-oh, what's gone wrong now?' You start playing around with everything you can think of that might have gone wrong to see what has happened. After a while it suddenly dawns on you that nothing is wrong. This is what it is supposed to do.[16]

Ed Storms was one of only three scientists at Los Alamos to get a positive result from his 1989 experiments. In 250 experimental runs over a period of a year, thirteen made excess tritium (hydrogen-3), a sure sign – if correctly detected – of a nuclear reaction.

When sceptics said that his palladium samples must have been contaminated Storms started separate experiments in which he contaminated the palladium on purpose. 'Sure enough,' says Storms, 'it behaved differently.' By this time, though, MIT,

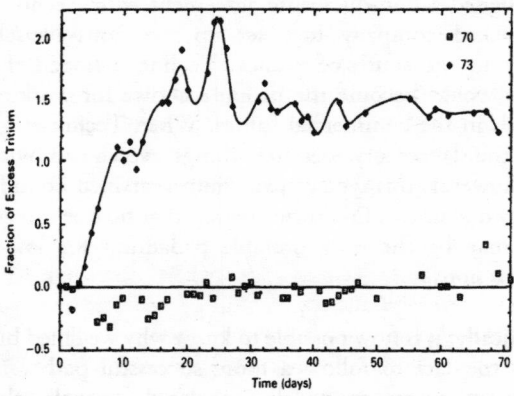

FIGURE 7.3 At the Los Alamos National Laboratory in 1989, Edmund Storms reported clear excess amounts of tritium in cell number 73, as compared with his control cell number 70.

CalTech and Harwell had already passed final judgement: Storms's efforts to raise further funding within Los Alamos hit a brick wall. So in 1994 he left Los Alamos, after thirty-four years of service, and set up his own laboratory 'down the road' in his newly built home.

Over the years since then he has refined his analysis of palladium, so that, instead of a one in twenty chance of success with cells, he can now predict whether a particular sample will work with 50 per cent accuracy. That's pretty good, but there are still problems with the raw material – problems that have dogged the whole cold fusion project since its inception, and have contributed extensively to its repudiation. The variability in palladium samples means that while certain types of palladium may 'work' in cells 50 per cent of the time, others may simply not work at all. It has taken many years to establish which types are most likely to work reliably, and now there are even problems with the availability of the researchers' favourite.

Pons and Fleischmann had found that Johnson Matthey's 'type A' palladium was the most reliable, but the precious metal supplier signed a non-disclosure agreement with Technova, the Toyota-backed company that set up the Pons–Fleischmann laboratory in the south of France. Technova hoped that this palladium would become the people's choice for working cold fusion cells in the commercial future. When Technova gave up funding the laboratory because things weren't moving fast enough, however, this type of palladium remained bound up by the secrecy document. Ed Storms regrets that no one can get hold of what may be the most suitable palladium for low-energy nuclear reactions.

> Ironically, it is now possible to know why we failed but it is too late to follow a more successful path . . . Without access to widely circulated journals, this negative attitude within the scientific community obviously cannot be changed. Even overwhelming proof, as demanded by many scientists in the past, can

have no effect because no mechanism exists for it to be communicated to the scientific professions.[17]

Despite the massive opposition to the field, Storms is one of those who believes it's still worth fighting to win over the sceptics by scientific argument. In a paper written in 1999 he set out his case:

> Rejection of CANR [chemically assisted nuclear reactions] has been premature. The cold fusion debate has struggled on for almost ten years with essentially no progress in converting skeptics to believers. Indeed the attitude of conventional scientists has hardened. On the other hand, new demonstrations of the claims have appeared, reproducibility has been achieved using several methods, and a relationship between heat production and appearance of a nuclear product has been determined. All of these successes were demanded by skeptics before claims could be accepted. So why has this acceptance been denied?[18]

Storms goes on to point out some of the gross paradoxes in the sceptics' resistance to progress. These include believing cold fusion should follow exactly the same reaction model as hot fusion (why?); that the Pons–Fleischmann process is the only claim to excess heat (in fact there are at least eight); that any nuclear products appearing in experiments such as helium, tritium, etc. must be the result of contamination; that data not peer-reviewed is, by definition, bunk (a circular argument, given that journals will no longer publish any papers on cold-fusion-related effects); and that all positive results must be the result of 'bad science'. Storms concludes: 'I suggest the field has been prematurely rejected and now deserves a second chance to prove its worth. To do otherwise is to deny mankind the potential for clean, unlimited energy and science the possibility to understand a new mechanism of nuclear interaction.'[19]

Final Words . . .

Crystal ball gazing for cold fusioneers has not yielded very reliable results so far, but nevertheless its protagonists now have more than ten years' worth of achievements, disappointments and resistance on which to base future prognoses. Scott Chubb at the Naval Research laboratory takes the long view:

> I'm optimistic. Compelling evidence exists that PF cold fusion is quite real. Eventually, science will accept this fact and vindicate PF, but when? It could take a very long time.[20]

CHAPTER EIGHT

Randell Mills – BlackLight's Power Struggle

'The Company's technology is projected to dominate the household and microdistributed power market over competing technologies such as fuel cells. With a focus on large scale production of microdevices, the Company anticipates rapid penetration of the electric energy market.'

BlackLight Power Website

Gerald Celente is the founder of the Trends Research Institute, a 'futurist' advisory body which publishes *Trends Journal*. He is also a regular writer for *USA Today* and regular expert guest on serious television shows. At the end of 1999 Celente made a significant prediction about the attractiveness to investors of the new energy-generation technologies:

> The energy revolution will be the single biggest investment opportunity in the twenty-first century. Its ramifications will extend to practically every aspect of human and planetary life. To profit from the trend, potential investors should begin familiarizing them-selves with the field thoroughly and immediately, and keep abreast of developments before they become official.
>
> A new global age is being born on the ashes of the dying industrial age and the fossil fuels that powered it.

Promising developments, so advanced they almost seem to challenge the laws of science, lead us to forecast that, within the next ten years, technological break-throughs will spell an end to dependence on oil and coal. Energy-generating machines, operationally cost-free, will hasten an end to global pollution, global warming, and a foreign policy driven by strategic oil interests.

The breakthroughs won't result from the unrealized promises of solar or wind energy or the half measures of fuel cells, but from the visionary research into low-energy nuclear reactions, zero-point energy and hydro-catalytic hydrogen power.[1]

These public predictions will be music to the ears of the 150 investors who have so far put over $25 million into BlackLight Power. For the 'hydrocatalytic hydrogen power' Celente talks about is the patented process owned by BlackLight Power and discovered by Dr Randell Mills, the company's founder and president. Smaller private investors making their 'punt' have found themselves in good company: already two major utility companies – PacificCorp and Conectiv – have been sufficiently convinced by the demonstrations of Dr Mills's technology to commit a combined $5 million. PacificCorp is a multibillion-dollar electric company serving the state of Oregon, while Conectiv provides power to the mid-Atlantic states. Conectiv's senior vice-president David Blake is clearly convinced of the investment potential: 'We're past the scientific verification stage. The talk now is about commercial applications – perhaps within seven years.'[2]

From the professional investment world, RS Funds, Eastbourne Capital Management and 'executives retired from the top echelon' of Morgan Stanley have also invested. Early in 2000 it was reported that Morgan Stanley Dean Witter was planning to bring BlackLight public during 2001. The investment bank says that there are two requirements that will trigger the Initial Public

Offering (IPO): the first is a licensing agreement with a high-profile, 'household' name; the second is a more substantial *academic* validation of the company's technologies. There are also talks occurring between BlackLight and Daimler-Chrysler regarding some joint working or investment. At least three other major corporations are investigating a whole range of novel materials that BlackLight is planning to produce. In January 1999 BlackLight started spending some of the investment capital when it moved into its new $2 million New Jersey headquarters.

So what's all the fuss about? What has Dr Randell Mills discovered, if anything? And what on earth (or anywhere else for that matter) is hydrocatalytic hydrogen power?

Mills's claims for his BlackLight technology are not small: first, he believes he has developed an entirely new energy source. He says that it's a safe, pollution-free method of getting high-grade energy from hydrogen, which will soon be running our electrical power stations. If that weren't enough, he has also built an integrated theoretical model around his discoveries. He claims that his work will bring the rule of Einstein and quantum mechanics to an end. This, he confidently asserts, is the Holy Grail of physics: a grand unified theory – a theory that finally brings together all the forces of nature into one relationship. A theory of everything. Indeed he has written and self-published a 1000-page epic named *The Grand Unified Theory of Classical Quantum Mechanics*. It's little wonder that he has physicists all over the world frothing at the mouth: after all, if he really has done what he claims, then a lot of people are going to look, and feel, very inadequate.

Whether or not Mills is right about his Grand Unified Theory is, at this stage at least, somewhat irrelevant. The world argues by results, and until Mills can show that his technology works, he's going to have a hard job convincing the theoretical physicists that he's got there before them. So what evidence is there to support the technology?

Mills's power-generation system can be explained in

relatively simple terms: it is a way of getting heat energy from hydrogen. Hydrogen, the simplest element in the universe, is made up of just one proton and an orbiting electron. When hydrogen is burned it gives off significant amounts of energy. But simply burning hydrogen will never give you more energy than it takes to get the hydrogen (typically from electrolysing water) in the first place. Yet in Mills's patented process, hydrogen is persuaded – with the help of a potassium-based catalyst – to give up hundreds, even thousands, of times the amount of energy that can be released through the simple burning of hydrogen.

So where does the extra energy come from? Conventional 'atomic' hydrogen contains only a certain amount of atomic energy – a level of energy often described as the 'ground state'. This level of energy is actually a function of the relationship between the single proton nucleus and its orbiting electron. In conventional terms this relationship limits the amount of energy that can be extracted from burning, or oxidizing, the hydrogen. Mills's answer is, to most physicists, unbelievable. In a revision of Niels Bohr's Nobel-prize-winning 1913 quantum theory, Mills confidently asserts that hydrogen can exist at a number of energy states below the ground state. In other words, and contrary to current understanding, the electron can happily orbit the proton in a smaller orbit (a half, third, quarter, etc. of the normal orbit). When the electron is persuaded to go to this lower orbit, the energy once used to maintain the higher orbit is released as ultra-violet light. In turn, the energy of the ultra-violet light becomes useful heat. Mills claims that the heat produced from the Black-Light process is some thousand times greater than the energy that would be released by the simple burning of molecular hydrogen.

Mills calls the hydrogen molecules in their collapsed state hydrinos, and says that these simple particles – once relieved of their excess energy – behave in extraordinary, but highly useful ways. They either escape to float away into deep space, or, potentially more profitably, form novel compounds with other materials – novel compounds that appear to have a string of commercial applications. For instance, hydrinos combined with certain inorganic elements appear to produce conductive, magnetic plastics which would revolutionize electronic circuitry, and, potentially, make semi-conductors smaller and faster.

Meanwhile, says Mills, the energy released by the hydrogen may be captured in two possible ways. Originally Mills's idea was to simply capture the ultra-violet energy as heat and use a conventional combination of steam turbine and generator set to create electricity. However, BlackLight's new project is to develop a 'gyrotron' – a device which can turn the energy into electricity in a much more efficient process.

In BlackLight Power's New Jersey headquarters sits the prototype 'vapor phase cell' or power cell that is the subject of so much study, hope and experimentation. It doesn't necessarily look that much – just a metal vessel with some pipes going in and out – but if it does what is claimed, it could turn out to be the world's most advanced and valuable kettle.

Since early on, Mills has been confident enough to offer out his prototype BlackLight power cells for third-party testing by other, credible laboratories. So what kind of validation has Mills received for his process?

Dr Charles Haldeman was senior staff member at MIT's Lincoln Laboratory in Lexington, Massachusetts, when he was given the opportunity to test early models of Mills's cells. (The Lincoln Laboratory is particularly well known for its work in radar, laser and defence work, which it carries out on behalf of the US Air Force.) Haldeman was clearly convinced from his tests that the Mills cells were producing excess energy: 'I got pretty good gain compared to the power I was putting in. The effect wasn't as large as Mills was getting, but it was in the direction that was predicted . . . There's clearly incontrovertible evidence that there's something going on in the work of Mills and others that certainly deserves further study.'[3]

The BlackLight team says that the Lincoln Laboratory found an excess energy in a ratio of 4:1. In other words, for every watt that was provided to the cell, they were getting 4 watts of heat out.

Michael Jacox is another nuclear engineer who has tested a BlackLight cell. Although now working as assistant director of Texas A&M's Commercial Space Center for Engineering, Jacox used to work as a research scientist for the Department of Energy at the Idaho National Engineering and Environmental Laboratory. He had read about Mills's work, and decided in 1991 to carry out his own independent tests with the assistance of electrochemical experts working on battery development at the laboratory. At that time he felt compelled to study the Mills cell under conditions of 'relative secrecy'. Jacox describes the process:

> We actually purchased a total of three large electrolytic cells and conducted very controlled experiments. We followed the protocols Randy [Mills] suggested and followed his technique and we got the same result he had. We were encouraged but we determined that what we had was not sufficient to break a news release, especially with 'cold fusion' going sour so soon before.

Jacox was keen to carry out more thorough testing – including strict comparisons of Mills's cells and 'control' cells – when his superiors suddenly got cold feet. 'In the middle of the process there was a management decision that said we should pull the plug on the whole project and not disclose that we had been involved in the project at all.'[4]

Jacox left the Idaho lab soon after the clampdown. Now BlackLight says that the Idaho lab was getting 8.5 times as much energy as was being supplied.

The BlackLight website[5] lists a total of fourteen laboratories worldwide that have reported excess energy from their prototype cells. Twelve of these are in the US, one at Hokkaido University, Japan, and a further analysis at the Moscow Power Engineering Institute in Russia.

Dr John A. Spitznagel, chief scientist for Siemens Westinghouse Power Corp.'s science and technology centre in Pittsburgh, was apparently getting a 1.5 times energy gain from a

BlackLight cell – enough to intrigue him, but not enough to keep him intrigued. He says now that he 'remains in a monitoring mode'.

In October 1999 Dr Johannes Conrads, the former director of the Institute for Low Temperature Plasma Physics at the Ernst Arndt University in Greifswald, Germany, appeared in front of an audience at the American Chemical Society. He said that he had been able to produce 'remarkably high energy' from one of the prototype cells. He was not sure, though, whether this was as a result of the process described by Mills, or whether it could in fact be coming from an effect within dense regions of the plasma produced by the process.

The results vary tremendously: from 1.7 times energy gain to over 100 times energy gain. While these results look extremely impressive at face value, certain detailed questions need to be asked about the precise numbers and their interpretation.

One expert who is wholly convinced of Mills's technology is Shelby Brewer, who was responsible – under President Reagan – for the entire US nuclear power programme from 1980 to 1984. In his time as Assistant Energy Secretary, Brewer saw thousands of proposals for new energy-generation technology, and only found two or three worthy of further development. Having seen Mills's BlackLight technology, however, Brewer was so sure of its commercial worth that he not only committed personal funds but also became a board director of BlackLight Power. He has already initiated negotiations with the South Korean government to provide it with power plant technology based on BlackLight's developments.

Mills himself is bullish about the rapid technical and commercial development of the BlackLight technology:

> We have cells running here that produced a thousand times the energy of burning hydrogen. We are doing some tests with Atlantic Electric, and we're not unreasonable about showing that. There are independent validation reports put out on the web if you need validation.

We now have a commercially competitive process and I have people from Stone and Webster, Fluor Daniel, Westinghouse and, you know, a lot of big power companies who have said, 'If you can get this new vapor phase cell independently validated,' they said, 'we feel that this will be the dominant source of power for essentially all power applications.'

We have power densities equivalent to many electrical power plants. And we're getting validated energy [balances] of a thousand times the energy of burning hydrogen. So we know the process works and now [all that's needed is] the time it takes to retro-fit that into existing technology.

So, depending on how fast we are at executing that plan and how fast we are getting partners to push that agenda forward, it could happen very quickly. And the thing is, right now we're working on a 100 kW thermal unit up at Thermacore at Lancaster [Pennsylvania]. Once we've got that, then you can put that into cars, you can put that into distributed power generation. That could meet [the needs of] developing countries where they don't have transmission lines – that could meet an *enormous* percentage of the market.[6]

When it comes to 'the market' it seems that Mills is a shrewd operator. On the company website, the commercial and the scientific come together pretty seamlessly. Under the section on commercialization, we get a clear picture of the way Mills sees it all going:

The science and its empirical confirmation have been accomplished to the satisfaction of significant elements of the investment and energy communities. Consideration, let alone acceptance, by the scientific community is halting at best, consistent with the reaction to evolutionary advances throughout history. Following scale-up to a self-sustaining cell, currently in progress, the next major hurdles are in engineering – the demonstration of a modular cell applicable to energy generation on an economic scale, and the design and engineering of an energy conversion system. Practical, conventional engineering challenges remain – increasing cell power density, control of the catalytic reaction, transport of the energy released to a working fluid, detailed design articulation of the cell and heat transport systems, etc.

The commercialization strategy can be stated simply: leverage the concept into the marketplace through license agreements with power equipment manufacturers [OEM] and power producers. BlackLight Power [BLP] is a small technology company with no current aspirations to become a major OEM or energy producer. With fundamental technology license agreements, OEMs will develop specific application technologies and equipment in response to market factors. Process licenses with energy producers will engender a revenue stream for BLP as a fraction of the avoided cost to energy generation. The 1992 Energy Policy Act and the 1996 FERC Open Access Rule, which spawn more competitive forces in the utility marketplace, are positive forces advancing BLP's commercialization strategy. Parallel advances in enabling technologies including high-temperature materials, manufacturing, power electronics, computers and data communications are creating the environment needed to support the rapid development and commercialization of the BLP process.[7]

The fact that BlackLight talks about a 'self-sustaining cell' is crucial. In the end, despite the best measurement techniques of government and university labs, the only real test of a technology which claims over-unity, which liberates energy from a hitherto unknown source, is whether the energy it produces is sufficient to initiate its own process in the first place. This would mean that the heat energy released by the patented 'hydro catalytic' process could be captured efficiently and used to create high-pressure steam to put through a turbine, which would turn a generator to make enough electricity to initiate the generation of enough atomic hydrogen to maintain the process. When Mills can achieve this and then 'turn off the mains' – let the reaction run on its own – he, and we, shall know he really has something remarkable.

Cold Fusion? What Cold Fusion?

Many people have bundled Mills's claims together with those of Pons, Fleischmann and some of the other cold fusioneers from the strange days of 1989. Mills himself has always sought to distance himself. In a recent interview he explained the differences between his process and those of others:

> I don't really pay much attention to that [cold fusion] . . . I don't even know if they're getting energy. I agree there are some experiments done in very reputable labs that said they're maybe getting 10 or 20 per cent heat from palladium and lithium electrolysis. And it turns out that palladium 2+ and lithium + is a transition catalyst.[8]

It is interesting that these are materials that Mills believes can also be used in his processes. 'So you could get some hydrogen transitions, get some heat, and then the nuclear products. But then there's a lot of junk there: talking about everything in the phone book – transmuting the periodic chart, a lot of really strange stuff that really isn't – I don't think – well done experimental work.'[9]

But how much has Mills suffered from being tarred with the cold fusion brush? It's difficult to say exactly, but certainly since April 1989 any new process for excess energy generation has to suffer at least a small part of the ridicule that was heaped upon Pons and Fleischmann.

As we've already seen, this ridicule may well have affected the academic end of the energy research business more than the commercial. It is interesting that Mills has chosen a very commercial route to develop his technology. He is not doing this under the supportive umbrella of any university or government body: this is strictly business. And that, it's pretty safe to assume, is how Mills likes it. It's also exactly the way that most academics loathe it. Some would say there's one very good reason for that: it's green, it's nasty and it's called professional jealousy.

For if Mills is right, both with his technology and with his theoretical physics, he will have achieved something that most living scientists can only dream of. And whereas Einstein suffered the grief of seeing his scientific understanding being used to erase Hiroshima and Nagasaki, for Mills there is the possibility that he will see his energy technology bringing an end to the threat of global warming.

Even if the technology works, though, will it really be safe? Mills is dogged in his promotion of hydrinos:

> A 200 horsepower car going 60 m.p.h. using this process will go a 100,000 miles on a tank of water . . . with no pollution because what you form is a lower chemical form of molecular hydrogen that does not react. It's lighter than air, so it goes out into space. And if you are worried about something in the gas, it's non-reactive. Every time you breathe, 80 per cent of the air you are breathing is nitrogen that doesn't react with anything in your body. This is much more stable than nitrogen.[10]

Mills claims that hydrinos would not even stay in the human body – instead, they would simply diffuse out into the atmosphere. Would there, though, be any effect on the upper atmosphere? Would hydrinos worsen the thinning of the ozone layer, for instance? Mills thinks it is possible that some of the hydrinos might – if struck by cosmic, high-energy rays – revert to 'normal' higher-energy hydrogen. This might actually offer some screening effect in the ionosphere, and thus help to offset ozone thinning. In any case, he believes, the effect of hydrinos would be negligible.

In all this excitement, it's worth asking the question: Who is Randell Mills? What's his background? How did Mills arrive at the point where he is claiming to be reinventing physics? Randell Mills's resumé makes interesting reading. He grew up on a ninety-one acre grain farm in Chester County, Pennsylvania, which was run by his father, Robert Mills Senior. From the age of sixteen he was part of the team that ran the farm. He graduated in chemistry in 1982 at Franklin and Marshall College in Pennsylvania before going on to Harvard Medical School, where he earned an MD degree in 1986. While at Harvard he conducted applied research and filed patents on several innovative medical technologies.

He was strongly influenced by his mentor at Harvard, Dr Carl Walter, a professor of surgery and a 'prolific inventor and researcher'. In fact Dr Walter has founded over a dozen companies, including four that became multinational. Randell Mills was encouraged by Dr Walter to focus on invention and, having returned to his home state of Pennsylvania following his studies, he founded a number of companies which secured patents on a range of technologies.

Initially Mills's focus was on the medical arena. His first patent was for a medical imaging technology called Magnetic Susceptibility Imaging, which provides high-resolution 3-D internal vascular images. This was followed by a cancer therapy called MIRAGE or Mossbauer Isotopic Resonant Absorption of Gamma Emission – a pretty fancy name for a form of radiation therapy that reduces the amount of radiation applied to the patient by a claimed factor of a million. Under the second company Mills formed, Luminide, he developed a new drug delivery system. BlackLight Power was not formed until 1991.

In 1986 Mills had taken classes in electrical engineering at MIT. Here he first started to tangle with orthodox atomic theory, but it was work that developed during his other activities. Even from the beginning Mills had no shortage of self-belief:

> I knew the old theory was wrong. It doesn't work. It causes a division between classical – the large-scale – physics, and atomic physics. And Niels Bohr, back in the early twentieth century, said he couldn't get the theories to work out and be in agreement with classical theories, so he just said it just obeys different physics, which was a very bad move.
>
> And we've inherited that ever since. So what I said is physics has to apply on all scales, because everything is made out of atoms – and the laws that apply on the large scale must apply on the atomic scale. It's just that they did not solve the equations correctly.'[11]

Mills believes that his solution to the problem of atomic theory is actually what Einstein dreamed of but never found: 'He [Einstein] was correct, though. His part of it was correct and his intuition was correct. But he couldn't finish it. I think I've finished what Einstein's dream was.'

Many scientists, though, adamantly oppose Mills's basic assertion that hydrogen can really exist in energy states below its ground state.

> That's OK, because this . . . is something that's really quite new and it's been ingrained in them that there is something called 'the ground state', and the reason they're ingrained with that ground state is because that's a postulate of quantum mechanics in order to solve the hydrogen atom.
>
> So people have been taught that 13.6 eV is the lowest, or the ground state, of the hydrogen atom, but

in fact it's not. There's no reason why it can't go lower. In fact, the potential energy between the proton and the electron could release a million extra electron volts of energy. And it doesn't and you ask, well why can't it go to these lower states, because it does it spontaneously when you form a *molecule* of hydrogen? It goes to the lower states when you form water?

And then I looked in the literature and alas! There is a ton of data in the literature that supports the existence of this new form of hydrogen and explains many, many problems that before could not be explained. There's things from solar flares; there's light from interstellar media; there's microwave background from deep space, there's transitions [of hydrogen] in the solar corona, there's been nuclear hyperfine transitions, there's proton atom scattering . . . that has the characteristic feature of being caused by a one to one-half fractional hydrogen transition.[12]

So Niels Bohr, the great Danish Nobel prize winner got it wrong about ground states? That takes some swallowing for the quantum establishment. They're certainly not going to take this lying down.

'The Empire Strikes Back'

Philip Anderson is a physics Nobel laureate at Princeton University. When asked for his opinion of Mills's theories, he was blunt to the point of fury: 'If you could f**k around with the hydrogen atom, you could f**k around with the energy process in the sun. You could f**k around with life itself . . . Everything we know about everything would be a bunch of nonsense. That's why I'm so sure that it's a fraud.'[13]

Dr Robert Park, who has gained a reputation as a debunker of anything that smacks of 'pseudoscience', has also launched an attack on Mills. Park is a spokesman for the American Physical Society who also expounds his views from regular columns in the *Washington Post* and the *New York Times*, as well on as his Internet science weekly *What's New?* Since he first became aware of Mills's work, he has questioned its validity. In his new book *Voodoo Science: the Road from Foolishness to Fraud* Park attacks both Mills's experimental validation and the theory behind the work: 'Those who bet on hydrinos are betting against the most firmly established and successful laws of physics . . . what are the odds that Randell Mills is right? To within a very high degree of accuracy, the odds are zero.'[14]

Credibility is the name of the game for any commercialization route, and in an effort to protect himself and his interests against these kind of attacks, Mills recently took out a lawsuit against Park in order to stop the publication of his book. The launch date was indeed delayed, and it is possible that Park has had to tone down some of his comments about Mills in the book. In May 2000, though, an extracted article from the book entitled 'The Alchemists of Energy' appeared in the influential *Forbes* magazine.

> A number of prominent scientists, including Nobel laureates, have publicly dismissed Dr Mills's claim as nonsense. Their comments were not welcomed by BlackLight, which is planning a public stock offering this year or next; it has retained Morgan Stanley Dean Witter as its investment banking firm. BlackLight's lawyers have sent those scientists strongly worded letters threatening legal action. You could dismiss this hydrino notion as just another laughable attempt to repeal the laws of physics, but for one thing. Some people with deep pockets are taking Dr Mills very seriously.[15]

Things Turn Nasty

On 15 February 2000, BlackLight was granted its key US patent No. 6,024,935, for 'Lower-energy Hydrogen Methods and Structure', detailing 499 novel aspects of their work (see Appendix 8). This again attracted the attention of the furious Dr Park. In an article in March 2000, the *Village Voice* journalist Erik Baard talked to Dr Park:

> 'I am shocked that they issued a patent on this. This indicates that the troubles at the patent office continue.'
>
> Nobel laureates in theoretical physics have blasted Mills's concept as impossible. Park described BlackLight Power's energy process in the most heretical terms possible: 'a perpetual motion machine'. The patent office, however defended itself against the attack: Their spokeperson Brigid Quinn spoke out: 'We do not give patents on perpetual motion machines. That this was granted a patent means it met the criteria that it is new, useful, and non-obvious, and fully disclosed as to how it works.'
>
> BlackLight's patent lawyer, Jeffrey S. Melcher, spoke of the issuance in glowing terms: '[This] marks an historic event in the field of energy production. By issuing this patent, the Patent Office has recognized that Dr Mills's energy cell and method of extracting energy from hydrogen has utility and is novel over conventional methods of producing energy. In securing his patent rights, Mills presented to the Patent Office overwhelming evidence that his energy cell and method provide an unlimited source of power never before contemplated.'
>
> Randell Mills himself was more than upbeat about the technology's value: 'This is more fundamental than the light bulb or the internal combustion engine.'[16]

At the same time Mills was told that BlackLight had been granted the '935 patent (US Patent No 6,024,935), he was informed that a further key patent (US Patent No. 6,030,601) based on the new hydrino compounds formed by the process – some of which would be part of BlackLight's battery technology – would also be granted two weeks later on 29 February 2000.

However, two days after the first patent was issued, BlackLight received some very bad news: the patent office issued a notice that at the request of the director of the Special Program Law Office, the US Patent Office was withdrawing the '601 patent from issue, 'to permit reopening of prosecution'. A further four applications which had also been 'allowed' were also to be reinvestigated. In the history of patent issuance this was unheard of. How could a company, which had been already told it was going to receive a patent, and which was basing its commercial activity on this information, be suddenly told that its technology was being reinvestigated? Even the officer of the patent office who

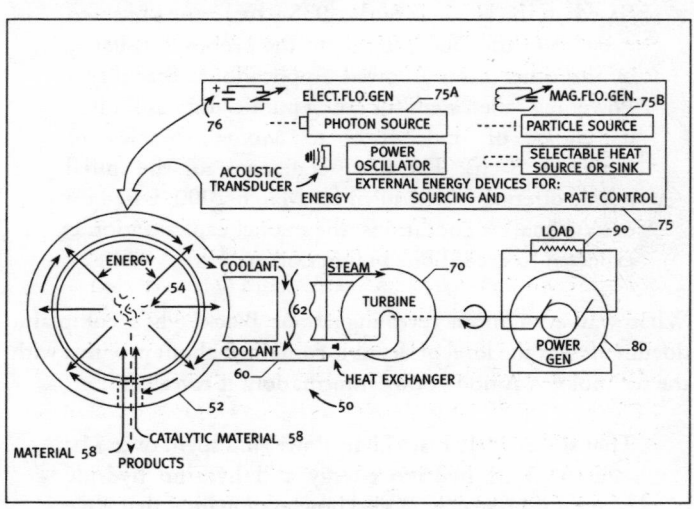

FIGURE 8.1 Image from BlackLight Power system from US Patent No. 6,024,935.

made the announcement, Ms Frances Hicks, was unsure why. When pressed by BlackLight's patent man, Jeffrey S. Melcher, she spilled the beans:

> Counsel was subsequently told by Ms Hicks that the petition had been issued at the demand of Robert Spar, the Director of Special Programs, who believed, based on the publicity arising from the issuance of the '935 patent, it was not patentable as it was based on 'unproven science' related to cold fusion.[17]

Mills could not stand back and watch the Patent Office, influenced by the media and other insiders, attempt to destroy his business. Within weeks BlackLight filed a legal suit against the Patent Office to halt its actions. This 'complaint' was revealing about BlackLight's plans:

> Based on the issuance of the '935 patent, the proposed issuance of the '601 patent and the proposed issuance of the other Four Allowed Applications, BlackLight Power has taken steps for going public and has limited its choice of underwriter to Morgan Stanley or Goldman Sachs. The filing statement for the initial public offering is scheduled for March 2000. Based on current market conditions, the market capitalization is expected to exceed one billion dollars.[18]

What was even more revealing about BlackLight's complaint document was the level of detail it contained about progress with the technology. Among other information, it revealed:

> That since 1991, BlackLight Power has spent over $10 million in its hydrino energy and hydrino hydride compound research. Well-known companies that have invested include AMP Corporation, Conectiv, and Pacific Corp.

That over twenty-five well-known independent laboratories have demonstrated that 'the technology is based on sound scientific principles'.[19]

Jeffrey Melcher attached a strongly worded letter addressed to Esther Kepplinger of the USPTO, to let the Patent Office know just how high the stakes were in this case: 'BlackLight Power's current private market capitalization is already in excess of $340 million, based on the last private placement that was over-subscribed.'[20] He was also keen to show the kind of support that the technology was attracting: 'These positive tests [of Mills's technology] have not escaped the attention of the US government. Following a thorough review, the United States Navy has taken affirmative steps to develop applications based on the Mills technology in co-operation with BlackLight Power.'[21]

The outcome of the case may well determine whether BlackLight can continue with its development plan unfettered, or whether the doubting Thomases – such as Robert Park – may get their way in crushing the BlackLight patents. Without the patents BlackLight may struggle to develop its technology commercially, since investors will steer clear of a technology without patent protection. Is it really possible that an orchestrated campaign of bad press comment could kill a technology that promises so much?

This is not the first major hurdle that BlackLight power has faced. It's certain not to be the last: for the foreseeable future the power struggle goes on . . .

Epilogue

In another bizarre twist to the story, Dr Robert Park was struck by a falling tree while out jogging in a park in the summer of 2000. He has since recovered.

CHAPTER NINE

Zero-Point Physics and the

Cosmic Free Lunch

> *'The energy of the vacuum remains one of the deep mysteries of science. We know from quantum mechanics that it is not empty. We have much to learn.'*
>
> Michael Turner, Fermilab, 1997

> *'A piece of space the size of a sugar cube that looks like it's empty is actually full of electromagnetic energy: so much so that it would run the whole world for a billion years!'*
>
> Dr Robert Forward, 1984

> *'There is no such thing as a free lunch – except in quantum mechanics.'*
>
> Charles Seife, *Nature*, 1997

Many of us have heard the buzz-phrase 'paradigm shift' used freely to describe . . . well, to describe all sorts of changes: changes in the economic model; advances in computing; even radical style movements in fashion or music. Few people are aware of the origin of the phrase in an apparently obscure, yet seminal, scientific book first published in 1962 called *The Structure of Scientific Revolutions* by an American philosopher of science named Thomas S. Kuhn. Kuhn's unique vocation was to grapple with the strange, non-linear fashion in which science progresses:

Discovery commences with the awareness of anomaly,

i.e. with the recognition that nature has somehow violated the paradigm-induced expectations that govern normal science. It then continues with a more or less extended exploration of the area of anomaly. And it closes only when the paradigm theory has been adjusted so that the anomalous has become the expected.[1]

While small progressions in science and technology may be linear, predictable movements along a straight track, the really big changes have required the overturning of almost everything that went before. These major changes in the scientific model are what Kuhn called 'paradigm shifts'. Charles Darwin's work on the origin of species is an example of a paradigm shift, in which one set of creationist beliefs seem to have been replaced by a theory of biological evolution. Einstein's general relativity undermined Newton's laws of motion with one imaginative leap. The fact that we still use Newton's laws for most calculations of motion (even in space programmes) demonstrates one aspect of the interesting relationship between theory and technology: that theory is often so far ahead that it takes a very long time before the technological implications catch up. Einstein's ideas have, for instance, spawned some new ideas about time and space travel. And yet it's not always theory that leads: it took Galileo's telescope to provide observations which revealed the earth's motions relative to the sun. Without the technology, theoretical progress would have been impossible. With paradigm shifts, it's often a question of which came first – the theory or the phenomena?

In the field of new energy technologies, phenomena such as over-unity and excess energy don't appear to fit too well with the law of conservation of energy. When these kind of David and Goliath clashes occur there are really only limited ways forward. If the law is strong, and not subject to adaptation or special cases or reinterpretation, it will stand firm and reject the phenomena without further questions. There must, the law says, be a problem in the observation and measurement of the phenomena. A law of science is strengthened as much by what it can reject as by what it can accept. If the phenomena persist, and the evidence for the persistence is strong, then the law has to consider options for its survival: it may have to extend its range to cover certain exceptions; it may even have to limit its range and admit that it only applies under certain conditions, as Newton's laws of motion had to with the arrival of Einstein's theories. The alternative, after all, is the oblivion of the theoretical scrapheap, where, logic dictates, most theories will eventually end up. In fact the law of conservation of energy, and its close cousin the second law of thermodynamics (which states that entropy, disorder and heat are forever increasing) are unlikely to be under total threat. There are, though, researchers who would want a reinterpretation, or a redrafting of these laws in the light of emerging physics.

Technology has the advantage that it is 'real'. Theories, even laws (their elders), are, ultimately, only our best current model. The inevitable consequence of this is that they have a limited lifespan: they will one day be replaced with a better model. There is a strange paradox in science: while there is an appearance of building knowledge on knowledge, there is the likelihood that, at any time, a model will come from left-field and replace all that we currently understand. It's not something most career scientists like to talk about: many live with high levels of uncertainty, and spend a lot of time trying to pretend, or wish, that life were more stable.

As I write, a debate has started over the speed of light. An American scientist has claimed to have measured light travelling at 300 times the speed of . . . light! Things appear to be arriving before they have left. This extraordinary measurement of a phenomenon will, of course, need to be tested, replicated, analysed and generally torn to shreds to see if it survives. Theorists everywhere are quaking in their boots. Could this be the end of Einstein? The end of relativity? The end of $E=mc^2$? 'C' was always meant to stand for that reassuring constant 'the speed of light'. Now what? Do we have to face the quantum weirdness (again) that effects and causes don't have to be in the right order? Will trains arrive at their destinations before they leave? Will history have to be rewritten to allow for this? Will all my life's work be as nothing? Will I lose my job at the lab? . . . Perhaps it will be simpler, for a while at least, to try to forget about the aberrant measurements and go back to thinking that light moves at the speed of light. In this way the paradigm is left intact. For the moment, at least.

Thomas Kuhn wrote extensively about the history of electricity and the parallel history of theoretical physics. In 1962 he successfully predicted an argument about space and the vacuum, which has now come alive in the field of new energy technologies: 'Space, in contemporary physics, is not the inert and homogenous substratum employed in both Newton's and Maxwell's theories; some of its new properties are not unlike those once attributed to the ether; we may someday come to know what an electric displacement is.'[2]

While we may think that space is an empty vacuum, physicists discovered earlier this century that the universe is not just made up of bits of stuff with empty space in between. It is, it turns out, a strange *Alice in Wonderland* world, in which nothing is not quite what it seems. 'Empty space' is not empty: it is actually suffused with vast amounts of energy. Aristotle may not have known just how right he was when he declared that 'Nature abhors a vacuum.' In the 1960s Professor John Wheeler of MIT put it in more modern language than Aristotle: 'No point is more central than this, that empty space is not empty. It is the seat of the most violent physics.' Wheeler went on to calculate the energy density of the vacuum at a staggering 10 to the power of 94 grams per cubic centimetre – a calculation with implications that have still to be fully taken on board some forty years later.

So how was this energy discovered? By experimentation. If we created an ordinary vacuum in, say, a vacuum jar, and were then to cool the empty space to absolute zero, we would find a level of energy. This energy has become known, for obvious reasons, as zero-point energy – the energy which remains when nothing else is left.

Yet what is zero-point energy? How does it compare with the classical idea of 'ether'? What are the implications of zero-point energy? Can this energy be captured by machines to provide useful electrical energy? Does this development in theoretical and experimental physics explain claims of excess energy and over-unity which might otherwise be dismissed as aberrant thinking or poor experimentation?

Aristotle's dictum that 'Nature abhors a vacuum' was accepted as a reality right up until the seventeenth century. When Aristotle made the assertion he truly meant that a vacuum was an impossibility. This concept of a vacuum was only interrupted when an Italian named Torricelli – who had been secretary to Galileo – invented the first barometer in 1644. It had a mixed reception, sparking controversy which was only settled in Torricelli's favour a few years later when Blaise Pascal designed a series of experiments which confirmed Torricelli's original findings. The idea of a gasless, empty vacuum and its 'properties' tantalized scientists of the time and prompted some curious and eccentric experiments. In 1654 Otto von Guericke, burgermeister of the German town of Magdeburg, constructed a hollow globe from two copper hemispheres, which he then evacuated with a pump. To each hemisphere he attached a team of eight draught horses and commanded both sides to pull in opposite directions. Pull they did, but the vacuum held the globe intact, so establishing the power of the vacuum.

It was not until the late nineteenth century that the concept of the vacuum was extended to include not just an absence of matter and gas but also an absence of heat. This advance was not so much the result of improved heat measurement techniques as the conceptual development of radiation and electromagnetic fields (of which heat is an example). With this new model, a true vacuum could only be achieved if it were possible to cool the vacuum to absolute zero – something which, at the time, was not technically possible.

The arrival of quantum mechanics in the 1930s and '40s brought a significant change to our perception of the vacuum. In particular, Heisenberg's uncertainty principle brought a new spin to the law of conservation of energy. With 'uncertainty' it became permissible for charged, energetic particles (quanta) to appear out of the vacuum's nothingness and then to disappear again without upsetting the law of conservation of energy. In the words of Heinz R. Pagels, the virtual quanta in the vacuum: 'should properly be thought of as pairs of particles consisting of a virtual particle and its anti-particle springing into virtual existence at a point in space and then immediately annihilating each other'.[3]

What had been thought to be a calm flat sea turned out to be topped with a boiling, bubbling froth of 'quantum fluctuations' – fluctuations that could, in theory, exert a force on things around them. Despite King Lear's assertion that 'nothing will come of nothing', something could indeed come of nothing, and physicists soon found ways that they could measure it.

In 1948 Hendrick Casimir, a Dutch research scientist working in the Philips Research Laboratory, predicted that two plates placed very close together in an 'absolute' vacuum would still experience an attractive force between them. This way because the forces of the electromagnetic radiation around them are more powerful than those between them – they are effectively 'shading' each other from this force and reducing the repulsive force in between them.

Yet it was not until 1958 that experiments were carried out to verify the existence of the so-called Casimir effect. M.J. Sparnaay, another Dutch physicist, placed two small metal plates very close together in a relative vacuum. As he cooled the environment around them close to absolute zero, he discovered that a residual force of attraction remained between them. Timothy Boyer, a classical (rather than quantum) physicist, described Casimir and Sparnaay's achievements:

> Whatever the magnitude of the Casimir effect, its very existence indicates that there is something funda-mentally wrong with the nineteenth century idea of the classical vacuum. If one is to fit classical theory with

experiment, then even at zero temperatures the classical vacuum cannot be completely empty; it must be filled with the classical electromagnetic fields responsible for the attractive force Sparnaay measured. Those vacuum fields are now referred to as classical electromagnetic zero-point radiation.[4]

It's worth noting that Boyer's interpretation of the Casimir effect does not appeal to quantum theory. As a classical physicist he prefers to see zero-point energy as, simply, a residual energy within the vacuum, rather than the result of quantum fluctuations. The important question for energy researchers, though, is not so much the theoretical model, but whether the effect of the energy is real.

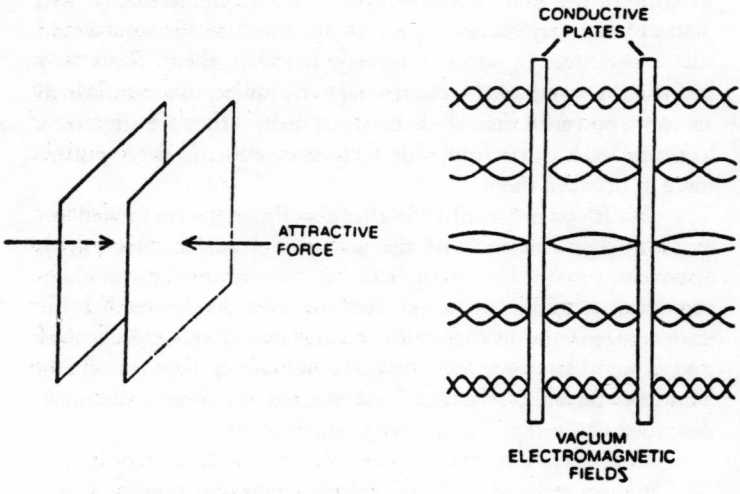

FIGURE 9.1 The Casimir effect demonstrates the existence of electromagnetic effects in the vacuum.

In January 1997 the Casimir effect was further confirmed by the work of Steven K. Lamoreaux of the Los Alamos National Laboratory. His experimental results for the size of the force – using a small metal plate and a tiny gold pendulum – were within 5 per cent of Casimir's projected value. Lamoreaux was, unsurprisingly, delighted to have confirmed the effect so close to its fifty-year-old projection.

Let's Get Practical

Why, if these energy effects from zero-point energy appear to be so subtle, should anyone be thinking about them for providing our energy needs? One thing is clear with zero-point energy: scientists differ greatly in what they think it is capable of. For some quantum hardliners, it's still a case of simply witnessing short-lived particles which live and die in fractions of a second, unbalancing and rebalancing the energy conservation equation on a continuous basis. Any ability to 'take' energy from the vacuum would, to some physicists, be a transgression of the law of conservation of energy. For others it would simply be a case of taking it from one place and using it in another – what you might call vacuum mining.

Harold Puthoff, director of the Institute for Advanced Studies in Austin, Texas, has written many high-profile physics papers on zero-point energy for respected journals such as the American *Physical Review*. His work has also been featured in the *Economist* and the *New Scientist* on a number of occasions. Puthoff continues to speculate that we may eventually be able to mine the vacuum for usable amounts of electrical or propulsion energy.

> As it turns out, even though the zero-point energy in any particular mode of an electromagnetic field is minute (equivalent to half a photon's worth), there are so many possible modes of propagation (frequencies, directions) in open space, the zero-point energy

summed over all possible modes is quite enormous; in fact, greater than, for example, nuclear energy densities. And this in all of so-called 'empty' space around us . . .

Those with a practical bent of mind may be left with yet one more unanswered question. Can this emerging Rosetta Stone of physics be used to translate such lofty insights into mundane application? Could the engineer of the future specialize in 'vacuum engineering'? Could the energy crisis be solved by harnessing the energies of the zero-point sea? After all, since the basic zero-point energy form is highly random in nature, and tending toward self-cancellation, if a way could be found to bring order out of chaos, then, because of the highly energetic nature of the vacuum fluctuations, relatively large effects could in principle be produced.[5]

When questioned by sceptical physicists who deny such possibilities as 'useful zero-point energy', Puthoff quotes the Russian physicist R. Podolny, author of *Something Called Nothing*: 'It would be just as presumptuous to deny the feasibility of useful application as it would be irresponsible to guarantee such application.'[6]

Puthoff has already worked with a number of energy researchers to provide theoretical underpinning to their work. In the late 1980s he teamed up with Ken Shoulders (see Chapter 10) to offer an interpretation of physics which supports the potential of 'charged cluster technology' as, among other things, a new energy source. Shoulders claims that he can get electrons to form 'charge clusters' ('Electrum validums' or EVs he calls them), in which hundreds of billions of electrons pack together in tiny spheres only a millionth of a metre across which are as dense as a solid. He says that these EVs occur naturally in lightning discharges. When EVs are fired at targets they can produce very high energy impacts – creating local heating to tens of thousands of degrees. What is even more unusual, and particularly promising for energy production technology, is that these impacts can be created with very small energy inputs – often as small as 20 microjoules.

This process of electrons all huddling together shouldn't normally be possible, since electrons are all similarly charged and would be expected to repel each other. Shoulders says that his EV technology enables, or encourages, the electrons to cluster without much fuss – a result which is surprising: conventionally it can only be done with a very powerful (and energy-intensive) magnetic field. Puthoff believes that the clustering effect may be a variation of the Casimir effect.

When the charge cluster work was first announced in 1989 it was featured in an *Economist* article entitled 'Does Jupiter Have New Bolts?':

> Mr Shoulders's compression devices are, he says, simple and economical. His tiny nuggets of pure charge, as dense as a solid, zip around at one-tenth the speed of light.
>
> Dr Puthoff . . . suggests that the electrons in a ball of condensed charge may be acting like Casimir plates, shielding each other from the vacuum pressure. The vacuum pressure would squeeze electrons into an EV ball, which would be stopped from collapsing altogether by their natural repulsion.[7]

Dr Puthoff is keen to extend the reach of vacuum effects; he also cites the work of the late Andrei Sakharov in support of the vacuum's importance. It was Sakharov who first suggested, in the 1960s, that even gravity itself could be the result of vacuum fluctuations:

> Specifically Sakharov suggested that gravity might be an induced effect brought about by changes in the zero-point energy of the vacuum, due to the presence of matter (*New Scientist*, Vol. 90, p. 277). If correct, gravity would then be understood as a variation on the Casimir theme, in which background zero-point-energy pressures were again responsible. Although Sakharov did not develop

the concept much further, he did outline certain criteria
such a theory would have to meet.[8]

In Sir Arthur C. Clarke's *3001: the Final Odyssey*, Puthoff's work
on gravity and inertia is specifically mentioned as contributing to
the development of the future's space drive technology. If
Puthoff's theoretical work were ever to find full support from the
mainstream, it would certainly put zero-point energy on the map
in a wholly new way.

Some theorists go even further than Puthoff with their claims for
zero-point energy. Moray B. King, an electronics engineer and
author of the book *Tapping the Zero Point Energy* has already
connected zero-point effects with the work of T. Henry Moray.
(They are not, it should be noted, in any way related!) In a 1998
article with the fancy title 'Vortex Filaments, Torsion Fields and
the Zero-Point Energy' King made the potentially helpful
observation that there are already some seven different models for
the vacuum. For those struggling to grasp more than one, it was a
relief:

Paradigm Camps Regarding the ZPE:

1) Quantum physics is wrong. Quantum events can
be explained classically using . . . fields. The ZPE does
not exist.
2) Relativity is wrong. A material-like ether exists.
3) Quantum physics is correct, but the ZPE is a
theoretical artifact; it is not real.
4) The ZPE physically exists, but its magnitude is too
small to be an appreciable energy source.
5) The ZPE physically manifests large energetic
fluctuations, but they cannot be tapped because of
entropy; they are random and ubiquitous like a
uniform heat bath.
6) The ZPE is a manifestation of chaos in an open

nonlinear system. Under certain conditions it can exhibit self-organization and therefore become available as a source.

The seventh and last is, perhaps, the most difficult to understand for the lay person, although, along with 6), it offers the strongest evidence for the vacuum as an energy source:

7) The ZPE is a three-space manifestation of electric flux from a physically real, fourth dimension of space. It can be twisted into our three-space, yielding alterations to space-time metric. It can be tapped as a source, and doing so locally alters gravity, inertia, and the pace of time.[9]

While this last description may sound like a cross between Stephen Hawking and *Star Trek*, it's simply another way of saying that there may be ways to 'stress' or affect the 'time-space' continuum in order to produce energy effects. Technologies that claim such methods, such as the late Sparky Sweet's Vacuum Triode Amplifier (VTA), have, though, a hard time proving their methods, since there aren't yet too many time-space stress-meters on the market.

There's no doubt that there is huge disagreement in the field about the vacuum's potential. Interestingly it is the Western academics who favour the quantum (but energetically 'useless') 3, 4 and 5 models in opposition to the classical (but also energetically useless) 1 and 2. Models 6 (as favoured by Puthoff) and 7, which offer potential for real energy sources, are taken particularly seriously in Russia, where the idea of a flexible space-time is seen as a modern-day version of the ether concept which ruled prior to relativity. This ether is not dissimilar to T. Henry Moray's concept of *The Sea of Energy in Which the Earth Floats*. It's interesting to note that even Einstein himself was – particularly in later life – extremely uncomfortable with the fact that his theory of relativity had removed the ether concept from scientific culture.

Moray B. King acknowledges that with this kind of diversity in the theory of vacuum physics, it's going to take an experiment that produces a large energy effect to focus the explanatory model. He also claims that the main hypothesis for tapping the zero-point energy is the kind of stimulation of plasma that is witnessed in the free-energy devices of Ken Shoulders, Paulo Correa (see Chapter 10), T. Henry Moray and two other researchers named Papp and Graneau. With Moray's device, he claims that it was the radioactive Swedish stone cathode which helped produce a 'glow plasma', thus inducing a zero-point energy effect. King is primarily, though, a theorist. When quantum push comes to quantum shove, it's likely to be the experimenters who will lead this area out of the vacuum darkness. So who are the likely candidates to demonstrate to the mainstream the connection between zero-point energy and a genuinely useful energy source?

One of the first to show up was Dr Robert Forward. In 1984 Dr Forward, an experimental physicist, published an article in the American *Physical Review* entitled 'The Extracting of Electrical Energy from the Vacuum by Cohesion of Charge-foliated Conductors'[10]. This strange and obscure-sounding title described an attempt to create a zero-point energy battery which was able to store energy that had been taken from the vacuum. It is, again, another technology that uses the Casimir effect, which has yet to be developed to a useful scale. Forward, along with Moray King, holds the view that there is an abundance, an infinity, of energy which can be made available via the vacuum if the right technology can be perfected.

Perhaps the most ground-breaking development in the field occurred on 31 December 1996 when the US Patent Office granted its first patent for a device utilizing zero-point energy as its power source. The patent was awarded to Dr Frank Mead of the Edwards Airforce Base, and is described in the abstract: 'A system is disclosed for converting high frequency zero-point electro-magnetic radiation energy to electrical energy.' In the patent Mead is bullish about the potential usefulness of zero-point energy in future technologies: 'Zero-point electromagnetic radiation energy, which may potentially be used to power interplanetary craft as well as provide for society's other needs, has remained unharnessed.'[11]

Then, in January 2000, it was reported in *New Scientist* magazine that NASA had awarded a three-year grant to Jordan Maclay, a former professor of Electrical Engineering at the University of Illinois at Chicago.[12] Maclay has formed a company called Quantum Fields, to carry out research into the extraction of zero-point energy from space. NASA's Marc Millis, head of the

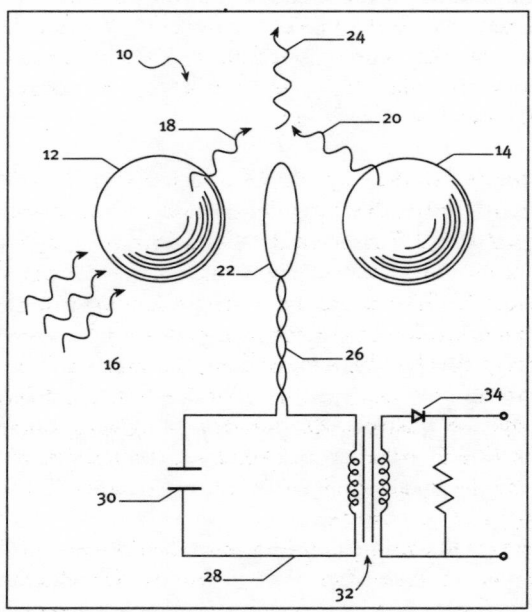

FIGURE 9.2 Diagram from Mead's US Patent No. 5,590,031.

Breakthrough Propulsion Physics programme, is optimistic that this kind of approach will eventually lead to a new form of space propulsion. While space propulsion using zero-point energy may be considered 'easier' than electrical energy production, since small forces can be used in space to create large effects, any progress that is made will almost certainly have positive spin-offs for electrical energy production here on earth.

While the major developments in new energy technologies are being made by experimenters and inventors who work away in their laboratories, the parallel universe of theorists is struggling with a new paradigm of explanation. While they would prefer to lead the search, this is one adventure in which the theorists may be destined to be the followers.

CHAPTER TEN

Significant Others

'Theories and ideas have almost no value at all in our world. Laboratory demonstrations are worth very slightly more . . . it is only a properly engineered device that has real value.'
Kenneth Shoulders, developer of 'charge cluster' technology

This chapter focuses on some of the other main approaches to free energy technologies that researchers have adopted in the last hundred or so years. This grouping is by no means exhaustive, and for every researcher mentioned here there is at least another who has appeared, and – in some cases – disappeared. Of all the claimants these technologies represent the tip of a much larger iceberg. From magnets and electromagnets, water as a fuel, the creation of plasmas, cavitation and sonoluminescence, there may be – now or in the future – many ways to skin the free energy cat.

Can Permanent Magnets be Made to do Work?

Ever since the discovery of magnetic materials, there has been a fascination with what seems to be their forceful natures. Attractive and repulsive forces are, as we know, at the heart of matter: on the micro-scale atoms are conventionally understood to be held together by both strong and weak nuclear forces, the strong forces gluing together protons of like charges which would otherwise repel each other; on the macroscale gravity is the attractive force between any size of object, the force which allows us to circle the sun without going off at a tangent, and which keeps us, and everything else on the planet, from simply floating away. Magnetism, attraction, is essential to life at all levels.

In energy terms we use the force of gravity in a number of ways – the main technology being the production of hydroelectric energy. We are helped in this process by the work of the sun on the sea and the atmosphere in recycling water back to higher portions of land in order to repeat its energetic fall. The conventional understanding of magnets, though, is that they cannot perform 'work' in the scientific sense of the word. Yes, they can hold things up, and stop things falling down, but they cannot act as the motive force which moves another object unless they themselves are moved.

This fact has not stopped people from trying to turn magnets into 'prime movers' in their own right. As early as 1269 Peter Peregrinus, an Italian, put forth a treatise in which he described his perpetual motion machine utilizing the 'virtue', or power, of magnets:

> In this chapter I will reveal to you the way of constructing a continually moving wheel, elaborated with marvellous ingenuity, in the pursuit of which invention I have seen many people wandering about, and wearied with manifold toil. For that they did not observe that they could arrive at the mastery of this by means of the virtue, or power of this stone.[1]

Patents and designs for motors and perpetual motion machines running from magnets have been appearing regularly over the last few hundred years – all, apparently without exception, the subject of a delusion that it is possible to get ordinary magnets to do work. They often involve a pair of wheels, each with magnets positioned around its rim. In some mysterious way the interaction of the magnetic fields between two magnets coming into relatively close proximity is intended to pass on some energy from one to the other, and in so doing the motion of the first wheel induces even greater motion of the second wheel – thus 'creating' energy. We would expect all devices to adhere to the relevant laws of energy – the law of conservation of energy, and the law of conservation of momentum. Despite the years of experience with these laws, some inventors think there may be either special cases in which anomalous events occur, or that the law itself needs to be reinterpreted in the light of advances in physics.

In Germany in the mid-1980s an engineer named Ulrich Schumacher started to take orders for models of his permanent magnet motor, which promised outputs of between 3 and 12 kilowatts. Researchers came from many countries to his workshop to see the machine and talk to the man. He claimed that Japanese scientists had attempted to steal the invention's design, and that the brother of Colonel Gaddafi of Libya had visited, showing interest in the design. Japanese visitors had indeed taken secret pictures: shots of the machines from Schumacher's workshop appeared in Japanese energy journals only weeks after their visit. I accompanied a group of potential investors, who were sponsored by the Sultan of Brunei, together with a scientist from the University of Sussex, in a group travelling to see the machines. Demonstrations were interesting for a variety of reasons, but were certainly far from conclusive in demonstrating any excess energy effects. Nevertheless, Schumacher received a large sum of money to develop the machine further. He was taken to Hong Kong to do laboratory work, but was unable to demonstrate anything useful to his investors, who eventually decided he was a time waster, and pulled out.

In Japan an inventor named Kohei Minato has become relatively famous for his permanent magnet wheel motor, which also secured a US Patent (No. 5,594,289) in January 1997 (see Appendix 9). Following a conference in Seoul, Korea, in the 1990s, a report was circulated by an independent researcher named Henry Curtis, who had been given the opportunity to test the machine in action:

The inventor is Kohei Minato, a Japanese rock musician, who reports that he has spent a million dollars out of his own pocket developing magnetic motors, because the world needs a better source of energy. He has several patents in various countries. His latest patent that I am aware of is US Patent No. 5,594,289 . . .

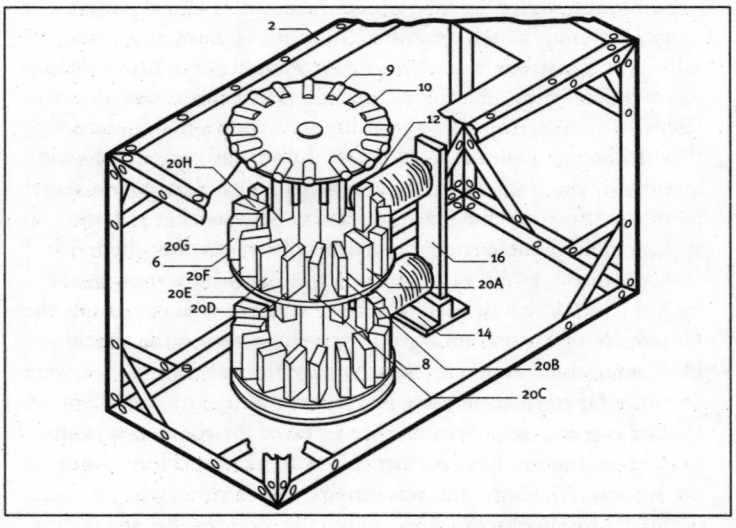

FIGURE 10.1 Image from Minato's US Patent No. 5,594,289.

He had a working prototype of this design at the conference and reported that it used 150 watts power input and produced 450 watts output on a sustained basis. About a year ago CNN (in the US) had a ten minute segment about him and his motors.

The motor is actuated by moving the N pole of a

large permanent magnet (the drive magnet) toward the wheel. As this magnet is moved toward the wheel, the wheel starts to spin. As the magnet is moved closer to the wheel it spins faster.

The acceleration of the wheel is rapid. So rapid in fact, as to be startling. To put it another way I was very impressed. The motor works. And it works very well.

In the film clip a slight pumping action of Minato's hand holding the magnet is apparent. When I braced my hand so that there was no pumping action, the motor still ran. In fact it seemed to run better. Pumping action by the hand-held magnet is not the power that drives the motor. When the drive magnet is moved away from the wheel it coasts rather quickly to a stop and comes to rest in a manner typical of any spinning bicycle wheel. Again when the wheel is at rest and a large magnet is moved up to the wheel it starts to spin. At no time is it necessary to touch the wheel to get it to rotate.

Simply bring the N pole of a large magnet several inches from the wheel. The particular orientation of the wheel when it is at rest seems to have no effect on how well it starts to turn. Irrespective of how the wheel and the magnets on it are sitting; move the drive magnet near, it starts to spin. Move the magnet closer it spins faster. Move the magnet further away it slows up . . .

Apparently the geometry of the magnets on the wheel is very important and subtle. I have built several small models, none of which have shown the free energy effects of Minato's machine.[2]

On 4th March 1998 a report appeared of a public demonstration by Minato:

Mr Minato demonstrated at the Japanese Energy Expo '98 his large unit, connected ten-feet-long units that can power thirty homes, and several smaller table top units.

CNN, NHK and other TV networks took videos of his devices, and of the whole Expo, but he did not know when it was re-broadcasted [sic]. Minato's staff had their own video on for the four-day event . . . There were not any instruments connected to the large unit to measure energy input to output but his table top unit was connected and it showed 48 watts input to 550 watts output. Minato's demonstration attracted a lot of public attention by the large daily crowds and also from a number of interested Japanese corporations.[3]

Since then no more news of any commercial production has appeared.

There are at least four other permanent magnet motors or devices currently gaining attention within free energy circles, which claim to demonstrate excess energy or effects which may be engineerable into energy-producing machines. Whether Werner Heisenberg's 1923 prediction that magnets will become our future energy source, though, still remains to be seen.

Energy From the Solid State

Between 1923 and 1926 a German inventor named Hans Coler, a captain in the German army, developed a device which was thoroughly tested by numerous scientists and practical engineers – some from the German military establishment. It was found, in nearly all examinations, to be producing an energy output significantly larger than its input. Coler himself, who was not an expert in electromagnetic theory, was not able to give any conventional technical explanation as to the functioning of the machine. Indeed, he admitted that he had come upon the effect of the machine as a result of trial and error. The machine itself appeared relatively simple, being made up of a number of linked electronic circuits. The description given by British Intelligence officers of 1946 is, probably, the best available:

The principle circuits (called the anchor) in which the energy gain probably occurs consists of metal plates between which transformer coils are connected, the whole being connected to one large plate coil (Plattenspule). On each of the single windings on this is coupled a large flat coil (Flachspule) (called field).

These flat coils are interwound in two groups. These groups represent the turns of a transformer. This couples on one hand on the flat coils of the other group (as secondary coils), and on the other hand on the anchor-plate coil, which is placed between them.

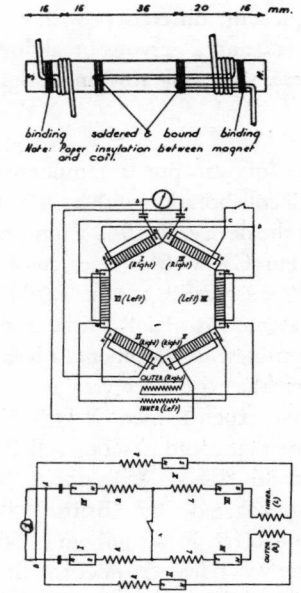

FIGURE 10.2 Images from British Intelligence Report showing Coler's circuit diagrams.

The third electrically independent circuit (called the directing circuit) (Steuerkreis) regulates this transference.

In consequence of this arrangement, different types of current are created in different conductors (pulsed direct current, alternating current, etc.) The transformer coils, connected between the anchor plates, are connected in a peculiar way through thin permanent magnet rods. Their main object seems to be to pre-magnetize the transformer cores . . .

During the years leading up to the Second World War Coler was able to attract some investment funding for his machine. From confidential military reports made at the time, these relationships were not productive for reasons that were far from clear.

Due to unpleasant differences with the financiers, mostly foreigners, and a nervous breakdown of Coler, because of these, the apparatus and original theories were lost.[4]

While the outbreak of war put a temporary end to Coler's experimental work, a collaboration with a Dr Modersohn brought new possibilities for the device. In 1942 a funding application was made to the German OKW (the research department of the German Admiralty) for assistance to put a working device together which could be presented to Adolf Hitler for his blessing and further support. These new developments appeared to yield some significant results, but the experimenters – now joined by a highly qualified measurement expert named Dr Frohlich – were not able to produce a machine that could function reliably.

After the Second World War, during which Coler was captured and interrogated by British Intelligence, this information was kept secret. It was only in 1956 that this limited information on Coler was released under the British ten-year rule for certain sensitive documents. It is not known what became of Coler or his collaborators. Even if Coler had been able to achieve excess energy results for some time, it is far from clear whether he was able to repeat his successes. Some observers, though, have chosen to take a more suspicious view of Coler's unknown fate.

Plasma From Behind the Iron Curtain

In the late 1980s when the Soviet Union's Communist stronghold was breaking up, a physicist named Alexander Chernetskii, working at the Georgi Plekhanov Institute in Moscow, announced what he believed to be a breakthrough in energy production. Chernetskii had been working with plasmas – ionized gases made up of highly energized gas molecules that have lost electrons and become positive ions. The news of his breakthrough claim was first broken by an extensive (and relatively technical) NOVOSTI (Moscow news agency) press release, bylined Andrei Smokhin:

> Classical physicists cannot explain what happens when a plasma discharger placed in a Chernetskii circuit is started. For no apparent reason the ammeter pointer suddenly shows triple strength of current increase and energy output is suddenly much more than one! No magic is involved. Additional energy outputs at specific plasma discharges have been established in several independent 'expert reports' by staff from the V.I. Lenin All-Union Institute of Electrical Engineering (Moscow) of the Ministry of the Electrical Equipment Industry. This effect has been checked by different methods. Where does this mysterious energy come from?

Where indeed? Perhaps Chernetskii's own history is a useful starting point. In Russia he was the author of the first ever study paper on plasma diagnostics equipment. He also had twenty inventions registered to his name, and had worked in the plasma field for some forty years. In the 1970s he and his fellow-researcher Yuri Galkin worked on the development of a new type of high-frequency plasma generator which could operate without the usual 'unwieldy energy converters'.

In one of their tests, measurements showed that there was a

'gap' between the energy input and the output – a gap in their favour. Chernetskii was surprised, but curious:

> I knew electron drift begins in plasma and sought to deduce a combination of variables in which fluctuating plasma instability emerged in discharge. Gas-discharge plasma was meant to serve as a powerful stimulator of electromagnetic modes and, all of a sudden and in defiance of the law of conservation of energy, a strange energy imbalance was produced. Many experiments with different circuits proved that the energy output was always greater than the input in these cases.

Having discovered this extraordinary effect, they decided to play devil's advocate:

> In a bid to explain the experimental data, the researchers actually tried to prove the impossible and one of their proofs turned out to be very violent. The one megawatt substation at the Moscow Aviation Institute, where Chernetskii and Galkin were staging an experiment with a powerful plasma unit, burned out. When the discharge currents reached criticality, superstrong current was 'born' in the generator and went back into the network, playing havoc with the safety devices calculated for short-circuit events.

Once they had established the reality of the effect they sought to find a theoretical basis for the energy effect that they were seeing. They were already familiar with the ideas of quantum physics, which may allow for a very different view of new energy sources:

> The researchers relied on the present-day quantum physics idea of 'zero-point oscillations' in the physical vacuum. Such oscillations signify the birth and

annihilation of virtual pairs, particle and antiparticle, distinguished from the normal elementary particles by a negligibly short lifetime of a mere 8.1×10^{-21} seconds. Emerging below the zero energy level from 'nothing' and returning to 'nothing', virtual particles seem to defy the law of conservation of energy. Quantum electrodynamics explains this strange paradox through the Heisenberg uncertainty principle under which all the precise particle features cannot be determined simultaneously, and, therefore, one must not require from nature 'punctual' abidance by the law in such a short time as the virtual pair lifetime. The observer fails to notice anything while every virtual pair is more than real, carrying an energy of about half a million electron volts during its lifetime. The energy potential in [an] electric bulb vacuum is enough to boil the earth's oceans, Americans John Wheeler and Richard Feynman have calculated.[5]

Chernetskii explained his claims in scientific terms:

The self-generating discharge emerges when the discharge currents reach a definite critical density, when the magnetic fields they create ensure magnetization of the plasma electrons and they begin to perform mainly cycloid movement. The interaction of currents with their magnetic field forces the electrons to deviate to the cylinder-shaped discharge axis and the electrical field emerges. It has been demonstrated that this switches on the physical vacuum. In this field the vacuum is polarized and consequently the virtual pairs begin to move in a definite direction, instead of chaotically. The virtual positrons accelerate plasma electrons, giving them part of their energy. The current in the circuit builds up and additional energy is discharged on the resistor switched into the discharge circuit. Clearly, only part of the tremendous vacuum energy is extracted.

We've developed several circuit versions which can find application. In the latest experiment which had an input power of 700 watts, the generator produced 3 kilowatts for load resistance, or nearly five times as much. This is only the start and not the limit. The calculations for more powerful plants show that many megawatts of free electricity can be produced from minimal power sources.[6]

Dr Keith B. Hindley of Technology Detail, a scientific consulting organization based in York, England, traced Chernetskii's work back to the 1960s:

He began working on instabilities in plasma at high current and high frequencies in the late 1960s, moving to higher and higher frequencies and reaching many tens of megahertz by the early 1970s . . . As the equipment steadily improved, it became clear that the plasma had acquired a new energy source at the sudden transition point. This effect quickly became so pronounced that more energy was being discharged by the plasma than that needed to drive it. By 1975, Chernetskii christened the effect the 'self-generating discharge'. Detailed observations of this transition provided by Chernetskii provide the strongest evidence yet that what is observed truly is a plasma detaching from the electrode drive and instead being driven by an entirely new, internal source – possibly the universal zero-point energy field.[7]

Dr Hal Puthoff of the Institute for Advanced Studies in Austin, Texas visited Chernetskii at the Georgi Plekhanov Institute in 1991, and was impressed with what he saw: 'It was a dramatic demonstration . . . I was impressed [and] didn't sleep that night.'[8]

He attempted to organize for Chernetskii to bring his equipment to Texas for independent verification. Unfortunately Chernetskii died the following year, and for some time it appeared that no one was willing or able to progress his work. More recently, however, there have been reports that Yuri Galkin, Chernetskii's main collaborator, is now developing the technology in Ekaterinburg, Russia, under a military-sponsored contract.

On 28 November 1988 a press release was issued by SOFIA BTA, a Bulgarian press agency, headlined: 'POTENTIAL NEW ENERGY SOURCE THEORY DEVELOPED'. The release had been taken from an article in a monthly science magazine called *Orbita*. The report focused on Kiril Chukanov, a Bulgarian engineer who claimed to have generated large amounts of energy from a process in which he had created artificial ball lightning.

> By a high-frequency generator he created a high-frequency field of about 20 MHz in which he brought a quartz generator, filled with helium. As a result of the action of the high-frequency field, the helium was fully ionized and formed a plasma cord or an oval, shining with a bright white light and surrounded by a bright red crown. The inventor called this cord a 'quantum plasma macro object'. It emits without loss a great amount of energy and is essentially an unknown source of energy.
>
> The technological handling of this energy is not particularly difficult . . .
>
> The *Orbita* weekly writes that the practical use of this discovery would be immense. First of all there is generation of energy without fuels. The helium or the hydrogen are not fuels but only a medium where the energy is generated or taken. The process is completely clean and wasteless from an ecological point of view: no X-rays, radioactive substances, etc. are emitted. The technological construction of the reactor would be quite simple while the efficiency immense.

In its article on engineer Kiril Chukanov's discovery, [the] *Orbita* urges the competent Bulgarian institutes to prompt the survey of his development and – if it proves to be a real discovery of the Bulgarian Academy of Sciences – to quickly start the development of a test reactor for the study of the quantum theory.[9]

Nothing has been heard of Chukanov since then, and it has proved impossible to trace him. Whatever he did achieve, and whatever has happened to him, he is part of a movement which firmly believes that plasma effects may have interactions with the energy in the vacuum. To find a plasma energy technology that is currently under open commercial development, we need to look to the West: more precisely to Canada.

Paulo and Alexandra Correa are based in Ontario, Canada, from where they recently announced that they have discovered a new non-polluting energy source and that they are preparing for manufacturing development. Their story starts back in the late 1980s when, while involved in development work on X-ray tubes, they noticed strange and anomalous behaviour in 'glow discharges' from the cathodes in the tubes they were working with. After a thorough literature search, followed by intensive experimentation, they discovered that particular kinds of cold cathode discharge tubes may, under certain circumstances, give off large bursts of energy.

By 1995 they had developed their Pulsed Abnormal Glow Discharge (PAGD) reactor to a point where it was producing short, repetitive pulses of multi-kilowatt energy, which they were able to convert to useful DC electricity. They claim that the energy released in this reaction is 'tens to hundreds' of times that required to initiate the reaction. These claims have now been enshrined in their three US patents which were secured during 1995 and 1996 (Nos. 5,416,391, 5,449,989 and 5,502,354 – see Appendix 10). The central patent, though predictably technical, does not hold back on the over-unity energy claims:

The Correa grid-independent Energy Conversion System utilizes an energy reactor whose function is based upon heretofore unknown spontaneous emission properties of certain metals in vacuum and involves an anomalous cathode reaction force conforming to Dr H. Aspden's law of electrodynamics.

The associated Motor Drive provides for direct electromechanical transformation of the energy accumulated within the reactor. The reactor may be conceived of as a portable vacuum battery made active only when needed. The Correa technology employs cold-cathode vacuum discharge plasma reactors to set up self-exciting oscillations, in the form of pulsed

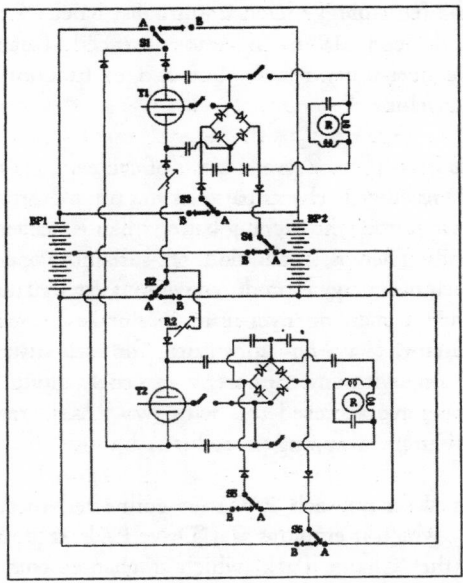

FIGURE 10.3 Circuit diagram from the Correas' US Patent No. 5,594,289.

abnormal glow discharges triggered by auto-electronic emissions, in order to produce power. The circuit is driven from a direct current source of impedance sufficient to prevent establishment of a sustained vacuum arc discharge. In combination with a special circuit, electrical power in excess of the input power needed for operation can be extracted.

Unlike the cold fusion process, which claims to output low-grade heat, the Correa technology directly generates electricity at power voltage levels, without any utilization of cold or thermonuclear fusion principles.[10]

The data that has been amassed and the technological development have impressed many people who have been given access to the technology. Science journalist Michael Carrell saw the PAGD device in 1996, and was convinced of its ability not just to give over-unity results, but also to function as a self-sustaining machine.

The Correas present several kinds of evidence . . . that a PAGD reactor can charge batteries and run motors, using less energy from the exciting battery than is delivered to the loads. There is, in addition, self-sustaining operation in which net energy is produced without external input.

When discussing over-unity performance, endless measurement is no substitute for self-sustaining operation with no apparent external input. The Correas have achieved this with two PAGD reactors and a battery swapping procedure.

In the typical set-up each PAGD is connected to two battery packs – one which it employs as a 'Drive Pack' or power source, the other, the 'Charge Pack' which it charges with its excess energy:

The Charge Pack must always be at a lower voltage than the Drive Pack. Two center-tapped battery packs are used. The full pack is used to drive the reactors, each of which charges half of the second pack. The roles are then switched.

In one test cited in the patent, the battery swapping was continued for eight hours, with both packs gaining charge. There was no external energy input. Dr Correa indicated that this is done automatically in more recent implementation not covered by the available patents.[11]

The Correas say that they are currently progressing beyond the prototype stage, having overcome some early problems in which the cathodes were being eroded too quickly to make the device reliable. While they claim to have a device capable of producing 1 kW – enough to run an electric kettle – they are now working on a version which will output 5 kW. At this stage they are unsure how difficult it might be to scale up the technology to a commercial product. Nevertheless they have started the process of demonstrating to organizations who they believe would want to support their invention. Paulo Correa has, however, been amazed by the lack of competence in examining his technology:

If you need to know, the most basic bottom line is typified by the following two examples – one from the Alcoa company, which took six months to have their legal team negotiate from scratch another confidential agreement with us only to decline our offer to demonstrate, even free of charge, the technology; then, it returned the two packages of our confidential documentation without those it had assigned to make an evaluation having ever opened them! Or Charter Power Systems, which took a year and a half to make an evaluation of the submitted materials and data, and then, by mistake enclosed two internal memoranda addressed to their director of Battery Engineering and

Development in the confidential materials returned to us, the first of which read: 'Quite frankly, I find myself unable to objectively judge what the documents are saying, probably because my background is in chemistry rather than physics. What I do see is a technology that is full of promises yet to be fulfilled; ten years of work which does not appear to have been snapped by anybody in spite of lofty claims.' And then the second, from another would-be appraiser who tersely wrote: 'You can see that [so-and-so] is not convinced of their claims either.' Is this the attention these people are paid for, by their stockholders, to dedicate to their business? And is this the peer review one deserves?[12]

Despite these knockbacks the inventors have gained a level of commercial support with which they intend to move forward towards commercial prototype production.

Clusters' First Stand . . .

How do you get 100 billion electrons to huddle together? No, this isn't a joke, but a serious scientific riddle which may have implications for our energy future. The discoverer or creator of 'charge clusters' – the name for a bunch of 100 billion electrons – is Kenneth Shoulders. Shoulders was a staff scientist at the Stanford University's SRI for four years, and has a track record in invention. He has created a number of gadgets over the years from tiny radios to backpack flying machines, but he is probably best known for his work with vacuum micro-electronics – a field in which he is considered pre-eminent – involving the miniaturizing of vacuum tubes to offer a more efficient alternative to the tiny transistors on silicon chips.

His relationship with charge clusters – also known as EVs, from the Latin for 'strong electron', *electrum validum* – started around 1980, and has now led to the development of a number of useful devices that have little to do with energy *per se*. He has developed EV-based X-ray machines, radar and large flat-screen TV technology which may soon be seen on the side of motorways displaying bright full-colour information in daylight. But Shoulder's interests are broad, and extend to the promotion not just of the technology of charge clusters but also of the theory that supports their existence. In 1986 Shoulders met the well-known genius and physicist Richard P. Feynman of the California Institute of Technology. Disbelieving what he was being told, Feynman sent Shoulders packing for the audacity of his ideas about charge clusters. But after a few weeks he had a change of heart, and wrote to Shoulders: 'When you were in my office I could not see how 10^{10} or 10^{11} electrons could be kept as a ball in a vacuum without ions. So I was skeptical and didn't let you tell me about them. I must apologize for it has come to my attention that it is indeed possible . . .' Dr Feynman had spoken to another physicist, Curtis Michael, who had explained how this might be possible. 'Now that I understand how it might work, I should be glad to discuss it again anytime you wish.'[13]

Through years of long and comprehensive testing Shoulders has shown graphic proof for the existence of charge clusters. Photos from scanning electron microscopes show the effects that these highly charged particles can have when they are fired at a target.

Throughout the development process, there has been an energy production dimension to charge clusters that Shoulders has been happy to keep under his hat. At an energy conference in Maryland in 1999, however, Shoulders let his guard down a little and showed his conviction that the existence of charge clusters may well have huge implications for clean electrical energy production.

> Throughout much of this work on EV [charge clusters] energetics it has been obvious that we get more energy out of certain experiments than we put in. The really good stuff for legitimate products is still to come and

we are working on it. Trying to market a bad, free energy (or cheap) approach is not good for the field even if it sounds wonderful at first.'[14]

As a precursor to an energy production technology, Shoulders's development company is currently working on using EVs to make a positive-ion particle accelerator that is about one million times more effective than current particle accelerator technology. The purpose of the device is to provide on-site transmutation of the highly radioactive spent-fuel pellets from nuclear power plants. If it works, it could, like Paul Brown's nuclear photodeactivation technology (see Chapter 3), offer a new lease of life to nuclear fission energy.

Hammering Energy from Water

When the firemen of Albany, Georgia, get back from a hot and sweaty firefight, they get in the showers at the fire station and turn on the taps. They don't have a conventional boiler at the station to heat the water, but nevertheless out comes the water, hot and steamy. Back in the late 1980s the fire station bought an early model of a machine invented by a local engineer named Jim Griggs. Griggs's machine is called the Hydrosonic Pump and it employs a novel process called 'cavitation', which heats water to very high temperatures without the need for any form of combustion. To Griggs's surprise, it has become the object of study by those who believe it may be an over-unity device. Indeed, after the facilities manager for Dougherty County investigated the fire station's hot water system, he testified that his calculations 'prove [the] unit produces more energy in BTUs [British Thermal Units] than it consumes.'

Griggs's interest in this 'cavitation' or hammering effect started in 1985 while he was working on an energy conservation project at a manufacturing plant in Missouri. He noticed that a cold feed water-supply line to a heating system was warm. When he mentioned this to a maintenance person he was told that they were presently experiencing a 'water hammer' problem on the supply line and that the cold water pipes became warm when that occurred. Griggs became intrigued and began to search for information on this effect. He found very little information, but did confirm from textbooks that when a shock wave passes through liquid, a portion of the energy is converted into heat energy and is dissipated into the mass. Those same texts also refer to this thermodynamic aspect of the shock wave as being so small that for most purposes it can be disregarded.

Over the next two years, Griggs experimented with the idea of producing heat by harnessing shock waves and capturing the heat energy released. In autumn 1987, he explored the idea of spinning a rotor or solid disk inside a housing that contained water. With this prototype he was able to significantly increase the temperature of the water coming from the device. This indicated that it was possible to intentionally produce heat energy by producing shock waves in a fluid. After two more years, during which he designed, tested and discarded hundreds of rotors, Griggs reached his initial design goal. In 1989, the first Hydrosonic Pump was built, driven by a conventional electrically powered motor, but producing steam and hot water with very high energy efficiency, using shock-wave technology.

So what actually happens inside the machine to heat the water? Griggs claims that the water undergoes a number of mini-processes as it passes through the pump.

> A shearing stress occurs as the water first enters the chamber and a small amount of heat energy is created and released into the water . . . As the rotor begins its rotation and reaches sufficient trip speed, liquid is drawn into the cavities or dead-ended bores by the centrifugal force created as the rotor spins. A pressure drop or vacuum is created within the bore.
>
> When the pressure in this pocket exceeds the pressure created by this centrifugal action, the flow

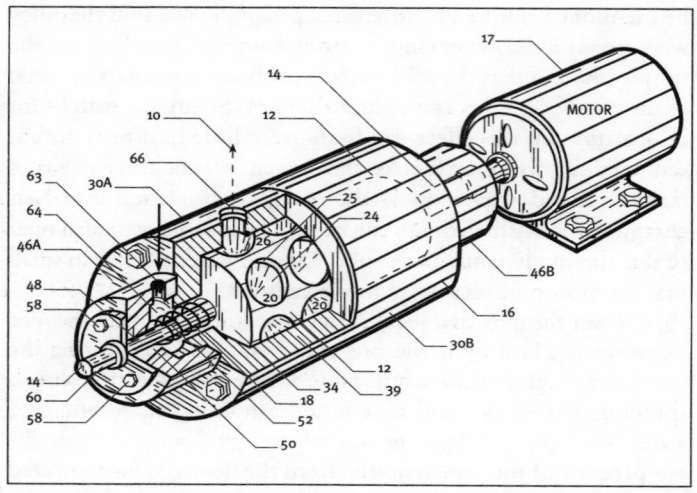

FIGURE 10.4 Image of hydrosonic pump from US Patent No. 5,385,298.

direction of the water is reversed and the water is forced out of the hole only to be instantly drawn into another hole. The process continually repeats itself, thereby creating millions of shock waves per minute. As these shock waves travel through the fluid, microscopic bubbles are also formed at the boundary layer of the liquid in contact with the surface. This particular effect is commonly called 'cavitation'.

Years of research have produced a pump design that forces the bubble collapse to occur within the bore of the rotor and not at the surface where standard cavitational damage could erode the metal. Therefore, all of the energy from the bubble collapse is transferred in to the liquid in the form of heat. As the heated water reaches the outlet side of the pump it will leave as 100 per cent steam, a combination of steam and hot liquid, or 100 per cent hot water . . . depending on the desired result for the commercial application.[15]

This cavitation effect had in fact already been the subject of some laboratory study before Griggs got hold of the idea for his commercial product. It is linked with another effect known as sonoluminescence – literally 'sound into light' – which has been examined as a possible free energy source. Sonoluminescence is a phenomenon in which bubbles in water are seen to give off pico-second pulses of light and heat when they become subject to a high-frequency sound field. While some of the energy measurements involved in the process are particularly difficult to carry out, theoretical projections of the peak temperatures in the bubbles can be as high as 10^9K.

An explanation is emerging for sonoluminescence, the mysterious underwater phenomenon in which air bubbles, compressed by sound waves, implode, releasing 50-picosecond flashes of light which are up to a trillion times more concentrated in energy than the initial sound waves. A new round of experiments and calculations over the last year has done much to elucidate the details of the phenomenon. C.C. Wu and Paul Roberts of UCLA propose (in the 31 May *Physical Review* letters, 1993) that the mechanism for sonoluminescence consists of spherical shock waves generated in the collapsing bubble. According to the hypothesis, the shock waves travel to the bubble's center at supersonic speeds, compressing air inside the bubble and heating it to such high temperatures (over 5000 K) that a plasma is formed. Electrically charged particles in the plasma release flashes of light in the process of accelerating.[16]

Griggs claims that the energy transformation between mechanical and heat energy is 100 per cent efficient, although there are some researchers who believe that the Griggs machine may in fact be an over-unity device which is providing more energy than its input energy by releasing some form of sonoluminescent phenomenon in the water. A third-party investigation into the pump's possible over-unity operation is under way, but so far there are no conclusive measurements to decide either way.

Sonoluminescence Meets Cold Fusion

On March 4 2002, in an annoucement that drew parallels with the Pons/Fleischmann cold fusion event of 1989, Oak Ridge National Laboratory in the States published a paper in *Science* that claimed they had achieved nuclear fusion in a 'table-top' apparatus. Suddenly it was déjà vu all over again. Rusi P. Taleyarkhan, the leader of the multinational team suggested that they had managed, using sound waves, to get tiny bubbles to implode releasing heat, light and – potentially – fusion products such as neutrons and tritium. Could it be that sonoluminescence can create such high temperatures in these bubbles that fusion of hydrogen nuclei becomes possible?

Other laboratories are now competing to confirm, or deny, the claims, and – just as in 1989 – things have gone strangely quiet. Except, of course, for the sceptics such as Bob Park who immediately dashed to print: 'Hark: A COLLECTIVE GROAN CAN BE HEARD . . .' Park is convinced already that the scientists are wrong . . .

*

These are by no means the only researchers who have made, and are still making, contributions to the research into new energy technologies. Just how many of these technologies emerge as real and commecialisable energy sources remains to be seen. To pick any one as our key energy technology for the future would be a high-risk venture. Only experienced time travellers and the most expert crystal ball gazers need apply.

CHAPTER ELEVEN

Of Conspiracies, Charlatans and Sceptics

'Mundus vult decipi – *The world wants to be deceived.*'

Anon.

'If it can't be done, it interests me.'

Joseph Newman

On my desk I have an audio tape from October 1988 of an Australian inventor and businessman named Brian Collins claiming – to an assembly of church folk in rural America – that his 'Project Alpha' free energy generator is about to bring to an end the evil rule of the 'oil barons'. The generator would, coincidentally, also provide a wonderful investment opportunity to people of faith. He goes on to tell his audience that in a mystical experience during a heart operation, he was given the design for the device by God, and has now developed it with the good people at the University of Sussex in England, to a point where, Lord be praised, it now works! Hallelujah!

> God gave me this invention and I believed the Lord has done it in such a way that instead of it being given to the oil barons it's being given to the Davids of the world and not to the Goliaths . . .
>
> We're six weeks away from a working generator . . .

next time I'm here I'll have a generator working . . .[1]

In some accompanying material he describes the machine:

> . . . measuring just 12 inches by 3 inches [sic] and weighing only 10 pounds produced enough electrical energy to completely power an average size home. No doubt you will agree that such configurations can only underline a breakthrough unrivalled anywhere in the world. With the availability of unlimited amounts of affordable electrical energy, individuals can at last pursue their creative aspirations in a new age of society.[2]

In a longer description of the device, published at the same time, the claims are even more generous:

> The prototype of the 'Collins Generator' which was conceived by myself and researched, developed and built by my specialist scientists and technologists . . . produced electrical energy in excess of 1000 kW [kilowatts] or 1360 hp [horsepower]; enough power to satisfy the energy needs of 100 domestic dwellings at average load demand.

This whole account is both extraordinary and typical of a particular confidence trick. What is extraordinary is the audacity of the perpetrator, Brian Collins. Firstly, Collins the 'conceiver' had not invented a useful free energy device: he was an engineer and businessman who simply put some money into a research contract with the University of Sussex – supplying them with something he called the Collins Energy Device.

Dr Denis Edwards was the head of the Electrical Engineering Department at the time of Collins' contract, and dealt directly with Collins. When I spoke to him in late 2000, Denis Edwards was damning of the device's value:

He might call it the Collins Energy Device. In fact it was a non-working piece of hardware. It never did work, nor in my opinion could it have worked. It was a very crude device. It did nothing.[3]

Dr Edwards and his associate Gunnar Sandberg – who died in April 1996 – both believed that Collins was attempting to replicate the work of a British inventor named John Searl. Despite Collins' denials that he had known much about Searl, Dr Edwards was convinced:

I think it was an attempt to implement Searl's ideas.[4]

None of this stopped Collins going around the world saying that the University's scientists were right behind him and convinced of his brilliance:

The scientists say I should be getting a Nobel prize.[5]

Denis Edwards rejected these claims:

I am aware that Brian Collins has made some extraordinary claims, some of which purport to include the University of Sussex. He has on occasion sought my support for his claims, which I have been unable to give. The University of Sussex would not wish to be associated with such claims, and I hope that you will respect this position.[6]

Back in 1998, though, the University was unable to stop Collins' methods for raising money. The good people of rural America, with the encouragement of 'Kingdom-Age Technologies' of Boise, Idaho, were being offered the opportunity to invest in the promise of free energy. The offer was temptation itself:

This final opportunity is extended to anyone who has

the faith to believe that free energy is possible . . . and would like to invest a minimum of $500 US within the next 30 days. Anytime after 31 January may be too late as Stage 1 will probably be completed and faith will no longer be required . . .

Benefits to be received are as follows:

1. A return on investment funds of 5 to 10 times the original amount. This is expected to take place during the first quarter of '89.

2. To be among the very first to receive a generator once production begins. There is no telling when generators will be made available to the general public.

3. An off-shore account will be established for the investor . . . into which future funds from the production and sales of the generator will be entered. These funds are a piece of the pie specially set aside for this purpose. The amount to be received by each individual will be based on the $ amount invested. This is a legacy . . . and can be passed from one generation to the next.

Faith investments should be sent . . .[7]

The Sting

There are a number of features of this case which are typical of this particular offer, and which have formed a pattern for a few modern-day charlatans out to fleece the masses. Whether it's cures for baldness, penny shares or get-rich-quick from free energy schemes, there's a gullible public out there who only need the right buttons pushed in order to hand over the cash.

Here's how the sting works. First, the perpetrator goes to America's religious heartland. There are many religious people who also believe in The Great Conspiracy that the government and the federal reserve have conspired against the American people to deprive them of their freedoms, and these beliefs are often played on. Second, offer them an exclusive, inner track to God's kingdom: this can be done in a few different ways but the basic formula is to equate investing (handing over the cash) with a demonstration of faith in the Lord (and his scientific servants). This is similar to the ancient practice of 'selling indulgences'.

At the same time another equation can be made: that to be sceptical of all the claims being put forward is to be a 'doubting Thomas' and to lack faith. In Collins's Kingdom-Age Technologies literature this button was pushed hard:

> In the spring of 1987, an opportunity to invest in the development of the C.E.D. (Collins Energy Device) was extended to myself and a few friends and associates. This offer ended in June of '87 in anticipation of Stage 1 being completed that same year. Unfortunately, unforeseen problems caused the project to take an extra year.

Why is it that these kind of problems are always 'unforeseen'?

> These delays worried some of the small investors, causing a few of them to become very impatient. This resulted in at least a few of them requesting their investments to be returned. I think you will agree that 'Doubting Thomases are a dime a dozen'. It is those with faith and understanding that will persevere . . . and be rewarded.

In a taped talk to some of his US 'faith investors', Collins made some big financial promises to help the Christian Patriots get through the 'end time' with dollars in their pockets:

> The special few who sent funds . . . for every dollar that they sent, they'll see more money than they ever believed possible, because I'll tell you: they're in a special little group that my attorney in Australia is

putting . . . it's . . . well, it's a privileged place that
they're in: in the next few weeks there could be some
amazing things happening that could see many, many
times the funds returned to everybody. And then you
just sit there and have a free ride from there on . . .

Not only that: as soon as we get the generators going
you people will be able to pick as many generators as
you want for your own use or anything else . . .[8]

Truly a promise of bliss. A promise that Collins just couldn't hope
to keep.

It's not known exactly how much Collins and his colleagues
were able to secure in investment, and Collins was recently
unwilling to divulge the figure. When I spoke to Brian Collins in
1988, he was staying at one of London's most expensive hotels. I
wondered how his American farmer friends would have felt had
they known what their money was contributing to. And as soon
as the scientists at the University of Sussex declared the
technology unworkable, the notion of wonderful gleaming
C.E.D.s disappeared in a puff of illusionist's smoke.

Once money's been handed over, scams often fold and
disappear, leaving the investors to lick their wounds and try –
usually unsuccessfully – to get their money back through some
form of legal redress. What is most galling for the original
investors is that the 'inventor' often reappears with the same scam
in a new guise only a few years, or even months, later.

Collins now maintains that he still intends to pay his
investors back, that it was very unfortunate, and that he had been
misled as to the progress of his technology. He is, though, still in
the free energy business – he claims to have three different devices
located in three different places around the world, which he will
soon be releasing to the world. A lot of people have decided not
to hold their breath.

The Dennis Lee Roadshow

Inventor Dennis Lee has recently been touring the United States with his Free Energy Roadshow. In this exhibition of extraordinary (as well as very ordinary) phenomena, Lee demonstrates a number of devices and machines which he claims will create a whole new energy future. He also tells people about the conspiratorial forces which have acted to prevent the success of these technologies that God wants him to give to the people. In the final act of his presentations people get to sign on the dotted line and commit the cash – as much as $10,000 for one of the 200 'exclusive dealerships'.

Eric Krieg is a free energy sceptic and the initiator of a $2000 challenge issued to any inventor of a free energy device who is able to submit their invention successfully to his tests. He couldn't resist the chance to see Dennis Lee when his roadshow came to Philadelphia in 1996:

> I saw a full-page newspaper ad promising a demonstration of amazing technologies, including one that will make free electricity from the air. On the night of 23 September, I and a few other members of the Philadelphia Association for Critical Thinking (PhACT) went to see this 'amazing' technology for ourselves. The city hockey stadium had been rented out for the grand finale of a thirty-four-city tour. There was a feeling of excitement (dare I say electricity?) in the air. After a brief prayer huddle with assistants, Dennis Lee took the stage amidst thunderous applause. Thus began a five-hour, non-stop demonstration of a whole array of curious machines in the middle of the arena.[9]

Krieg soon saw that Lee was promoting the Great Conspiracy Theory as the reason why these devices hadn't yet made their mark on the world:

The charismatic Lee said he has been victimized by a massive international, multigenerational conspiracy to keep such amazing technologies out of the marketplace. The audience gladly signed 'declarations of energy independence' that boldly declared they would no longer accept governmental suppression. His presentation focused more on his unique blend of patriot politics and religion than on proof of his claims. He claimed he couldn't make good on his advertised promise to demonstrate a wonderful radiation-neutralizing invention by Yull Brown. Apparently, he had inside knowledge that government agents had infiltrated the presentation, ready to make arrests. Lee claims to have invented the world's most efficient heat pump, but conspirators sabotaged his efforts, stole his company, and incarcerated him.

For about ten years, Lee has claimed that he can produce free energy from ambient heat by connecting his heat pump to a Fischer low-temperature phase-change machine. Not surprisingly, the audience warmed to the assertion that God had given Lee the final technical help to make this possible. (In Lee's literature, he quotes many of God's exciting revelations to him.) Unfortunately, Lee's only proof of this device was to have an audience member confirm that one part of the machine was hot. Each new bold pronouncement was interrupted by ecstatic applause.

Throughout the meeting Krieg tried to get Lee to respond to his direct challenges:

> Throughout debates, I tried to keep shepherding people back to the primary issue: Does the free-energy machine work? Lee and his people rebuffed my appeals to examine his machine. I then made an open offer to spend tens of thousands of dollars promoting his device

among people with the experience and equipment to validate his machines if he would just let me verify it first. Lee simply told his army that they should pay no attention to me because I was the 'enemy.' He certainly didn't respond to inquiries such as, 'How much does your company pay the power company and gas stations?'[10]

Once Lee had shown people some of the technological claims, it was time for him to get down to the nitty-gritty: the investment opportunity. 'Lee promised that people paying $10,000 to become dealers would be installing smaller versions of this machine in private homes across America before the end of the year. Since then, he has claimed that 2000 dealers signed up but that there will be a few delays.'[11]

With 2000 dealers each paying $10,000, there's a pot of $20 million to go towards the technologies. Those 'dealers' will all want know where their money is going. This is how the business plan works.

Dennis Lee has determined that in order to make an economical production run of the free energy units he must produce a minimum of 2000 machines. In this quantity the machines will cost roughly $10,000 each to build, even though some people say they can be made from simple parts available at a hardware shop.

This funding is accomplished through a pretty complex process which, it's believed, has tax advantages. It uses $200 Certificates of Beneficial Interest (COBIs), which are deposited into a trust fund and then loaned to the International Tesla Electric Company. ITEC (which has nothing directly to do with Nikola Tesla, who is possibly rotating in his grave at the use of his name) is a new company belonging to Dennis Lee and others. Individuals purchasing a COBI are entitled to have a free energy electrical generator installed in their home within one year.

After the organization's 'trustee', a pastor named Charlie, has collected fifty certificates (worth $10,000), he loans $1000

(10 per cent) to ITEC as a down payment for one free energy unit (the balance is given as a letter of credit, payable upon machine delivery). Once it is manufactured this unit is used as collateral for a conventional loan to finance the building of a second unit. The second unit is used as collateral for the third unit, and so forth, until fifty units (one for each COBI holder) have been created from the dealer's original $10,000 investment.

Once a free energy machine is installed in someone's house, they are given an allowance of 26,000 kWh (kilowatt hours) per year. The dealer can then sell any excess over this amount (the machine supposedly produces 100 kW continuously) to the electricity companies at 3 cents per kWh, which is less than their own cost of producing electricity.

So what happens if Lee is not able to deliver on his promise? Who loses out? If a free energy machine is not delivered to a COBI holder's house within one year of purchase, the contract states, the holder is entitled to recoup only 90 per cent of their investment. Given that Lee and his friends have taken $20 million, they'll only have to give back $18 million and will be hanging on to $2 million. Not only that, but they may also benefit from the annual interest on the capital in the meantime – which could be another million or so.

Some people believe that the technology that Lee is using for these devices is an already discredited form of heat pump called the Zeromotor, designed by a man named John Gamgee, who was never able to turn it into an energy-producing machine. Eric Krieg believes that Lee has failed to satisfy on a number of occasions: '[Lee] seems not to have told his latest 2000 dealers that all but six of 2000 dealers of a similar effort years ago gave up on him.'[12] Lee's record on customer satisfaction is not good: the *Utah Desert News* of 22 January and 16 February 1993 reports that Lee was indicted for fraud in New Jersey in 1975, charged with fraud in the state of Washington in 1985, and pleaded guilty to two felony counts of consumer fraud in California in 1990 in connection with the sale of his energy-saving heat pump kit.

This time he's been talking to his lawyers, and he's making sure that while some people may get the impression that some free energy technologies are working, he's very careful not to state outright that he has the answer: 'We're not saying that we have a black box. But wouldn't it be neat if somebody could give you a black box that makes free electricity?' No one's disagreeing with that. He says some other things that sound pretty tempting too: 'We have a plan for setting you free from the grid' and 'We can make commercial-sized units on a flat bed trailer.' These Lee calls 'power wagons':

> We are working with Edison Electric in New Jersey to power a substation with a 20 megawatts power wagon.

> It costs nothing to run – it takes its power from the magnetic field of the earth. I could do that right now and pump money out of the earth!

> I could have them pay me not to bring this thing out!

> 'Concentrated power' is no good for the people of a free country!

> I have been offered a billion dollars for this development by commercial interests!

> The State of Israel want me to power the country!

He claims that conventional investment institutions have rejected him, and he has turned away from them in order to favour people of faith:

> I have a unique relationship with God! He told me he wants me to bring this to you instead! He told me to go across the country on a tour – we will find who the true believers are!

I have just showed you the most amazing discovery in the world.[13]

But is his discovery a machine to provide the world with electrical energy, or just a device for taking money out of people's pockets?

The Energy Machine of Joseph Newman

On 18 September 1999, as Lee was still touring with his roadshow, he suffered an enemy attack by press release from another 'free energy developer' – Joseph Westley Newman:

> WARNING TO EVERYONE REGARDING DENNIS LEE:
> It was just brought to my attention that Mr Dennis Lee (also operating under the name of 'Better World Technologies, Inc.' or 'United Community Services of America') ran a full-page advertisement in *USA Today* on Friday, 17 September 1999. He specifically stated that he would be 'selling magnetic motors that are more than 200 per cent efficient.'
>
> All people be warned: Dennis Lee came to my national demonstration at the Louisiana Superdome in New Orleans in the mid-1980s and he even wrote me a letter offering $1,000,000.00 for permission to use my Pioneering Energy Invention to operate a device he had already been promising to people.
>
> I turned him down and told him, 'If your device works, then you don't need my Magnetic Motor Pioneering Technology.' Even at that time I was suspicious that he was deceiving people. NOW I KNOW THAT HE IS!
>
> If he is in ANY WAY claiming that 'He and his company have invented a Revolutionary Magnetic Motor' (that can operate at over 100 per cent efficiency), then I consider him to be *lying scum*! [14]

While there's little love lost between these two self-professed Christians, Joseph Newman is like Lee in being another researcher who seems to have frustrated as many seekers after free energy truth as he has apparently satisfied. The controversy surrounding the Energy Machine of Joseph Newman has rolled on for over fifteen years and continues to this day, undimmed, it seems, by negative publicity. Its inventor claims that it is anything between 300 and 2500 per cent efficient – producing many times the energy it requires to drive it. And yet it has never been seen running as a self-sustaining machine. Does the machine have real value, and is Joseph Newman a genius, a fraud or a self-deluded maverick?

Joseph Newman's publicity blurb says that he has made his living as an inventor for the past twenty-five years or so. He currently holds eight patents for 'useful devices'. These include: plastic-covered barbell sets; a mechanical orange picker; a bike that does wheelies; a knife that always lands point upwards; and a new type of automobile rain-deflector. He does not, however, hold a US patent for his energy device: a fact that enrages Newman as much now as it did nearly twenty years ago when he first filed for patent validation.

Newman's own formal education ended after his junior year of college, when he left to pursue a career in inventing. Since then he says that he has continued to educate himself through a combination of brains and books. The starting point for his study of energy was the work of Michael Faraday, the British 'father of electricity' who invented the first electric motors, and who established the laws relating to magnetism, electro-magnetism and motion.

After fifteen years of his own study, Newman published his first major document on energy production. In this he predicted that 'because all mass is made up of electromagnetic energy, and if the proper, mechanically designed mechanism is built, one can change mass into pure electrical energy and/or rotational motion in a 100-per-cent conversion process.'[15]

The means by which Newman expected to be able to

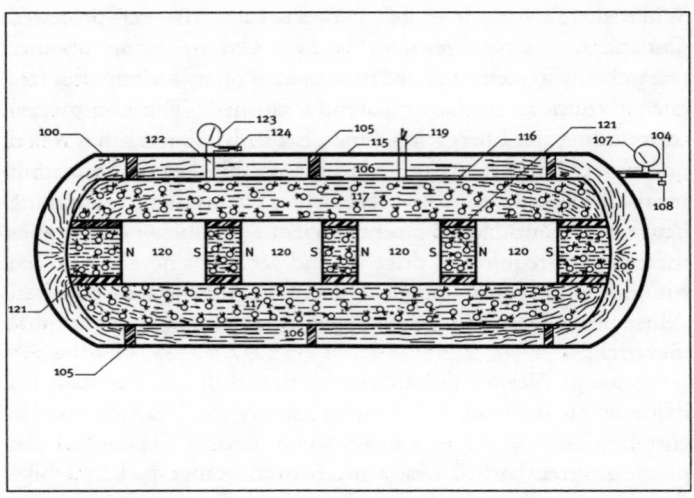

FIGURE 11.1 Image from Newman's Patent No. WO 08,300,963.

achieve this miracle of physics was revealed a few years later with the building of three prototype machines – one small, one medium and one large model which weighs over 5000 lbs and contains a 600-lb rotating magnet.

In essence the machines all consist of large powerful permanent magnets which rotate or reciprocate either within, or near to, a coil consisting of a very large number of turns of copper wire. The coil is normally energized using a set of batteries, and the magnetic field produced by the coil provides the turning force required to turn (or reciprocate) the permanent magnet. A mechanical commutator reverses the direction of current flow through the coil each half cycle.

So far, I've just described a normal electric motor, although in this case it would be more accurate to call it a two-pole, single-phase, permanent magnet armature DC motor. What makes the Newman motor unusual is the scale of certain elements, and the effects that Newman claims for these scalings. Both the magnet and the coil are extremely large: the magnets can weigh up to 600 lbs, and the coils contain as many as 100,000 turns of copper wire. This makes the coil's resistance very high, and means that the motors operate with very high voltages, but with very small currents. At one of Newman's demonstrations he showed a prototype motor turning a 16-inch fan blade at more than 500 r.p.m. This was claimed to have been achieved with a minuscule current of .0008 amps at a voltage of 3000 volts – a total of 2.4 watts.

Roger Hastings, Ph.D, a professor of physics from St Paul, Minnesota, and a supporter of Newman, made a statement to the Subcommittee on Energy, Nuclear Proliferation and Government Processes on 30 July 1986:

> How much torque can this motor produce? Try to stop the motor by holding the two-inch diameter shaft. This will not be possible for a normal human, although the motor will never draw more than 0.003 amps or 9 watts. This motor is a scale model of a motor which Newman intends to build to power an automobile.[16]

In 1986 the US National Bureau of Standards (NBS) undertook a series of tests on one of Newman's machines following his patent application. The test results showed that Newman's machine was incapable of producing an output larger than its input, but Newman challenged the findings, saying that the tests had been rigged. For him this was proof that the Great Conspiracy was against him. Court cases followed, but for Newman a satisfactory outcome was never reached. He does, however, hold a number of patents internationally, including one from Mexico. He still hopes that under an international treaty (NAFTA) this will be 'converted' into a US patent before long.

Newman has appeared on numerous television programmes, and in hundreds of newspapers and magazines across the United States and the rest of the world. As far as is known none of these has put the machine under serious scientific scrutiny. Newman has, however, allowed a select band of researchers and engineers to investigate his machine and make assessments. One of these was Milton Everett, a mechanical engineer who used to work for the Mississippi Department of Energy, who issued a notarized affidavit on 7 September 1999.

> I first visited Joseph Newman's home in Mississippi for the purpose of proving him wrong. Instead, not only myself, but I also witnessed numerous other credible scientific individuals verify his work. Like myself, these individuals initially disbelieved the technology and then listened to Joseph Newman's mechanical unified field theory. They then tested several prototypes with oscilloscopes, torque tests, heat tests while comparing the performance of Joseph Newman's motor/generator to conventional motors. All of these scientific individuals then signed Affidavits *that Joseph Newman's invention works and that his mechanical theory of the Gyroscopic Particle was also correct.*
>
> I was so impressed with Joseph Newman . . . that I influenced the premier electrical engineer of Mississippi State University to travel with me to Joseph Newman's home. After considerable testing of his motors, he stated that: 'Joseph Newman's Motors are 200 per cent efficient.' I myself stated on a national CBS evening news broadcast that 'Einstein would have to take a back seat to Joseph Newman.' I have also witnessed the terrible manner in which Joseph Newman has been treated by various agencies of our Federal Government and special interests in industry.

In his affidavit Everett goes on to describe how powerful and efficient he believes the Newman motor to be:

> Unnecessary friction losses found in the relatively crude, hand-built production motor are tremendously

greater than the input power at 100 volts which operate the Newman motor without any torque load on the motor's shaft. We are talking about a magnitude of 1200 per cent more unnecessary friction losses than input power. Of course, those unnecessary friction losses can easily be removed on the final, machine-built production motors.

As any mechanical engineer is taught in the first years of mechanics, such astounding results are impossible by conventional teachings. As a person of mechanical training and years of technical service, it is with great sincerity that I tell the people of this world that Joseph Newman's Energy Machine will greatly benefit everyone on the planet.[17]

What Everett is saying here is that the power that gets lost in the 'losses' is larger than the amount of power going into the machine. But why, his critics demand, has Newman not been able to reduce the losses and use this excess energy to close the loop and produce a machine that provides usable energy? Many people believe it's because there's a basic error in either the measurement techniques or in the Newman theory. Or, of course, both!

Newman has recently established a demonstration centre in Scottsdale, Arizona, where the machine has been viewed, apparently functioning 'successfully', by groups of the general public numbering some three hundred. On 14 August 1999 one of the Newman machines was set up alongside two other 'control' motors. All machines were connected to the same set of solar panels as their power source, and were required to lift a 14 lb weight from the ground.

From the test Newman concluded that only his motor was powerful enough to raise the weight using the electrical power supplied by the solar panels. At the end of the session one witness – who some claim was Newman himself – made a bold claim: 'Anyone who can't understand the importance of the demonstration is an idiot!'

After Newman's test methods were published on the Internet, they were torn apart by a variety of electrical engineers who believed that he had revealed a lack of knowledge of basic electrics.

Let's try to understand in simple terms what Newman was trying to demonstrate: the reason for using solar panels (in sunny Arizona) is that they limit the amount of power that can be drawn; a mains source would permit a higher current draw to be made by the motors. The point here is that the Newman motor – which does not seem to rely on a high current to produce a significant torque – appears to lift a 14 lb weight two feet off the ground in two seconds. The other two motors – both of which are current demanding – will not lift the weight. Newman's conclusion from this demonstration is that:

Conventional motor inefficiencies are CLEARLY PROVEN BY THE USE OF SOLAR PANELS IN THAT THEIR HIGH CURRENT DRAW DESTROYS OR WORKS AGAINST BATTERIES, GENERATORS, SOLAR PANELS, ETC., ABILITY OF A SOURCE OF POWER THAT PRODUCES VOLTAGE IN ACCORDANCE WITH E=MC^2, RELATIVE TO THE CONVENTIONAL MOTOR TO BE OPERATED!

The capitalization is Newman's, as are the syntactic errors. Newman is saying that the ability of his motor to operate efficiently at very low amperages means that it is, in some mysterious way, exchanging mass for energy. He goes on to extrapolate that the mass of the machine is related to its efficiency: 'As I make the Newman Motor larger and larger it uses less and less current and wattage, and PRODUCES MORE AND MORE POWER!'[18]

Critics Speak Up

Responses to Newman ranged from the polite and technical to the rude and unrepeatable.

While Newman trumpets his clarion call 'Join me in its mass production!' there are quite a few people who wish they hadn't. A number of people who have signed licensing options have seen nothing for their money. Some are afraid to challenge Newman, and hang on in the hope of making a profit one day.

One electrical engineer named Norm Biss was not afraid to incur Newman's wrath, announcing over the Internet what he thought of Newman's technology. He was in a special position too: he had built a motor for Newman.

> Many people have provided reasons why the figures on Joe Newman's latest solar panel tests are 'Sour'. To those who say: '*Norm, why don't you just back off? We are sick of this,*' I will explain my reasons for doing so.
>
> About one year ago, Joe Newman approached my company, and conned us into building a prototype of his 'Energy Machine' at a cost of over $31,000. On the night before final testing, Joe Newman stole the motor to prevent the test results from being made public. Had other victims of 'Newmanism' had the courage to publish their dealings with Joe Newman, we would have been saved from his scheming. It is my intent to give all the information I can, which will enable others to judge for themselves the validity of Joe Newman's claims for his 'Energy Machine'.[19]

At this point Newman, who absolutely refutes all these charges, threatened to sue Biss and others whom he claimed were threatening his livelihood. The case continues . . .

Machines Go Under the Internet Hammer

Meanwhile, if you want to own one of Newman's machines yourself, there may still be time to buy one. In a strange twist to the story, Newman has now started to auction up to a 1000 examples of his energy machine on the Internet. The first few have sold for between $2000 and $4000:

> A fully functioning, signed and numbered scale-model of the Energy Machine of Joseph Newman has now been placed for auction on this Internet auction site. This collectible is designated with the Serial No.1 and will be personally autographed by Joseph Westley Newman.
>
> The specific goal of offering such collectibles for sale via auction is to raise the capitalization necessary to produce full-scale production units capable of powering homes, businesses, factories, and farms. The collectibles offered through auction will directly demonstrate the operability of a revolutionary technology designed to transform our access to energy across the planet. As such, the collectibles will have great historical value as items that will herald the arrival of a new energy technology for humanity.[20]

If all goes well Newman will have raised a cool $2–4 million. He refers to the models as collectors' items and is careful not to claim that they are actually energy-producing machines – rather, they are scale models. However the machines are accompanied by a set of 'facts' about the 'original' Newman machine (rather than the scale model). They include:[21]

> Fact: The Newman Motor/Generator gives back higher voltage and current than inputed from battery system.
> Fact: Conventional wisdom before Joseph Newman's Disclosure states that is impossible.[20]

How can any of this be true? Why are the demonstrations so obscure? If he's saying that the machine is more than 100 per cent efficient, why can't he simply close the loop and make the machine self-sustaining? Some observers will draw their own conclusions from the fact that Newman has not even chosen to attempt such a feat.

Financial Health Warning

There are inventors who are looking to raise investment finance to develop their technologies, in order that they can eventually profit from them. This is to be expected. Whether the general public should become involved in schemes to fund such developments is another question. The record on these schemes is not good, and should be contrasted with companies who seek professional or institutional investors who have a professional attitude to risk management. For utilities companies to hedge their future positions with investments in new technologies is a very different matter to individuals committing their private savings in technologies which do not have a track record of successful independent testing.

In the words of many sceptics, 'Extraordinary claims require extraordinary proofs.' If the proofs aren't forthcoming, and the evidence isn't there, it doesn't matter how good the spiel is, how convincing the conspiracy story: there's unlikely to be gold at the end of the rainbow. What's most amazing, though, is just how long and how well some people can get away with selling not just the gold at the end of the rainbow, but the very rainbow itself.

CHAPTER TWELVE

Envisaging a New Energy Future

'Drill for oil? You mean drill into the ground to try and find oil? You're crazy!'

Response to oil pioneer Edwin L. Drake, 1859

'Whatever our resources of primary energy may be in the future, we must, to be rational, obtain it without consumption of any material.'

Nikola Tesla, 1900

'2010: The first Quantum Generators (tapping space energy) are developed. Available in portable and household units from a few kilowatts upwards, they can produce electricity indefinitely. Central power stations close down; the age of pylons ends as grid systems are dismantled.'

Sir Arthur C. Clarke, *2001 and Beyond*

Imagine a machine that sits in a cupboard in your home producing electricity. It requires no maintenance, and – if connected to your fuse board – will produce all the energy you need to run your home. After you have bought it you need never pay for any further electricity. It also has other, wider, advantages: unlike current energy technologies it produces no pollution (particularly carbon dioxide) and no waste products, and does not contribute to any other negative environmental impact.

Imagine also that larger versions of the same machine can be used to run factories and cars, and that people living in remote parts of developing countries could use the machine to pump water from long distances to irrigate crops on land hitherto barren.

Imagine how much you might be willing to pay for something that is so beneficial – individually and socially. For something that not only saves you money on electricity bills, but also makes sure that you don't contribute to adverse climate changes.

So what's it worth? And when can we have one?

In December 1997 representatives of 160 of the world's governments got together in Kyoto, Japan, to decide on the actions that would be required to prevent irreversible climate change. It followed the 1992 Earth Summit in Rio de Janeiro, at which the United Nations Framework Convention on Climate Change was adopted and signed. The objective of the Framework Convention had been to: 'achieve . . . stabilization of the greenhouse gas concentrations in the atmosphere at a level that would prevent dangerous anthropogenic interference with the climate system'.[1]

Even though the aim had been set, there were wide differences of opinion in Kyoto about what levels of greenhouse gases represented dangerous human tampering with the atmosphere. While everyone knew that reductions had to be made, there was hard bargaining and hard lobbying from interest groups in all the countries. While industries and utilities wanted to maintain liberal and cheap usage of energy, campaigning groups believed that it was time to make radical steps to reduce emissions. Inevitably there was a search for compromise – and it appeared in the form of a document called the Kyoto Protocol. The Protocol established – for each of the 160 participating countries – binding targets for their emissions of greenhouse gases, in an effort to stabilize the planet's atmospheric conditions.

The Protocol states that by 2010 all participants should have reached a specific level of emissions relative to their 1990 output levels. The most stringent target was for the countries of the European Union: an 8 per cent reduction relative to its 1990 level. The most lenient was for Iceland, which was actually permitted an increase of 10 per cent. The target for the United

States – the largest single polluter – was set at 7 per cent below its 1990 levels. To see how difficult these targets would be to reach, they need to be set against the background of the past . . .

The UK accounts for about 2.5 per cent of global carbon dioxide emissions – typically around 160 million tons of carbon. Energy production accounts for around 92 per cent of these emissions. Owing to the introduction of relatively cleaner technology – powered by gas rather than coal – the levels of carbon dioxide emissions actually fell between 1990 and 1997 by 8 per cent, which means that the UK has a fair chance of meeting this target so long as growth of demand does not start to outrun efficiency savings. The UK government, though, has already accepted that this cut will not be enough to stabilize the environment – the Royal Commission on Environmental Pollution's report in 2000 suggested that only by making cuts of at least 60 per cent in carbon emissions over the next fifty years could we hope to avoid contributing to the worst excesses of climate change.

In the United States, which accounts for a much larger proportion of global emissions, the picture is very different. The US D.o.E.'s own report for 1997 comes clean:

> Carbon dioxide accounts for the largest share of combined anthropogenic greenhouse gas emissions. US anthropogenic emissions totaled about 5.5. billion metric tons (1.5 billion tons of carbon) in 1996, 3.5 per cent higher than the year before and 18 per cent higher than in 1985. Nearly 98 per cent of this total was energy-related emissions, especially from petroleum consumed by the transportation sector, coal burned by the electric utilities, and natural gas used by industry, homes and businesses.[2]

It would be a struggle to significantly reverse this rise – 18 per cent rise in eleven years (which implies a doubling in less than fifty years) – and meet the Kyoto target. So when, in March 2001, the newly incumbent President George W. Bush formally withdrew from the

Kyoto process, no-one perhaps should have been surprised. For a President who was an ex-oil man, and whose cabinet was filled with ex-oil people, CO_2 emissions were not the main thing on his mind – particularly at a time when the US was looking a recession squarely in the face, and California was in the midst of blackouts. Foreign governments looked on in disbelief as the planet's champion polluter decided it would actually increase emissions. From now on its current 25% of the world's CO_2 from 5% of the world's population would only be a baseline.

And yet the US is far from being the only problem. Globally the picture potentially is even more threatened by the exponential growth of output from Latin America, China and the rest of Asia. China is already committed to increasing its energy production capacity by some 15 gigawatts each year.

A Climate Of Change

As the twenty-first century gets older, and atmospheric levels of carbon continue to climb faster than they have in the last 3 million years, it is a virtual certainty that there will be more environmental disasters. The Global Warming International Center in the United States lists thirty-four major climatic 'extreme events' during 1999 which resulted in large-scale devastation, homelessness, death, disease and famine. This is only the tip of the global-warming iceberg. A news flash from August 1999 made for chilling reading:

> For the first time in history, man has possibly permanently altered the energy balance in our general circulation (GC) system . . . The man-made alteration of energy balance in the system determines how chaotic our atmospheric and oceanic systems will be. At the present time we measure this man-made Greenhouse Forcing to be at 2.4–4.3 W/m^2. A change of 7.5–10 W/m^2 will completely alter seasonal characteristics, e.g. from winter to spring.[3]

In other words, and as the report goes on to emphasize, we're well on our way to irreversible change:

> The result of this Greenhouse Forcing is not a simple parallel shift in the climate of our well-known ecological zones . . . Global warming causes 'extreme events' and bad weather in the near term. In the long term it may cause the earth to transition to another equilibrium state through many 'oscillations in climatic patterns'. The magnitude of these oscillations could easily 'exceed' the difference between the end points.[4]

In simple terms we have been playing with a system that we simply don't understand, and are in mortal danger of making irreversible and catastrophic changes.

A Search for Solutions

There is clearly an urgent need for new, clean and economic ways to produce electrical energy. Fossil fuels are not only dirty; they are also limited. A variety of projections sees oil, coal and gas all used up between 2020 and 2080. Any sapient race of *Homo sapiens* would be looking for new forms of energy now, rather than later. Conventional nuclear power is no longer likely to be acceptable, for safety and cost reasons. Renewable energy sources have so far struggled to make an impact, for a number of reasons – mostly connected with cost of capital equipment, and their return on investment; the road to commercial acceptance is long and very winding.

So how can a new energy technology ever hope to take a place in this complex and highly competitive marketplace? What will our energy sources be in fifty or a hundred years' time if we are to have a sustainable climatic situation? Do any of the technologies we've looked at in this book have a chance of making it to a place at the top of the energy charts?

The Barriers to Adoption

The energy market is a cruel and uncompromising parent: while it may not kill its children off, it will neglect its weaklings until they perish. If it is to adopt a new child, that child must be fit, healthy and cheap to run. It must also be able to create employment for the people and profits for the shareholders. Ideally it should also support other industries and contribute to the GDP of the country. If it has export possibilities, then all the better – so long as there are no national security issues through such an availability. And while Nikola Tesla may have sought a fuelless power source, many power brokers in the energy market prefer a fuel-based system since there is continual income based on the processing and sale of fuel.

For a new, clean, fuelless technology to succeed in the energy market it will have to take the place of those who are already dining at the top table. It will only be able to do this if it can 1) demonstrate its technical feasibility and secure its patent rights without posing a threat to national security; 2) demonstrate its economic feasibility and attract investors; and 3) demonstrate its superior marketability and attract customers through advantageous pricing. In each phase it will encounter resistance to change. Earlier in this book we have seen some of the problems and challenges involved in the first two phases. And yet an energy technology can only become a 'player' if it can meet and overcome the difficulties of the third 'marketing' phase.

This challenge is particularly difficult since it involves asking people to dump their existing equipment – which they may still be paying for – and spend money on new equipment. The customer may be an individual looking for a domestic power plant, or a utility company looking to generate and supply to the grid. The logic, though, will be similar: there will have to be a significant long-term cost saving to make a change worthwhile. Here the key criterion will be the 'payback period' – in other words, if I spend a pound today, how long will it be before I get that pound back (through savings) and how much will I continue to save (or make) from that time onwards?

To accountants and finance directors this criterion is known as return on capital employed (ROCE) (or return on investment (ROI) in the US) and is a key business target. Each person or organization will have a different answer to the question of their desired ROCE, which will depend on a number of complex economic and investment factors including the prevailing interest rate and the potential investment return from other sources. It is something that every technologist will, at some point, need to address.

BlackLight Power Case Study

BlackLight Power is an interesting case study in its approach to the market. Its literature is a powerful example of using an economic business case to sell a new technology. While the company is still in the technological validation phase of its evolution, it has laid out a developed plan to penetrate the energy market.

This plan is based on an analysis of current costs and current market demand trends. It encompasses two important approaches to the delivery of electricity: firstly, the licensing of the BlackLight hydrino process to utilities companies, who would build large power plants to supply the grid; secondly, the manufacture of small, domestic scale 'stand-alone' 5 kW power plants which could produce $2500 worth of electricity each year (at current prices) running on water and a simple potassium-based catalyst.

BlackLight claims that for a 100 kW power plant with a life of fifteen years, it will be possible to generate electricity at less than 1 cent per kW hour. That compares with typical costs of 4–5 cents for electricity from most fossil fuels such as coal, oil and gas, 5–7 cents for nuclear energy, 4–7 cents for hydroelectric, 5–9 cents for wind power, 10–12 cents for solar (heating), and 30–40 cents for photovoltaic.[5] If the BlackLight technology really turns out to be practical, utilities companies should be falling over each other to buy licences to build such plants; with that kind of increase on current profit margins the return on investment should be very tempting. Many would want to see someone else do it successfully first, though, and keep an eager eye on any engineering and safety problems that might be met along the way. Also, until one plant has successfully fulfilled its complete lifecycle the true costs of a technology are not known – as the nuclear industry is now grudgingly having to admit. And given that the lifecycle of this technology may be fifteen years, it's easy to see just how long it could take for a new technology to gain acceptance.

It's also not difficult to see why some businesses might fear such a technology. If such a cheap way of making electricity really hit the market in a big way, with power providers able to offer electricity at, say, a half or a third its current price, there would be a huge impact on oil, coal and gas producers all over the world. With the expectation of a long-term fall in demand, prices could crash and whole industries go under. If it's not going to be worth getting oil out of the ground, there isn't going to be an oil industry.

General Motors and the rest of the world's car makers will need to rethink, regroup and retool as the transportation landscape changes. If we were to move to a water-based, electricity-driven economy, cars would be electric and those prototypes that car manufacturers bring out at shows might actually get to run on the roads. While financial market pundits may cower at the panic potential of such a change, the truth is that their bark is probably worse than the economic bite. These changes could actually take years to implement – power plants don't get built in a day.

Also, those in the existing marketplace have a choice: either they try to oppose the newcomer and strangle it at birth; or they invest in it and see if they can profit (and avoid loss) by becoming a leader in the new technology. Will they be 'reactive or proactive', as business gurus might ask? That's what the utilities companies who have bought into BlackLight are doing – and by doing so they are hedging their position.

Dr Hal Puthoff of the Institute for Advanced Studies in Austin, Texas, who supports the potential of cold fusion energy technologies, as well as those based on zero-point energy, has an 'adoption' strategy which echoes this approach. In a conversation with radio science talkshow host Bob Hieronimus, Puthoff explained:

> Hieronimus: You do not believe that cold fusion is going to spell the end of power companies. In your conversations with Chris Bird you noted that the Arab oil producers in the Middle East should be brought into the investment picture, which I thought was really interesting as to why. Because that would keep them from standing in its way?
>
> Puthoff: That's exactly it. In our business plan, under the assumption that we might really bring this to market, we have looked at all the potential 'enemies' and in every case there is a way to work out a win-win situation. And so, in terms of talking to the ordinary oil companies here, I had a chance to talk with Scotty Hahn, president of Penzoil, and research directors and presidents and vice-presidents of a number of other oil companies, talking to them about the zero-point energy future. They said they would definitely welcome it, because right now if they take oil out of the ground and make pharmaceuticals and plastics they have a big profit margin, and they do not use much of the resource. But when they put it into cars and homes it is sort of like burning Van Goghs and Picassos to heat your house . . . They said you wouldn't have any trouble with us, but you might have trouble with the people who get it out of the ground. So there our approach is simply to go to them and let them know this is happening. If they capitalize the development of it, then as oil goes down their investments will still win.[6]

Conspiracy? What Conspiracy?

There are those who believe that the only reason we don't have free or fuelless technologies already is because of some grand, or not so grand conspiracy (or even a set of smaller conspiracies) that has bought out, suppressed or simply killed off technologies and their inventors before they had the chance to hit the market.

Stories abound of 200-miles-per-gallon carburettors which have appeared in a newspaper one week, never to be heard of again. Depending on your mindset, you'll either believe that 1) they're all true; 2) some of them are true; or 3) none of them is true. As with many things in this field the evidence can be as elusive as ever.

Professor Martin Fleischmann believed that there were forces within governments that acted against the early developments of cold fusion. But how can an intelligent, rational scientist believe that people in government offices would do such things? Surely you'd expect to see governments getting involved in promoting research on future energy technologies – after all it's in their long-term interest. Like many other countries, including the UK, the United States has a Department of Energy with a specific commitment to develop future energy technologies. Yet some critics have claimed that not only does this department ignore new energy technologies, but that there is evidence it has been actively hostile to them.

In early 1999 a patent examiner at the US Patent Office named Tom Valone (who had researched the N-machine for his postgraduate study many years earlier – see Chapter 4) decided to set up a Conference on Future Energy (COFE) in Washington DC. Through the Integrity Research Institute – a non-profit-making organization of which he is the president – Valone sought the support of the departments of government which he believed had an interest in the topic. He started at the State Department, gaining its interest and sponsorship to hold the conference under the Secretary of State's 'Open Forum' initiative. The speakers for the conference included researchers into wind energy, Ken

Shoulders talking about charge clusters (EVs), Paul Brown reporting on his betavoltaic batteries, Edmund Storms addressing the cold fusion low-energy nuclear reaction field, and a number of other experimentalists looking at topics such as fuel cells, biomass gasification, and non-combustive helicopter propulsion.

Valone had not bargained for the actions of Dr Robert Park of the American Physical Society and Peter Zimmerman, the newly incumbent science advisor to the Arms Control Agency at the State Department. Dr Park is an avowed enemy of anything he views as 'pseudoscience' and publishes weekly diatribes against scientists he regards as 'fringe' in his *What's New?* webzine for the American Physical Society. When he heard about the up-and-coming conference, he e-mailed his friend Zimmerman: 'Pete, if you can't get that killed, what's the point of having a State Department?'[7] Zimmerman took Park very seriously: 'I like challenge and here was a chance to influence an event . . . A decision had been made. But, you know, I work in Washington and those of us who work in Washington are quite aware that nothing's ever finally decided until the day for it to occur has passed . . .'

Within days the conference was cancelled at the State Department, and when attempts to get interest from the Departments of Commerce and Energy were made, Zimmerman's influence was still felt.

Zimmerman and Park both spoke about the conference at a meeting of the American Physical Society on 22 March in Atlanta, Georgia. Zimmerman, an appointed official of the government on a salary consisting of US taxpayers' money, made a proud boast about managing to get the conference moved on from the State Department: 'That's one of the accomplishments I'm proudest of within the last year.'[8] He also announced that he and Robert Park intended to work to exterminate every trace of cold fusion from the federal establishment. (They had mistakenly got the impression that the conference was majoring on cold fusion.) He called upon the audience to join him in the crusade, and, only half-joking, he asked them to report to the highest authorities any rumours about unauthorized research and groups of more than three people caught discussing cold fusion. The crowd of physicists cheered and clapped.

Later one of Zimmerman's e-mails, meant for an unknown recipient, was accidentally sent to Tom Valone's office:

> Oh, the shame of it all. How dastardly we were to poor Mr Valone. He and his Aussie friend are embarrassed and it's all our fault. How can they ever forgive us? How can we ever cleanse our souls of this black mark?
>
> I had a wonderful time at the Physical Society meeting at Atlanta, and you and I were hailed as heroine/hero for getting the conference moved out of State. I have reason to believe that a 'Higher Power' will get them evicted from Commerce too.[9]

Whoever the 'Higher Power' was, Zimmerman was right about the Commerce Department. It cancelled its support. The Department of Energy also turned turtle. The conference was eventually held at a Holiday Inn in Bethesda, Maryland, on 29 and 30 April and 1 May 1999. It continued to attract negative comment from Park in his columns, as well as condemnation from the major science journals *Nature* and *Science* who both believed erroneously that the conference was majoring in cold fusion. David Voss wrote in *Science*: 'None of the dozen or so talks showed any understanding of modern science.' Voss had failed to notice that even Peter Zimmerman had, in fact, given Paul Brown's 'photodeactivation of nuclear waste' – a way of getting energy from radioactive waste by bombarding it with X-rays – a vote of confidence:

> What is interesting is Brown's selection of an electron linac [linear accelerator] rather than a proton one, and his use of photo-fission rather than relying on only neutron-induced reactions. Assuming that all of the engineering works out properly, he will certainly obtain

a net gain in energy relative to the beam power in the accelerator.[10]

Soon after the conference Tom Valone was removed from his position as a patent examiner, following what he believes was a concerted campaign by Park and Zimmerman to discredit him in the eyes of the Commerce Department. He is said by some to have had a nervous breakdown following the events, and although he is now again active in promoting new energy technologies, it is likely that he will, in the eyes of mainstream science, be branded a heretic until further notice.

Perhaps the key question here for new technologies is just how important public or peer support is for a new technology. Obviously mainstream scientific acceptance is useful for an organization trying to raise funds: a bad press, or a 'nay-saying' campaign against a technology, can make getting investment that much harder. And without investment many technologies will simply not progress. In the field of new energy technology, where conventional theory may contradict the claims being made by a technology's creator, investment can be that much harder to secure.

There is certainly no guarantee that just because something works at a prototype level it will make it through the phases of market acceptance. This point raises the possibility that there have been technologies that have worked, but which have been lost along the way. Is T. Henry Moray's radiant energy device an example of this? Will BlackLight Power overcome its enemies in the scientific mainstream and forge a successful energy technology for this century and beyond? While there is strong evidence to support a positive answer to the Moray device, BlackLight's future remains unanswered. What happens depends on many factors: on the technology itself and how difficult it proves to be to engineer it, on the Patent Office's ongoing attitude, on the investors' nerves and their interests, on the press's attitude, the consumer's interest – the list goes on . . .

Perhaps the question 'How bad do things have to get?' is relevant. When we're all threatened by the effects of climate change, self-interest may look more like altruism. At the moment many of the mainstream purse-holders are still afraid to look outside the conventional. As the crisis deepens, and the real costs of climate change hit home, the search for radical and novel solutions such as those explored here will look increasingly attractive. How long it will take to reach this point is anyone's guess.

APPENDIX 1

An Energy Primer

'Energy is eternal delight.'

William Blake

What is Energy?

Specifically, energy is defined as the ability of a system or device to do work. When people talk about energy, however, the term is often confused with other terms such as force, power and work. To understand energy it's helpful to explain the relationship between all these terms.

Force is the most fundamental unit of energy, and there are four basic forces in the universe: gravity, electromagnetic (light, X-rays, infra-red, ultra-violet, etc.), weak interactions (which are responsible for radioactive decay) and, finally, strong nuclear forces, which are responsible for holding atomic nucleii together. Force is measured in either newtons (in the metric measurement system) or foot-pounds (imperial). If I apply a force of one *newton* to an object, causing the object to move one *metre*, then one *newton-metre*, or *joule* of work (or energy) is said to have been expended.

Power is the rate at which energy is used, or work is done. So if I am able to exert a *joule* every second, my power 'rating' is actually one *watt*. One of the first power rating measurements was based around the horse – hence the term 'horsepower'. In watts the power of the idealized horse is 745 watts – the ability to supply

745 joules of energy every second. If a machine (such as a horse) were to supply this power for an hour then it would have provided 745 watt-hours. The electricity we buy from utilities companies is actually measured in watt-hours, or more specifically, *kilowatt-hours.*

Energy Forms and Conversions

Energy exists in many forms in the universe: chemical, kinetic, electrical, gravitational, electromagnetic, sound, nuclear and heat. Energy transformations are a constant activity of the universe, and of life on planet Earth. The sun is undergoing nuclear fusion, which generates huge amounts of heat and radiation. An amount of this heat reaches our planet and helps the chemical, biological and kinetic processes which create the atmospheric and soil conditions that are required for certain kinds of life. Plants undergo chemical changes which are assisted by heat and light energy from the sun. Animals – including humans – use the chemical energy locked up in food to assist them in their kinetic energy (movement). There are also electrical processes which go on in the body and brain which are fuelled by the chemicals in food.

Our technologies involve transformations between different kinds of energy: motors turn electrical energy into mechanical energy; batteries turn chemical energy into electrical energy; light bulbs turn electrical energy into light and heat; wind generators turn the kinetic energy of the wind into electricity; nuclear power plants turn the energy of matter into heat, and then – via a generator – into electricity. Energy transformations are the key to our civilization, and they are governed by some fundamental laws.

The Basic Laws of Energy

The main law which describes the behaviour of energy in transformations is the law of conservation of energy. This states that energy cannot be created or destroyed: it can only be changed from one form to another. Therefore the total amount of energy in the universe is fixed and it simply undergoes changes in form: from kinetic to gravitational, from chemical to heat, etc.

The laws of thermodynamics were first formulated in the nineteenth century, following the pioneering work on heat engines by a French engineer named Sadi Carnot. The laws of thermodynamics were intended, initially, to describe and define the workings and efficiencies of all heat engines. The first law of thermodynamics is a restating of the law of conservation of energy as it applies to heat engines or systems. It is actually expressed by a mathematical formula ($\Delta Q = \Delta U + \Delta W$) and simply says that the increase in internal energy of a system is equal to heat supplied to the system plus the work done on the system. If the system is an isolated or 'closed' system we can say that the internal energy of this system is constant – hence the total energy within a system is conserved.

The second law of thermodynamics is often referred to as the law of entropy, and says that in any system there is a general movement of all other forms of energy towards heat – the lowest form of energy. Entropy also means that there is a increase in 'disorder' – exemplified by the random motion of heated molecules. The main implication of the second law of thermodynamics is that it takes more energy to raise heat to another form of energy (e.g. chemical, kinetic etc.) than it does to generate heat from the same form of energy. It is harder to climb up the 'energy hill' from heat back up to chemical, mechanical or electrical energy.

This introduces the concept of efficiency. While the overall energy in a system is never lost, an energy-generating transformation such as a conversion from coal to electricity involves a number of steps in which some heat is irretrievably lost to the environment.

Heat from combustion, heat from friction within bearings, heat within the windings of generators, and heat within transmission cables all contribute to a loss of useful energy. Only around 20–30 per cent of the chemical energy stored in coal is finally available as electricity to the consumer. Within a closed system, no energy transformation technology can ever be 100 per cent efficient.

The second law of thermodynamics is usually cited as the reason why the universe will eventually die a 'heat death', as all other forms of energy in the universe eventually degrade to heat. The second law is also given as the reason why all attempts to create perpetual motion machines are an impossibility, since, while machines can approach 100 per cent efficiency, there is always some process in such a closed-system machine that yields unrecoverable heat to the surrounding environment, and, thus, a loss in the machine's motion.

Many sad and wasted years of research have gone into the creation of various wheels, magnets systems and water flows in an effort to create a self-perpetuating machine. Patent offices around the world still continue to receive many designs each year for perpetual motion devices. Some inventors are inspired, however, by the fact that there appear to be many apparently perpetual processes occurring in the universe: having been set in motion, the planets continue to make their orbits for extremely long periods of time. At an atomic level electrons appear to continue spinning around their nucleii without any signs of slowing . . .

Voices of Dissent

While the principles of the second law of thermodynamics are extremely widely accepted, there are those who ask for widenings, reinterpretation or even – in some cases – restrictions on its use. There are those who argue that it was only developed to apply to closed-system 'heat engines', and does not apply to all natural processes.

In 1912 Charles P. Steinmetz, chief engineering consultant

at the General Electric Company and one of the most highly respected electrical engineers of all time, wrote an article entitled 'The Second Law of Thermodynamics and the "Death" of Energy, with Notes on the Thermodynamics of the Atmosphere'. While accepting the conventional interpretation of the law in relation to engines that 'without expenditure of some other form of energy heat flows only from higher to lower temperature' Steinmetz demonstrated how: 'attending the escape of molecules from the attraction of earth into cosmic space, there is a heat energy flow from a temperature of 10 degrees Celsius to one of 60,000 degrees Celsius'. His detailed explanation of this process left him in no doubt of the scientific consequences. In his words, it 'leads to the conclusion that this law of thermodynamics is not of universal application, but applies only within the limited range of thermodynamic engines from which it has been derived'.[1]

Since Steinmetz's time, the general 'wide' application of the second law of thermodynamics to many cases has continued – particularly with regard to the physics of the universe. There have, however, been a number of dissenting voices which have argued against the universal application of the second law. Steinmetz himself objected:

> The second law of thermodynamics is well founded on our experience. The reasoning from this law as to the death of the universe is logical. At the same time, the conclusion that the universe must run down is not reasonable. If the universe is eternal, has existed since infinite time, then it should have run down an infinite time ago. But if it is not eternal, but had a beginning, what was before? How could energy begin without offending the first law, that of the conservation of energy? Thus, in the final reasoning, we arrive at a contradiction.[2]

So in these terms the Big Bang represents the ultimate free energy event. It would also represent a massive increase in the universe's level of order. Steinmetz is by no means the only scientist to notice this logical fallacy at the heart of thermodynamics. A number of scientists have argued that there are local examples of order increasing within the universe, and on the planet, without the input of additional energy. Ken Rauen, an engineer at the New Energy Research Laboratories, recently presented a number of cogent examples: 'How could increasing randomness be absolute when molten earth has solidified into pure and crystalline minerals nearly everywhere that bedrock is exposed? How could galaxies be accelerating apart if the universe is winding down from entropy generation? The story has yet to be told.'[3]

Dr Harold Aspden, formerly of Southampton University and IBM, and author of *Modern Aether Science*, has developed his own theory of electrodynamics, and echoes Steinmetz's challenge:

> If the universe did appear in a flash billions of years ago then it must have suddenly acquired all its energy freely from somewhere in that first moment of time. Otherwise, we are part of a living universe that has a way of drawing upon the free energy resource of the quantum underworld of space to create particles of matter.[4]

Aspden is alluding to the apparently eternal quantum fluctuations of the vacuum which give rise to particles and antiparticles, and which, in the opinion of many scientists, may offer an unlimited source of energy. If it really is possible to tap this energy, then the idea of a closed system – as defined in the second law – may not apply. A model of the universe in which specific technologies are able to tap vacuum energy is an open model, and not bound by the strictures of the second law.

While this model could explain a number of apparently anomalous observations and technologies, it would, however, represent a major paradigm shift in scientific thinking. Chapter 9 is a full discussion of the evidence for zero-point, vacuum energy, and the potential significance of this development.

APPENDIX 2

Nikola Tesla's US, UK and Canadian Patents

US Patent 11,865 'Method of Insulating Electric Conductors'
US Patent 334,823 'Commutator for Dynamo-Electric Machines'
US Patent 335,786 'Electric-Arc Lamp'
US Patent 335,787 'Electric-Arc Lamp'
US Patent 336,961 'Regulator for Dynamo-Electric Machines'
US Patent 336,962 'Regulator for Dynamo-Electric Machines'
US Patent 350,954 'Regulator for Dynamo-Electric Machines'
US Patent 359,748 'Dynamo-Electric Machine'
US Patent 381,968 'Electro-Magnetic Motor'
US Patent 381,969 'Electro-Magnetic Motor'
US Patent 381,970 'System of Electrical Distribution'
US Patent 382,279 'Electro-Magnetic Motor'
US Patent 382,280 'Electrical Transmission of Power'
US Patent 382,281 'Electrical Transmission of Power'
US Patent 382,282 'Method of Converting and Distributing Electric Currents'
US Patent 382,845 'Commutator for Dynamo-Electric Machines'
US Patent 390,413 'System of Electrical Distribution'
US Patent 390,414 'Dynamo-Electric Machine'
US Patent 390,415 'Dynamo-Electric Machine or Motor'
US Patent 390,721 'Dynamo-Electric Machine'
US Patent 390,820 'Regulator for Alternate-Current Motors'
US Patent 396,121 'Thermo-Magnetic Motor'

US Patent 401,520 'Method of Operating Electro-Magnetic Motors'
US Patent 405,858 'Electro-Magnetic Motor'
US Patent 405,859 'Method of Electrical Power Transmission'
US Patent 406,968 'Dynamo-Electric Machine'
US Patent 413,353 'Method of Obtaining Direct From Alternating Currents'
US Patent 416,191 'Electro-Magnetic Motor'
US Patent 416,192 'Method of Operating Electro-Magnetic Motors'
US Patent 416,193 'Electro-Magnetic Motor'
US Patent 416,194 'Electric Motor'
US Patent 416,195 'Electro-Magnetic Motor'
US Patent 417,794 'Armature for Electric Machines'
US Patent 418,248 'Electro-Magnetic Motor'
US Patent 424,036 'Electro-Magnetic Motor'
US Patent 428,057 'Pyromagneto-Electric Generator'
US Patent 433,700 'Alternating-Current Electro-Magnetic Motor'
US Patent 433,701 'Alternating-Current Motor'
US Patent 433,702 'Electrical Transformer or Induction Device'
US Patent 433,703 'Electro-Magnetic Motor'
US Patent 445,207 'Electro-Magnetic Motor'
US Patent 447,920 'Method of Operating Arc-Lamps'
US Patent 447,921 'Alternating Electric Current Generator'
US Patent 454,622 'System of Electric Lighting'
US Patent 455,067 'Electro-Magnetic Motor'
US Patent 455,068 'Electrical Meter'
US Patent 455,069 'Electric Incandescent Lamp'
US Patent 459,772 'Electro-Magnetic Motor'
US Patent 462,418 'Method of and Apparatus for Electrical Conversion and Distribution'
US Patent 464,666 'Electro-Magnetic Motor'
US Patent 464,667 'Electrical Condenser'
US Patent 487,796 'System of Electrical Transmission of Power'
US Patent 511,559 'Electrical Transmission of Power'
US Patent 511,560 'System of Electrical Power Transmission'
US Patent 511,915 'Electrical Transmission of Power'
US Patent 511,916 'Electric Generator'

US Patent 512,340 (HTML) 'Coil for Electro-magnets'
US Patent 512,340 (PDF) 'Coil for Electro-Magnets'
US Patent 514,167 'Electrical Conductor'
US Patent 514,168 'Means for Generating Electric Currents'
US Patent 514,169 'Reciprocating Engine'
US Patent 514,170 'Incandescent Electric Light'
US Patent 514,972 'Electric Railway System'
US Patent 514,973 'Electrical Meter'
US Patent 517,900 'Steam Engine'
US Patent 524,426 'Electromagnetic Motor'
US Patent 555,190 'Alternating Motor'
US Patent 567,818 'Electrical Condenser'
US Patent 568,176 'Apparatus for Producing Electric Currents of High Frequency and Potential'
US Patent 568,177 'Apparatus for Producing Ozone'
US Patent 568,178 'Method of Regulating Apparatus for Producing Electric Currents of High Frequency'
US Patent 568,179 'Method of and Apparatus for Producing Currents of High Frequency'
US Patent 568,180 'Apparatus for Producing Electrical Currents of High Frequency'
US Patent 577,670 'Apparatus for Producing Electric Currents of High Frequency'
US Patent 577,671 'Manufacture of Electrical Condensors, Coils and Similar Devices'
US Patent 583,953 'Apparatus for Producing Currents of High Frequency'
US Patent 593,138 'Electrical Transformer'
US Patent 609,245 'Electrical Circuit Controller'
US Patent 609,246 'Electric Circuit Controller'
US Patent 609,247 'Electric Circuit Controller'
US Patent 609,248 'Electric Circuit Controller'
US Patent 609,249 'Electric Circuit Controller'
US Patent 609,250 'Electrical Igniter for Gas Engines'
US Patent 609,251 'Electric Circuit Controller'
US Patent 611,719 'Electrical Circuit Controller'

US Patent 613,735 'Electric Circuit Controller'
US Patent 613,809 'Method of and Apparatus for Controlling Mechanism of Moving Vessels or Vehicles'
US Patent 645,576 'System of Transmission of Electrical Energy'
US Patent 649,621 'Apparatus for Transmission of Electrical Energy'
US Patent 655,838 'Method of Insulating Electric Conductors'
US Patent 685,012 'Means for Increasing the Intensity of Electrical Oscillations'
US Patent 685,953 'Method of Intensifying and Utilizing Effects Transmitted Through Natural Media'
US Patent 685,954 'Method of Utilizing Effects Transmitted Through Natural Media'
US Patent 685,955 'Apparatus for Utilizing Effects Transmitted from a Distance to a Receiving Device Through Natural Media'
US Patent 685,956 'Apparatus for Utilizing Effects Transmitted Through Natural Media'
US Patent 685,957 'Apparatus for the Utilization of Radiant Energy'
US Patent 685,958 'Method of Utilizing of Radiant Energy'
US Patent 723,188 'Method of Signaling'
US Patent 725,605 'System of Signaling'
US Patent 787,412 'Art of Transmitting Electrical Energy Through the Natural Mediums'
US Patent 1,061,142 'Fluid Propulsion'
US Patent 1,061,206 'Turbine'
US Patent 1,113,716 'Fountain'
US Patent 1,119,732 'Apparatus for Transmitting Electrical Energy'
US Patent 1,209,359 'Speed Indicator'
US Patent 1,266,175 'Lightning Protector'
US Patent 1,274,816 'Speed Indicator'
US Patent 1,314,718 'Ship's Log'
US Patent 1,329,559 'Valvular Conduit'
US Patent 1,365,547 'Flow Meter'
US Patent 1,402,025 'Frequency Meter'
US Patent 1,655,113 'Method of Aerial Transportation'

US Patent 1,655,114 'Apparatus for Aerial Transportation'

British Patent 1,877 'Improvements in Electric Lamps'

British Patent 2,801 'Improvements in Reciprocating Engines and Means for Regulating the Period of the Same'

British Patent 2,812 'Improvements in Methods of and Apparatus for the Generation of Electric Currents of Defined Period'

British Patent 2,975 'Improvements in Dynamo Electric Machines'

British Patent 6,481 'Improvements Relating to the Electrical Transmission of Power and to Apparatus Therefor'

British Patent 6,502 'Improvements Relating to the Generation and Distribution of Electric Currents and to Apparatus Therefor'

British Patent 6,527 'Improvements Relating to Electro-motors'

British Patent 8,200 'Improvements Relating to the Transmission of Electrical Energy'

British Patent 8,575 'Improved Methods of and Apparatus for Generating and Utilizing Electric Energy for Lighting Purposes'

British Patent 11,293 'Improvements Relating to the Utilization of Electromagnetic, Light, or other like Radiations Effects or Disturbances Transmitted through the Natural Media and to Apparatus Therefor'

British Patent 11,473 'Improvements in Alternating Current Electro-magnetic Motors'

British Patent 13,563 'Improvements in, and Relating to, the Transmission of Electrical Energy'

British Patent 14,550 'Improvements Relating to the Insulation of Electric Conductors'

British Patent 14,579 'Improvements in and Relating to the Transmission of Electrical Energy'

British Patent 16,709 'Improvements Relating to the Conversion of Alternating into Direct Electric Currents'

British Patent 19,420 'Improvements in Alternating Current Electro-magnetic Motors'

British Patent 19,426 'Improvements in the Construction and Mode of Operating Alternating Current Motors'

Canadian Patent 24,033 'Improvements in Dynamo Electric Machines'

Canadian Patent 29,537 'Improvements in Methods of and
Apparatus for the Electrical Transmission of Power'
Canadian Patent 30,172 'Improvements in Methods of and
Apparatus for Converting and Distributing Electric Currents'
Canadian Patent 33,317 'Improvements in Methods and
Apparatus for Converting Alternating into Direct Currents'
Canadian Patent 135,174 'Improvements in Fluid Propulsion
(Tesla Pump)'
Canadian Patent 142,352 'Improvement in the Art of
Transmitting Electrical Energy Through the Natural Mediums'

LETTERS and AFFIDAVITS

supporting the work of

T. Henry Moray

Letter from E.C. Johnson to Mr Cooley

Dear Mr Cooley:

This letter is being written to you for your information and in order to make a record of the electrical demonstration made 29 October 1926, by inventor T. H. Moray for Attorney Judd, Mr Knight and myself. As prearranged, I met Misters Moray and Judd at the Moray laboratory about 7.10 a.m. on 29 October 1926. We carried the electrical equipment into my car and left Mr Judd's car in the Moray lot, as there were only three of us to make the trip from Salt Lake and to meet Mr Knight at Orem, Utah. I remember that the speedometer registered 19 miles at Charleston and 26 miles as we left the last electric line near the mouth of Daniel's Canyon; also that speedometer registered 52 miles where we stopped to demonstrate, making the distance 52 miles from the nearest power line and 26 miles from the nearest one wire rural telephone line. Moray requested that we select a place near a stream of water so that the ground pipe could be sunk in its bed and be more effective, as the ground in the mountain was frozen. He stopped at a place about 10 miles south-east of the Daniel's Strawberry summit and about 200 yards west of the main road to Duchesne, this location being almost due east from what Mr

Knight called Haystack Mountain and perhaps ¾ of a mile east of the Strawberry Lake on a little stream which made a zigzag course through a gently sloping grassy flat to the lake.

The antenna wire was put up without any aid or instructions whatever from Moray, as it had been 'balanced', except that Moray suggested that the wire be stretched tighter to prevent so much sag at the center. This was done and the wire then appeared to clear the ground by 7 or 8 feet at its lowest point.

The balanced ground rod was pointed at the end to make its driving into the creek bed easy. The antenna wire was insulated from the poles with two quartz glass insulators about six inches long. A piece of wire about two feet long connected each insulator with the pole. The lead-in wire was fastened to the antenna wire at a point about 10 or 15 feet from the east pole. I helped Moray solder the connection where the lead-in wire fastened on to the antenna wire and also helped him solder the ground wire to the rod. I stepped the distance between the two antenna poles and estimated it to be 87 feet as I took 29 steps intended to be three feet each.

Moray took this electrical equipment out of the automobile and placed it on the running board of the car. Two dry boards were laid on the ground and a rubber mat used under my office chair was placed on the boards for Moray to stand on as a precaution against electric shocks. The running board was hardly large enough for the equipment so we took the seat cushion out of the front seat and placed it on the mat and Moray transferred the equipment to the seat cushion and connected it up there.

Very light snowflakes fell occasionally and a tarpaulin was hung over the top of the auto doors, when opened, to protect the equipment from getting wet. When all of the wire connections were made, and the device synchronized in resonance by Moray, it was just 1.05 p.m. by my watch. Before 'tuning in' he placed the key on the post he said it would be in contact with while the light burns but no light appeared.

After 'tuning in' for slightly more than 10 minutes the key or switch was put on the operating post and the light appeared immediately. It was slightly after 1.15 p.m. by my watch. Moray put the key, or switch, on the operating post two or three times before and during the tuning in operation but no light appeared until perfect 'balance' was established. 'While the lights were burning, the antenna lead-in wire was disconnected from the apparatus and the lights went out. Connected again and the lights appeared.' Moray disconnected the 'ground wire' and the lights went out. He then connected it and the lights appeared again.

This letter signed by
E. C. Johnson
Salt Lake City, Utah

Quotation from letter from R. E. Croquet, ex-Secretary of State of Utah:

In regard to the Moray Radiant Energy discovery, I have had it demonstrated to me to my full satisfaction and have read the reports of many reliable experts and have heard others express themselves favorably about what they have seen. One of these men T. J. Yates, is a nationally known electrical expert, a graduate from Cornell, with a Masters Degree, and a man of high character who has had many year's experience in the electrical field, some of his positions being Assistant Superintendent of Power Stations of the Utah Power and Light System, Superintendent of City Electric Service of the Utah Power and Light. He had charge of the Research and Experimental work of the American Smelting and Refining Company. He was Chief Engineer of the Utah Radio Products Company and a consulting engineer for many years.

Open Letter from Geo. R. Pyper

Salt Lake City, Utah
To Whom It May Concern:

I have worked in electricity all my life, was with the Utah Power and Light Company for thirteen years, and worked in all departments including sub-stations. I have been with the Kearns Corporation over seventeen years; and have charge of all the electrical work for the Tribune and Telegram Publishing Company, and in Kearns and Tribune Buildings. In December last, I witnessed a demonstration at Dr Moray's laboratory of his electrical marvel box. He let me see inside this box and there was a H. F. transformer, some of his cold tubes and some condensers. Dr Moray connected this box to a special balanced aerial and ground wire from the outside and two of us held a counter poise antenna attached to glass insulators in the room and when he connected the box to this counter poise antenna I saw the same results. During this demonstration and while the lamp and appliances were on I shorted the aerial and ground wires. There was no spark, it just turned off the power from the box. I then took hold of both of these wires. There was no feeling and they were both cold. He then took a larger box, about $18 \times 30 \times 15$ [inches] and connected it to the outside aerial and ground wire. From this box he lighted about fifty 100-watts, 120-volt lamps, ran a small motor specially wound at great speed, an original electric iron, and a 500-watt glow heater. Dr Moray then disconnected the appliances and lamp, and attached two long wires to the box and we pulled the main line Utah Power and Light Company service switch for his building. We attached the wire from the box to the building side of the switch and he lighted his building, heated iron heaters; in fact, everything the Utah Power and Light Company service would do except run motors which I understand have to be specially wound. Standard globes were used but they seemed to give a softer whiter light which was more daylight. I am satisfied myself from my experience in electricity that there was no fake of any kind of concealed batteries, or wires. Everything was in the open so I could see every operation. I did not see the inside of the larger box. It was a very remarkable demonstration and one which I will always remember.

[Signed] Geo. R. Pyper

Unattributed Letter

An experiment was given for a nationally known physicist, a professor in one of the greatest universities of the country, at which time he noted and mentioned the following (and this was verified by another Dr of Sciences): 'That when the oscillators are connected in the circuit, the condensers fill slowly, and the longer the current is applied to charge them, the greater the charge they take, up to their maximum for the applied voltage, much as in filling a bucket by pouring the water into it, instead of taking the charge practically instantaneously, as is ordinarily the case with condensers.' 'That the size of wire in the transformer could not carry the amperage passing through it without burning up, if ordinary current were used, yet the wires remained absolutely cool no matter how long the machine operated.'

'The above points show that there is developed something which is entirely out of the ordinary, and cannot be accounted for on the basis of induction from existing power lines or current from batteries.'

The above statement duly signed and verified.

Paul Brown's Open Letter to all

Working on Alternate Energy

1 November 1991
Paul Brown
c/o P.O. Box 201
Los Altos, CA 94023

Greetings,

I have been involved with alternate energy research since 1978 while still a college student. Over the years I have heard many nightmare stories about people who developed something significant only to be persecuted, harassed, prosecuted, and even killed. I was sure that these stories were exaggerated or possibly the result of the inventor's own paranoia or such. Further I met several inventors whom I felt were their own worst enemies (via fabrications of their imaginations) which confirmed my beliefs.

As time went on, and in about 1982, I became involved in work of some significance and received some minor criticism and skepticism that I found to be beneficial as well as practical, but no death threats or any other forms of persecution. I built experimental devices, learned things unavailable from books, filed for patents and in general felt very satisfied with my life, society and the scientific system.

However, things began to change slowly and alarmingly. The more success I had in my endeavours – the more I began to attract dishonest and greedy people (I know this now but was unaware of it then). My life became more uncomfortable as time went on but I was not sure of the problem.

In 1987 we decided it was time to let the world know what we were working on and the results we were getting. It was a proud time for me. I thought we were doing the right thing. But this was the real beginning of the worst.

Since that February 1987 I or my company have been persecuted by the State Department of Health; then the Idaho Dept of Finance filed a civil complaint against the company and myself; my license for handling radioactive materials was then suspended for six months; I began to receive threats (i.e. 'We will bulldoze your house with your family in it'); securities fraud charges were then filed against my company and myself; then investigation by the Oregon Dept. Finance; then the tax man; then the Securities and Exchange Commission; my wife was assaulted; I lost control of my company; my home has been robbed three times and vandalized on four other occasions; twice now I have been accused of drug manufacturing; I lost my home; most recently my mother's car was pipe-bombed. With each hardship I strive harder toward successful development of the technologies under my endeavour. But it only seems to get worse.

Someone once said: 'Paranoia is only a heightened sense of awareness.' He was right! It is hard for the average guy to comprehend these disasters happening to select people. I am here to tell you it is not coincidence. I now understand why some inventors drop out from society.

My advice is to keep a low profile until you have completed your endeavour; be selective in choosing your business partners; protect yourself and your family; know that the nightmare stories are true.

God speed. Good Luck in your endeavours, and Never Lose The Faith.

Sincerely,

Paul Brown

The Methernitha Video Tape –

Transcript of Narration

The Methernitha video tape was produced for the 1989 Swiss Association of Free Energy (SAFE) Conference held in Einsiedeln. It was available for a few years directly from the Methernitha community, although they no longer make it available. (Details of current sources will be available on the website www.freeenergy.co.uk)

This film shows the life and achievement of the spiritual community of Methernitha, as a whole, and in particular the research work in the area of free energy.

There exist two versions of the narration: the first a direct transcription of Methernitha's English version, which is printed below; the second a translation from the original Swiss-German version by Cindy Simmons in 1992 is made available via the KeelyNet Bulletin Board by Brian Prothro.

This first narration – transcribed from the English language video – is believed to be narrated by a member of the community. While the English of this version is not necessarily as good as the translation from the original Swiss-German, it appears to be closest in intention to the meaning of the original. Sometimes I have added words in brackets to help in understanding particularly difficult translations.

Transcription of Narration from English Language Version

This is the machine called Thesta-Distatica, an apparatus which allows to make use of the so-called 'free energy'. The Thesta-Distatica is a development of the spiritual community Methernitha, which is a co-operative in Linden officially established under this name since 1960. Ever since the foundation of Methernitha there has been a department for research, development and electronics which was concerned with the problem of alternative energy sources. Namely the technologies which were suited to exploit the inherent forces of nature and thus to unlock sources of energy for the benefit of mankind without disturbing nature's ecological balance of nature in any negative way. Any technology Man invents should serve him in short and long terms [sic] and this condition is not fulfilled as soon as it opposes nature in any way.

This team of researchers within Methernitha works completely autonomous and is financed out of the co-operative's own sources, without any outside support.

The efficient utilization of wind energy possible was one of the first objectives of Methernitha's research programme. At the beginning [wind] generators with special excitation were developed which allowed to load [charge up] the cells of accumulators even at low r.p.m.s in times when there are only moderate air movements.

Utilizing the kinetic energy of water currents was another field of interest of the development team, it was pursued more as a hobby. The key problem here was to transfer the slow revolutions of the water wheel to an extent that the excitation threshold of the generator could be surpassed by a minimal loss of energy. Also solar cells and solar collectors attracted the attention of our researchers since a long time. But since in these fields other institutions have attained outstanding results, Methernitha started – and this was already more than twenty years ago – to concentrate its efforts on lesser-known and even generally unknown sources of energy.

The result of this scientific work is the Thesta-Distatica, of which most of you will have heard already. The question arises: how it comes that Methernitha – nothing more than a private organization – could invest so much time, engagement [attention], perseverance and also financial resources in this kind of research? Research and development are integrated parts of the general idealistic concept of Methernitha. In order to make you understand these ideals and goals we will now introduce you to the practical sides of the spiritual community of Methernitha as it functions as a co-operative of people living and working together.

Linden is a calm [peaceful] village of farmers, just like dozens of others in the region of the valley called Emmenthal. However, Linden is also the home of a special form of human life which is capable of attracting more and more people from all over the globe, and which has again and again caused astonishment through its excellent functioning even in extremely difficult situations.

There is no doubt that the formation of Methernitha is also a good part of the life story of Paul Baumann [the inventor of the Thesta-Distatica]. Through his extraordinary technical abilities, but also through his astonishing practical wisdom, he opened relations to all kinds of people with ideals, and in many places, and pretty soon the idea to form a co-operative enterprise took shape.

In the name of God the Almighty people of equal thinking gathered and founded a co-operative which could serve as the basis for this spiritual community. We want to be a united group of brothers, and never separate, however severe the burden may be. This was the solemn vow. Renunciation of alcohol and smoking, and the will to realize a harmonious community life without dispute and discord – like in the original Christian

288 THE SCIENTIST, THE MADMAN, THE THIEF AND THEIR LIGHTBULB

communities – were the prerequisites to become a member. For the members, Methernitha is an ideal opportunity to live the fulfilled life practising charity.

A workshop building was erected. One house after the other grew on these premises. All construction was done out of own resources, and solely with the savings from the common work. Today Methernitha is an enterprise with several production companies and properties worth millions.

The people working here are almost without exception members of Methernitha. Not even the prospering development which took place over the following decades could impair or even suppress the global idealistic aims. On the contrary everybody works in his own interest with diligence and great joy towards the erection and support of their new homeland and according to the principle 'one for all and all for one'. With these words one can conquer anything. Also the ancient truth appeared again and attained respect.

The people living here feel themselves as members of a family: a group sitting in the same boat and proud but also grateful proprietors of their own homeland, which they may shape exactly as they wish to. Evidently this form of human social life can function only on the basis of idealistic principles.

The question arises, how the realization of a sincere religious philosophy of life may be brought in harmony with a successful economic management. It is not obvious, at all, that this is attainable. Nowadays there are many amongst us which [sic] are caught in the worldwide and dense network of social and economic dependencies and obligations and many also feel the confrontation with its problems. One member of the economic directory [board member] has recently phrased this in the following way: 'The fact that all essential functions of Methernitha are fulfilled without any external force, driven solely through inner conviction which causes everybody to help and take care of the other – this is, for me, the most astonishing effect which is produced by this form of living together. It seems to be a miracle.'

Another miracle within Methernitha is the Thesta-Distatica, which is the result of more than twenty years of research and contains the secret of the secrets. Here you can see the members of the research team which [who] took part in this development. One of them is Paul Baumann, who, with his high capabilities, and his outstanding knowledge about the acting laws of nature, but also through his high sensitivity has contributed very much to this invention.

This 'wonder machine' is learnt from nature. Nothing else. Nature is the greatest source of power as well as knowledge which man has. And it still conceals many secrets which are only revealed to those who approach and tie in with them with highest respect and responsibility. In order to understand nature and to perceive its voice, man is obliged to experience silence and solitude, and it was there where the knowledge about this technology was obtained.

For these reasons it was always a great concern of Methernitha to acquire properties untouched by man as far as possible, be it in valleys or forests, in the mountains or the shores of lakes, where one could study nature, one's own being and the creator of this universe in silence and concentration, and without being disturbed. The public never understood this properly: rather it interpreted it wrongly as an act of seclusion, assuming we had to hide something unclean. We actually had, and still have, to take great troubles to realize undisturbed, all the things we intended to accomplish. Whatever we can learn from nature, while being in nature, is the greatest benefit, not only for us, but for everybody. This, because all [everything] positive expands more and more just in virtue of inner laws.

Such undertaking in research and development necessitates considerable financial expenditure. Therefore we are quite often obliged to construct things with most primitive means and materials. What was thrown away by our affluent society we collect and possibly set up with it the cornerstone in the discovery of new forces and truth. We were fortunate in gaining the experience that paradoxically the most beautiful and gigantic results can be achieved by just using the most simple means. Never did we use any borrowed capital because we wanted to stay free Swiss citizens and do not want to be hindered or even bound in any way the pursuance of our aims.

The two counter-rotating disks generate an electrostatic charge. One disk represents the earth, the other the cloud. Using grid electrodes the charges are 'bound'. After that they are collected by non-contacting so-called 'antenna-keys', and then sorted. After being initially turned on by hand, the disks rotate by themselves according to the electrostatic laws of repulsion and attraction. A rectifying diode keeps the cycles in steady state, otherwise the impulses of attraction and repulsion would accumulate and cause the disks to run faster and faster. The correct [rotation] speed is of great importance, and for optimal power generation the disks have to run quite steady and slow.

By means of grid condensers the energy is stored and then uniformly discharged, at the same time reducing the high voltage and building up power with additional devices. Finally the machine supplies a uniform direct current [DC] which varies according to size of the model.

The machine furnishes about 3–4 kilowatts permanent output, depending on humidity, whereby the electrical potential ranges from 270 to 320 volts. High humidity of the atmosphere prevents the build-up of electrical potential [voltage]. The drier the air the better.

No doubt, through the so far achieved results, one main objective has been reached. Namely the proof that it is possible to use 'free energy'. Nevertheless the research work is not yet completed. To finish a model which can be handed out more or less to anybody, and without any health hazards, also to non-specialists, much work and also time will still be needed. To the educated physicist, many [much] of thing of this machine may seem impossible – maybe even crazy. Maybe he is also offenced [offended] by the conceptions [concepts] used to explain the whole [project].

Only partly we could use the concepts of conventional

physical terminology in order to explain and define only approximately the functions and properties of the various parts of the machine. After all, it will be necessary to create some more new concepts, like the one we have already used before when we termed the non-contacting collectors of electric charge as 'antenna-keys'. This machine puts experts who are just trained in conventional physics to a very hard test, because its mode of action is not explainable with the state of the art of officially accepted physical knowledge – or at the most only partially explainable. However also a trained specialist could remain free and independent in his thinking and should avoid to become limited by the temporal framework of publicly admitted knowledge in any science.

It has to be remembered that the established sciences were already many times forced to change amend or give up some of their very fundamental concepts. Think about Galileo Galilei in order to name only one example. Our human society almost condemned this man as a sorcerer and magician just because he investigated and discovered a truth which seemed unacceptable by the established science of the days. The 'book' knowledge of any time is not wrong, but it is incomplete, and therefore allows to draw wrong conclusions. We are part of a new era which brings to light many new facts and new knowledge. The clothing of nowaday science has become too tight, and should be stripped off, just like the larva of an insect does with its skin. Only this will allow a true metamorphosis to take its course, and finally at the limits and at the destination of all worldly knowledge, an universal and unlimited spiritual science – radiating and beautiful just as the completed imago [image] of an insect may give its blessings and benediction to a renovated humanity. To ever reach there an universal development of man has to take place. But this is only possible when man becomes aware of his true role within the whole of creation, and again learns to recognize his true tasks. Because the whole universe functions within a strict and precise structured order according to the will and work of the creator. Therefore man should also recognize and realize these universal laws which are valid within the whole and also within every part of this creation.

But the hard facts rather show how far man has left the divine order through his self-will and authoritarian way of action and that he has become the actual cause of all discord and evil on this planet. Unfortunately the ruling bodies which should be responsible for the well-being of the people work too often with the target to make life more and more difficult and to render impossible every free spiritual development. Instead of utilizing the achievements of science and technology for the benefit and preservation of all forms of life, they are abused carelessly, irresponsibly, in order to destroy and to kill – and thus turn them into a curse upon mankind. To change all this the evolution of a new technology is not enough – even if it were the most ecological and ingenious. To change this present status one has to go much deeper down: to the root cause of all this evil. And this is man's way of thinking, his state of mind.

The Ancients' divine commandments are still valid today and also show today the way and direction humanity should go, as clearly spoken by the prophet Micah: 'God has told you what is good. And what is it that the Lord asks of you? Only to act justly. To love loyalty [mercy]. To walk wisely for your God.'

Transcript of BBC Radio 4's

On the Ropes, 21 May 1997

An interview with Prof. Martin Fleischmann

This is a transcript of a radio interview in which Professor Martin Fleischmann talked to the presenter John Humphrys about the announcement of cold fusion on 23 March 1989, and the effect that the global reaction had on him.

John Humphrys: Imagine a world in which limitless energy could be created from a few buckets of water – so cheap they wouldn't even bother to meter it. We would solve the problem of global pollution at a stroke. No more need to pump carbon dioxide into our battered atmosphere. We might even end global hunger: the water of the oceans could be desalinated in vast quantities and pumped wherever it was needed to turn deserts into green fields. Oh, brave new world indeed. On 23 March 1989 it seemed that we had taken a great step towards that. Two hugely respected scientists, Martin Fleischmann and Stanley Pons, held a news conference at Utah University to announce that they had discovered the secret of nuclear fusion; the Holy Grail of science; the process by which the stars in their very heavens produce their power. For a few heady days the world celebrated the great news and dreamed wonderful dreams. Then for six nail-biting months scientists all over the world settled down to reproduce the experiment. And they failed. Or said they failed. From that moment on, Fleischmann and Pons were truly 'on the ropes'.

Professor Fleischmann, was that how it felt at the time for you? Did you feel beleaguered at that point?

Martin Fleischmann: I thought that it had gone wrong. I thought that the whole scientific process – in as much as it affected this particular process – had gone wrong. That's certainly true. Quite early on, the opinions were polarized into groups who behaved as sceptics – as they said 'they are sceptics' – and true believers. So the essential process of criticism was replaced by scepticism. That derailed the research . . .

John Humphrys: Right. We'll come to that in more detail. For those of us – like me – who are not scientists, let's try and understand a bit about this 'cold fusion'. I know it's a phrase you don't particularly like. We have split the atom. We have created nuclear fission. In layman's terms we've understood how to do that and we have therefore liberated vast energy. It's an explosion: we can contain it in nuclear power stations but in the process we produce a massive amount – or at least potentially – of pollution and risk and so on. It's very expensive to do and you can't exactly use that to put it in our vacuum cleaners to power them as we once dreamed that we would. Now 'cold fusion' – to use that phrase for the moment – is something quite different from that: it's joining the atoms together.

Martin Fleischmann: It's joining the nucleii together. If we break nucleii which are heavier than iron into fragments we get energy. If we join nucleii together which are lighter than iron we gain energy again. And of course, one of the chief objectives of fusion research is to join nucleii related to hydrogen – heavier nucleii than hydrogen: tritium (which contains two neutrons and one proton) or deuterium (which contains one neutron and one proton) in order to create heavier elements. And that is fusion.

John Humphrys: And the effect of doing that is to release enormous amounts of energy . . .

Martin Fleischmann: Like in the sun. The same type of process as the initial steps in the sun.

John Humphrys: And the only way previously that we had discovered how to do that involved huge temperatures.

Martin Fleischmann: Correct—

John Humphrys: Like the sun.

Martin Fleischmann: Yes. Huge temperatures or huge energy. And one thing, going back to your lead in . . . it is absolutely certain that the long-term future of the world requires the implementation of fusion. Now we did not actually say we had attained fusion. We said we had created large amounts of energy that could not be explained by chemistry.

John Humphrys: You had – again to put it very simply – a flask, a glass bottle. You had tubes sticking into that bottle. You had water in the bottle and what did you do?

Martin Fleischmann: Electrolyse the palladium electrode and – people know what an electrode is, I think – they are used to having batteries.

John Humphrys: I can grasp an electrode.

Martin Fleischmann: You polarize it negatively. You cram deuterium into the lattice and you get excess energy.

John Humphrys: It sounds very, very simple indeed: you put in a certain amount of energy and you created much more energy. Four to ten times as much.

Martin Fleischmann: Well, under certain circumstances . . . Let's be quite correct about this . . . Under some transient conditions about ten times as much energy out as we had put in.

John Humphrys: All of this was being done in secret.

Martin Fleischmann: Indeed.

John Humphrys: Why?

Martin Fleischmann: We did not like certain trends in research that we could perceive internationally.

John Humphrys: That is you and Stanley Pons.

Martin Fleischmann: Yes. And we did this really to satisfy ourselves whether or not carrying out these processes might have unfortunate consequences.

John Humphrys: Unfortunate in what sense?

Martin Fleischmann: Well, I think I have to come clean here. In the sense of national security.

John Humphrys: Why?

Martin Fleischmann: I mean the real reason we did this was because we thought this might be one way of inducing nuclear reactions which would be useful in a military context.

John Humphrys: You were worried about that: you did not want to enable that to happen.

Martin Fleischmann: If the answer to that was yes, we would have wanted the information classified. At least classified for the time being until the scope of the whole problem had been properly investigated.

John Humphrys: Something that puzzles me about this is that you'd put a lot of your own money into this: £100,000.

Martin Fleischmann: Well, we knew we couldn't fund it. We couldn't write a research application.

John Humphrys: Why?

Martin Fleischmann: It would not have been funded. First of all it would not have been funded, and secondly we did not want to reveal that we had, er, the notion that we could carry out these processes in this particular way.

John Humphrys: Your critics have since said that the reason for that was because you wanted to get ahead in this race, because, after all if we do regard this as a race—

Martin Fleischmann: There was no race!

John Humphrys: No race?

Martin Fleischmann: No. There was no race.

John Humphrys: We're talking here about the Holy Grail of science.

Martin Fleischmann: Oh yes, but we believe that nobody else was working in that particular way.

John Humphrys: Someone described you – one of your erstwhile colleagues – as a brilliant scientist with a mad theory. Is that the truth of it?

Martin Fleischmann: No. The theory isn't mad at all. The theory is . . . If you put down the framework in which you carry out an investigation, then this is not at all a mad concept.

John Humphrys: Let's—

Martin Fleischmann: I mean, many scientists might regard it as being mad, because they judge it within the existing paradigm. But if you . . . I'm quite convinced that the paradigm will change. It should have changed in the latter half of this century, but I think the paradigm will change. Then it will be seen that this particular research was just an example of many other research topics, and might very well lead to a positive conclusion. It doesn't follow that every piece of research, set up within a new paradigm, will be successful.

John Humphrys: But you believed . . . You carried out this research. You conducted those experiments, and on 23 March 1989 you held a news conference to tell the world that you had succeeded. Now let me just take you back to the moment of the experiment, and I doubt very much, because we all imagine the professor in the laboratory saying the equivalent of 'Eureka!' – 'We've cracked it!' I suppose it wasn't quite like that: you didn't rush out of the laboratory saying, 'My God, we've done it, we've done it, we've done it!'

Martin Fleischmann: No, science isn't like that.

John Humphrys: I was rather afraid it wouldn't be.

Martin Fleischmann: Well, eventually we will deposit our papers in a library somewhere and you will see that the usual comment was: 'The results are frustratingly interesting.' There is no reason to stop . . . perhaps no reason to go on . . . You see, it depends on the sort of person you are. Many people, when they get an unusual result, will say: 'This is unusual, I'll go and do something else.' But if you are a different sort of person you say: 'Should I stop or should I go on?' It depends on your attitude to the unusual result, and I was brought up in a research school where you always had to explain everything that you did – including the unsuccessful experiments.

John Humphrys: But now, what you did was you held a news conference. Instead of publishing the results of all of that research in *Nature* or some other respected scientific journal for your colleagues to pore over, and eventually perhaps someone would say, 'Yes, we think there's some rather interesting work here,' you held a news conference and the world went potty!

Martin Fleischmann: Well, that was something outside our control by that stage. We lost control.

John Humphrys: Why?

Martin Fleischmann: Another research group was working on this topic [Fleischmann is referring to Stephen Jones of Brigham Young University] and they believed they had observed neutrons of the correct energy—

John Humphrys: There was a race!

Martin Fleischmann: Well, it wasn't a race really. I think that the other group should have followed our wishes and held back the publication until September 1990. Their work would have been on a better basis, and our work would have been on a better basis. But when it became clear that this other research group wanted to publish its findings, we of course had to inform the university authorities of what we were doing, and we had to ask them the question: 'Do you believe that you need to take a patent?'

John Humphrys: And it was their decision, the university's decision, to hold a news conference.

Martin Fleischmann: It was their decision, not our decision. It was the university's decision that there had to be a set of patents, and that then dictated the subsequent events.

John Humphrys: The news conference . . .

Martin Fleischmann: That's right. The news conference was the consequence of the patent applications.

John Humphrys: And you regret that that happened?

Martin Fleischmann: Well, I was never in favour of it. I tried to stop the news conference even the day before. But . . . unsuccessfully.

John Humphrys: Because the result of that—

Martin Fleischmann: I knew it would go bad . . .

John Humphrys: And it did go bad.

Martin Fleischmann: Yes. I knew it was not a sensible thing to do.

John Humphrys: And the result of that was that it exposed, I suppose, apart from anything else, all the jealousies that operate in the scientific world.

Martin Fleischmann: Well, there were plenty of jealousies. It was a singularly unfortunate time to make this announcement. It was the fiftieth anniversary of the discovery of nuclear fission. And the hot fusion brigade were just gearing themselves up to ask for a lot more money. For the next step in the research in[to] hot fusion. So it was a singularly unfortunate time for two chemists to make such an announcement. That was certainly true, and of course, if we had not been put into that situation in March 1989 – if we could have delayed, even until December 1989 – we would then have published the full paper rather than the preliminary paper. And my recommendation was that this should be let out at the lowest possible level.

John Humphrys: Without a great fuss, you mean?

Martin Fleischmann: Yes. In fact, I wanted to have it published in the *Annals of Utah Science*, of which I believe they only print seven copies.

John Humphrys: Not a best-seller, exactly.

Martin Fleischmann: Not a best-seller. I wanted to really let it out in a really very minor way.

John Humphrys: There seems to be a great deal of difference between chemists and physicists that I'd not been aware of.

Martin Fleischmann: Yes, yes. Well, the joke statement is that the reason for the news conference was that chemists are interested in chemicals, but physicists are not interested in physicals. But I think that is only partly true: when a lot is at stake then physicists are really the principal offenders with regard to making premature announcements.

John Humphrys: So what followed then was a result in your view partly of professional jealousies.

Martin Fleischmann: It's very difficult. I always maintain that really this is a job for several investigative journalists to find out what really went on. It was very unfortunate. I thought it would be bad, but I didn't think it would be quite that bad. I was hoping that we would have constructive criticism, rather than scepticism . . . but it was not to be. We had scepticism and no criticism.

John Humphrys: I was going to say you had both, didn't you?

Martin Fleischmann: No, there was no criticism. There was no constructive criticism at all . . . really. I'm not aware of anybody who asked for our results, and who analysed our results. We had to ask for the results to be analysed. Independently.

John Humphrys: Some people went as far as suggesting you'd been guilty of some sort of fraud even.

Martin Fleischmann: Well, you know, this is why we say: 'The lady doth protest too much.' People who accuse other people of fraud, you could say, 'Well, perhaps they have done a little bit of fiddling somewhere.'

John Humphrys: Why? Again looking at this as a non-scientific outsider. Why should there be this sort of thing going on in this world?

Martin Fleischmann: It's distressing. I don't know. A precondition for science is total honesty. Of course I know scientists deviate from this. You know, even highly respected scientists try to make their results conform to some notion they have had, and later on it turns out that that notion is incorrect and if a new experiment is carried out you find out that it is really something different to the way they believed.

John Humphrys: But isn't the most simple explanation of all of this that you got it wrong.

Martin Fleischmann: I keep on checking. I must tell you that I am again checking up old data. You always worry about that. I don't know how often I have been through the past data to try to see where have I made a mistake. This is something you must . . . you see I do believe with Sir Karl Popper that you can't prove something right, you can only prove it wrong. So one of the things you have to do is check and check and check and check. Have you made a mistake? Where is the mistake? If you can't find the mistake then all you can say at the end is: 'I have done the following investigation. I cannot find a mistake.' And you have to stop there. The consequence of that is that we could go on and maybe create a successful energy source. I have always said: the only thing which people will believe in the end is a practicable device. So this research would have an end result. I am convinced that no one will believe any of the research results until there is a device. It's like the Wright brothers flying their aeroplane: nobody would believe that a 'heavier than air' machine could fly until they saw the plane flying. In fact the day before, the *New York Times*, I think it was, accused them of fraud.

John Humphrys: But what happened was that one team of scientists after another tried to reproduce – including the people here at Harwell – and failed. And therefore, after all this excitement, the conclusion was that the whole thing was anomalous.

Martin Fleischmann: No, but you see . . . The problem is . . . let's take the group at Harwell. The apparatus use at Harwell was deficient in many regards. You have to design the experiment and then you have to analyse the results. And this is . . . this problem of analysing the results is where most of the failures in science take place.

John Humphrys: This is puzzling, again to a non-scientist like me. This is puzzling. What's going on here? Why, if you can do it, and if you can take that set of results and analyse them in a certain way . . . Those of us who aren't scientists have always believed that the one thing you can be absolute about is science. All right, philosophy, poetry, music: heaven knows what any of it means. There are a million interpretations. But a scientific result – we've always wanted to believe at any rate – is a result, is a certainty!

Martin Fleischmann: Exactly, but you have to carry out the analysis. And if you cannot analyse your data you have to change your experiment so that you can carry out your analysis. I'm afraid that scientists are not very good at analysing their data. I always say to people who say they don't believe this: 'Write a research application which is going to deal strictly with the analysis of other people's data, and see whether you can get any funds. You will never get the funds, and you see research is driven by the research student syndrome. The supervisor in the – I can only speak for university research . . . The research supervisor tries to get the maximum number of results, and says, 'I will analyse those data later,' and of course he never analyses those data.

John Humphrys: Because he wants to carry on researching?

Martin Fleischmann: That's right. I mean, the biggest loss of information in science is the lack of analysis of existing data.

John Humphrys: But . . . you're not saying, Professor Fleischmann, are you, that you are the only one who's right: the rest of the army is out of step?

Martin Fleischmann: There are plenty of people out there . . . I mean this has all been published. It's all accessible . . . we don't need to talk about this any more. If people really wish to know what these research groups obtained it is in the literature.

John Humphrys: Although we wouldn't be able to understand a word of it. That's the problem.

Martin Fleischmann: You see, this is always the way. I think the problem is that science sometimes proceeds very slowly because of the misinterpretation of results.

John Humphrys: Well, all right then. Let's . . . In nice simple terms: you conducted the experiment. You got, as you put it, excess heat.

Martin Fleischmann: Right.

John Humphrys: The world got very excited about that. Other scientists tried and failed to reproduce the experiment and, adding on the very important caveat, to analyse the results in the same way that they came up with the same thing as you. Now—

Martin Fleischmann: No, no. Let me correct you. They just did not analyse their results.

John Humphrys: O.K. They didn't analyse their results.

Martin Fleischmann: Therefore their experiment is useless.

John Humphrys: But we're talking here about as important a piece of scientific work as it is possible to imagine. Certainly in layman's terms. In anybody's terms for that matter. And you're telling me that the reason the whole thing came to grief was that scientists didn't analyse the results of the experiments that they themselves carried out to try and replicate what you had done. Now, the question has to be asked again: why not? We're talking about something that is unimaginably important here.

Martin Fleischmann: The resources required for analysing data are much larger than the resources required for gathering the data.

John Humphrys: Here we're talking about work that—

Martin Fleischmann: It's one of the diseases of present-day science.

John Humphrys: But billions of pounds is spent on research in science. And this research, these experiments, if they had produced . . . delivered the goods in layman's terms, would be worth unimaginable sums of money. Billions! Trillions of pounds. For the sake of a few million . . .

Martin Fleischmann: Uh huh. That's the way it is.

John Humphrys: But that is stunningly stupid, if that's the case.

Martin Fleischmann: I'm afraid that is so, but that is the way it is. If the number of people who analyse their results in great detail and with sufficient, adequate care is really quite small . . .

John Humphrys: Well then, why isn't there someone out there now saying: 'Fleischmann was on to something, we believe . . .'?

Martin Fleischmann: Well, there are people who say that.

John Humphrys: Why aren't they putting hundreds of millions of pounds into it?

Martin Fleischmann: Well, you see, then you have the question of the sociology of the subject. How can you put a lot of money into a field of research that has been discredited?

John Humphrys: But it was discredited, you say, because the analysis of the results was not carried out.

Martin Fleischmann: Correct. I think we should take . . . people should nominate the pieces of research they believe are critically important, and those investigations have to be reinvestigated maybe ten times.

John Humphrys: Why are you not continuing to work on it yourself?

Martin Fleischmann: Well, I am.

John Humphrys: Where?

Martin Fleischmann: I would prefer not to discuss that at the present time. At the present time I am reanalysing – actually this is very interesting – I am reanalysing old research data obtained by ourselves and other research groups. And I am starting work with another research group.

John Humphrys: There are those who – the conspiracy theorists in this world and there are plenty of them – who believe the reason some of the great discoveries never get made is because there are vested interests. And if we did have limitless energy – not necessarily free, but compared with today's prices very, very cheap indeed and non-polluting – it would destroy whole industries. The oil industry, clearly. The people who make the internal combustion engine. And so on and so on. The implications of it would be profound beyond belief. Anything in that theory, in your view?

Martin Fleischmann: Er . . . it is always tempting to resort to conspiracy theories. But you should only do it as a last resort. However, one extremely intelligent person I know, scientist I know, says: 'When you have assembled all your facts, there has to usually be a single explanation of all the facts. And if the explanation of all these facts is that there is a conspiracy then you'd better take that seriously.' Am I answering your question?

John Humphrys: Well . . . so far. But then, as you would say: 'and then, and then . . .'

Martin Fleischmann: Well, I'm afraid that if you assemble the facts, if you assemble all the information about this subject, you have to come to the conclusion that there is a conspiracy.

John Humphrys: And who . . . ?

Martin Fleischmann: That you don't know. That you don't know. But it looks strongly like a conspiracy. Or several conspiracies . . .

John Humphrys: Well, I was going to say: you could understand that—

Martin Fleischmann: Conspiracies within conspiracies.

John Humphrys: You could understand why an oil-producing company would be concerned about cold fusion. It's difficult to understand why a government – which also spends a great deal of money on research – would not seize it with both hands and say, 'We must, for the good of mankind, develop.' So doesn't a conspiracy theory come unstuck at that point?

Martin Fleischmann: It depends on what the conspiracy deals with, doesn't it?

John Humphrys: How do you mean?

Martin Fleischmann: Well, what is the motivation of the conspiracy? If there is a conspiracy.

John Humphrys: Well: in the case of the oil company, for instance, it's to protect its interests.

Martin Fleischmann: That might not be the motivation of the conspiracy, may it?

John Humphrys: What other motivation might there be?

Martin Fleischmann: That is something that people have to work out for themselves.

John Humphrys: Well, you tell us you've been [. . .] for a long time . . .

Martin Fleischmann: No, I'm not going to put that on BBC. On Radio 4. No, I'm not going to say that on Radio 4. No, I'm sorry. I'm not.

John Humphrys: But can there be any reason why a government should be less than enthusiastic about—

Martin Fleischmann: Of course! Of course! Right at the beginning, in that article which perhaps you have read, I said at that time the head of the United States Department of Energy was Admiral Watkins. And I said: 'Would Admiral Watkins welcome the notion of nuclear research being carried out in chemistry departments?' It is ludicrous. Of course he would not. The motivation would have to be: this must stop. If this work is going to be done at all, it's going to be done in national laboratories – something which I agreed with at the time.

John Humphrys: But this is a matter of individual pride getting in the way.

Martin Fleischmann: No, it's not a question of individual pride, it's a question of sensible security. Why should this . . . Supposing you have this type of research carried out in university departments, goodness knows what will be discovered. Should it be done in university departments?

John Humphrys: Well then, why aren't governments, why is not the United States government taking your work and saying this will now be done in a government laboratory? Or perhaps they are?

Martin Fleischmann: Well, you don't know, do you?

John Humphrys: Do you know?

Martin Fleischmann: No, I don't know.

John Humphrys: Is it conceivable?

Martin Fleischmann: It's certainly conceivable, but I don't know.

John Humphrys: So how far are we away from another news conference – such as you held back in 1989 – with someone saying: 'Well, we have cracked it!'

Martin Fleischmann: Could happen at any time.

John Humphrys: Really?

Martin Fleischmann: Yes. I think it is one of these things . . . the production of a demonstrable, useful device could happen at any time now. That doesn't mean to say that it will happen, but it could happen at any time. The creation of a useful, a commercially useful device will take a considerable time.

John Humphrys: By which you mean years?

Martin Fleischmann: Years, years.

John Humphrys: But you, now in your seventies, are still working and you believe that in your lifetime you will see this work—

Martin Fleischmann: Well, you know: I'm not a spring chicken! And I'm not very fit, so I don't know whether it will be in my lifetime, but I think it is around the corner, yes.

John Humphrys: Professor Fleischmann, thank you very much indeed.

Martin Fleischmann: It's been a pleasure to talk to you.

Excerpt from BBC Radio 4's

'Today', 20 October 1998

Presenter: Do you remember cold fusion, the technology which promised limitless pollution-free energy to a world hungry for power? And do you remember the disappointment when researchers dismissed it as false hope? Well, one of the men who helped its development, or claimed to, said that there was a conspiracy to discredit his work while laboratories across the world contain scientists continuing the search for the technological Holy Grail. Michael Williams reports . . .

Williams: It's almost ten years since two professors at the University of Utah made an announcement which promised to change the world. Stanley Pons and his colleague, Martin Fleischmann, said they had harnessed the power of the sun – nuclear fusion – using a small piece of equipment which operated near room temperature.

Fleischmann: What is on offer here is the source of energy which is accessible to everybody all over the planet. We could create any sort of society anywhere we want.

Williams: Fleischmann and Pons believed that within their electrochemical cell, minute chunks of matter at the heart of atoms, the nuclei, were merging, liberating energy in the process. Theirs was a simple but remarkable claim that more energy came out of the system than went into it. But within six months, the work had been widely dismissed by many researchers around the world who tried and failed to reproduce the results. Perhaps the most definitive study came from the UK Atomic Energy Authority at Harwell, where Nick Hans is the spokesman.

Hans: I know that the scientists concerned desperately wanted cold fusion to exist. They looked very hard, but they weren't going to be fooled. They investigated it very deeply with all the skills of nuclear scientists and electrochemists and, in the end of the day, they could not ascribe a cold fusion process.

Williams: But the data from Harwell was analysed by others. Among them Michael Melich, who works for the United States military. He's a professor of physics at the US Naval Post Graduate School in California. He never gives interviews, but he did agree to issue a statement, a summary of his findings. In the data from Harwell, he says, he found evidence of cold fusion.

Reading of statement: Our re-analysis strongly suggests that they had at least ten anomalous heat generation events. My own view of cold fusion is that the system has properties which are not understood. Not least of which is the ability to produce relatively large quantities of power.

Williams: Martin Fleischmann is drinking in the Fox and Hounds, a pub near the Wiltshire village to which he returned after his years in Utah. The water in his beer, he says, could be made to give up some of its atomic components, producing enough energy from a pint to run an electric fire for almost a year.

Fleischmann: I have never been able to find the evidence that we were wrong. Therefore I continue, and other people continue too. I mean there are many people working on this in the world. There are clearly a number of industrial organizations who are interested and a certain number of government institutions.

Williams: There is a stigma associated with work in cold fusion. Distinguished scholars from around the world have dismissed the Pons–Fleischmann effect as mere experimental error. But there remains a small community of scientists who keep the faith. Among them Dr Michael McKubre.

McKubre: We have done enough work to know that there is heat being produced which is well beyond any amount of heat that you can account for by chemistry, by known chemistry. The most likely source of that heat, in my view, is a nuclear process.

Williams: He's an electro-chemist with SRI International which grew out of Stanford University in California and, in his lab alone, they've spent $7 million investigating the Pons–Fleischmann effect. Other more secretive laboratories are investigating too.

McKubre: We have an informal collaboration of four or five major research institutions in the United States, for example. The sponsors of these institutions may not want their involvement to be known.

Williams: Is the American government involved in research to your knowledge?

McKubre: Yes it is, to my knowledge.

Willaims: Can you tell me the nature of the involvement?

McKubre: I'd rather not. I can assure you that it's real. I know directly governmental sources are using US governmental funds directly and specifically to do this research but some people, influential people, influential people in Washington, just don't want that to be the case.

Fleischmann: You put me in a difficult position. I mean I can only answer this from my own experience. It had been my intention to explore the possible applications of this in military technology and maybe people are worried about that particular aspect. My own thoughts on this will probably – should probably – accompany me to the grave.

Presenter: That report was by Mike Williams. Fascinating stuff.

BlackLight's Patent

United States Patent 6,024,935
Mills, et al.
February 15, 2000
Lower-energy hydrogen methods and structures
Abstract

Methods and apparatus for releasing energy from hydrogen atoms (molecules) by stimulating their electrons to relax to quantized lower energy levels and smaller radii (smaller semimajor and semiminor axes) than the 'ground state' by providing energy sinks or means to remove energy resonant with the hydrogen energy released to stimulate these transitions.

An energy sink, energy hole, can be provided by the transfer of at least one electron between participating species including atoms, ions, molecules, and ionic and molecular compounds. In one embodiment, the energy hole comprises the transfer of t electrons from one or more donating species to one or more accepting species whereby the sum of the ionization energies and/or electron affinities of the electron donating species minus the sum of the ionization energies and/or electron affinities of the electron accepting species equals approximately $mX27.21$ eV ($mX48.6$ eV) for atomic (molecular) hydrogen below 'ground state' transitions where m and t are integers.

The present invention further comprises a hydrogen spillover catalyst, a multifunctionality material having a functionality which dissociates molecular hydrogen to provide free hydrogen atoms which spill over to a functionality which supports mobile free hydrogen atoms and a functionality which can be a source of the energy holes.

The energy reactor includes one of an electrolytic cell, a pressurized hydrogen gas cell, and a hydrogen gas discharge cell. A preferred pressurized hydrogen gas energy reactor comprises a vessel; a source of hydrogen; a means to control the pressure and flow of hydrogen into the vessel; a material to dissociate the molecular hydrogen into atomic hydrogen, and a material which can be a source of energy holes in the gas phase. The gaseous source of energy holes includes those that sublime, boil, and/or are volatile at the elevated operating temperature of the gas energy reactor wherein the exothermic reaction of electronic transitions of hydrogen to lower energy states occurs in the gas phase.

Inventors: Mills; Randell L. (Malvern, PA); Good; William R. (Wayne, PA); Phillips; Jonathan (State College, PA); Popov; Arthur I. (Philadelphia, PA)

Assignee: BlackLight Power, Inc. (Cranbury, NJ)

Appl. No.: 822170

Filed: March 21, 1997

US Class: 423/648.1; 422/129

Intern'l Class: C01B 003/02

Field of Search: 423/648.1 422/129

APPENDIX 9

Kohei Minato Patents

US 4751486: Magnetic rotation apparatus
Inventor(s): Minato; Kohei, Minato-Ku, Tokyo 105, Japan
Applicant(s): none
Issued/Filed Dates: June 14, 1988 / April 24, 1987
Application Number: US1987000042432

Abstract: The magnetic rotation apparatus of the present invention has first and second rotors rotatably supported and juxtaposed. The first and second rotors are connected so as to be rotatable in opposite directions in a cooperating manner. A number of permanent magnets are arranged on a circumferential portion of the first rotor at regular intervals, and just as many permanent magnets are arranged on a circumferential portion of the second rotor at regular intervals. Each permanent magnet has one magnetic polarity located radially outward from the rotors, and has the other magnetic polarity located radially inward toward the rotors. The polarity of each permanent magnet, which is located radially outward from the rotors, is identical. When the first and second rotors are rotated in a cooperating manner, the phase of rotation of the permanent magnets of one rotor is slightly advanced from that of the permanent magnets of the other rotor. One of the permanent magnets of one rotor is replaced with the electromagnet. The radially outward polarity of the electromagnet can be changed by reversing the direction in which a current is supplied to the electromagnet.

Attorney, Agent, or Firm: Brown, Martin, Haller & Meador;
Primary/Assistant Examiners: Harris; George;
First Claim: (only)

1. A magnetic rotation apparatus comprising:
a first rotor which is rotatably supported; a second rotor which is rotatably supported, and juxtaposed with said first rotor; cooperating means for enabling said first and second rotors to rotate in opposite directions; and magnet elements arranged at regular intervals on the peripheral portion of each of said first and second rotors, the number of the magnet elements arranged on the first rotor being equal to that of the magnet elements on the second rotor, characterized in that each magnet element has at least one magnetic pole located radially outward from each rotor, that, when the first and second rotors are rotated in a cooperating manner, any one of the magnets of the first rotor, and any of the magnets of the second rotor, which constitute a pair, move such that their magnetic poles having the same polarity approach and move away from each other periodically; that one of the paired magnet elements has a phase of rotation a little advanced from that of the other; that, when the paired magnet elements approach each other, a magnetic repulsion force is produced to exert a torque to the first rotor in one direction, and the torque of the first rotor is transmitted to the second rotor through said cooperating means, thus allowing the second rotor to rotate against a torque applied to the second rotor due to said magnetic repulsion force; and that one of at least a pair of magnet elements is provided with magnetic force switching means for changing the polarity of said one magnet element.

[Five further claims follow]

US 5594289: Magnetic rotating apparatus
Inventor(s): Minato; Kohei, Shinjuku-Ku, Tokyo

Issued/Filed Dates: Jan 14, 1997 / Dec 14, 1995
Application Number: US1995000574582

Abstract: On a rotor which is fixed to a rotatable rotating shaft, a plurality of permanent magnets are disposed along the direction of rotation such that the same magnetic pole type thereof face outward. In the same way, balancers are disposed on the rotor for balancing the rotation of the rotor. According to the magnetic rotating apparatus of the present invention, rotational energy can be efficiently obtained from permanent magnets. This is made possible by minimizing as much as possible current supplied to the electromagnets, so that only a required amount of electrical energy is supplied to the electromagnets.
Attorney, Agent, or Firm: Marks and Murase L.L.P.;
Primary/Assistant Examiners: Dougherty; Thomas M.;

[Twelve claims follow]

APPENDIX 10

Paulo and Alexandra Correa

Patents

Paulo and Alexandra Correa have secured a total of seven patents, including these three patents relating to their Pulsed Abnormal Glow Charge technology: US Patent Nos 5,416,391, 5,449,989 and 5,502,354.

US 5,416,391: Electromechanical transduction of plasma pulses
Inventor(s): Correa; Paulo N., Concord, Ontario, Canada
Correa; Alexandra N., Concord, Ontario, Canada
Issued/Filed Dates: May 16, 1995 / Oct. 15, 1992

Abstract: A direct current power transducer for driving alternating current devices utilizes a discharge tube connected across a current source, the construction of the tube and characteristics of the source being such as to maintain endogenous pulsed abnormal gas discharge within the tube. The tube is capacitatively coupled to an external load including an alternating current device, typically an electric motor. Electric motors of the asynchronous induction or synchronous types are particularly suitable, but other alternating current devices may be used. By adjustments to the current source, the capacitance in parallel with the discharge tube, and connections to auxiliary electrodes, the pulse repetition frequency of the discharge may be adjusted, thus allowing variable speed control of types of alternating current motor not normally amenable to such control.

[Thirteen claims follow]

US 5449989: Energy conversion system
Inventor(s): Correa; Paulo N., Concord, Ontario, Canada
Correa; Alexandra N., Concord, Ontario, Canada
Issued/Filed Dates: Sept. 12, 1995 / April 15, 1993

Abstract: An energy conversion device includes a discharge tube which is operated in a pulsed abnormal glow discharge regime in a double ported circuit. A direct current source connected to an input port provides electrical energy to initiate emission pulses, and a current sink in the form of an electrical energy storage or utilization device connected to the output port captures at least a substantial proportion of energy released by collapse of the emission pulses.

[Twenty-three claims follow]

US 5502354: Direct current energized pulse generator utilizing autogenous cyclical pulsed abnormal glow discharges
Inventor(s): Correa; Paulo N., Concord, Ontario, Canada
Correa; Alexandra N., Concord, Ontario, Canada
Issued/Filed Dates: March 26, 1996 / April 19, 1994

A cold cathode vacuum discharge tube is used in a circuit for generating pulsed autoelectronic emissions which are particularly intense and frequent in the abnormal glow discharge region, and involve much lower current densities than predicted by the Fowler-Nordheim vacuum arc discharge region law. The discharge tube is characterized by a large electrode area at least of the cathode, and a large interelectrode gap. The electrodes are preferably spaced at least 2 cm apart in a parallel relationship. A probe may be introduced between the electrodes to reduce still further the field required to generate the emissions. In another configuration the probe forms the anode and two plates form cathodes. The circuit is driven from a direct current source of having an impedance sufficient to prevent establishment of a vacuum arc discharge.

[Eighteen claims follow]

Patents can be examined at www.delphion.com and at www.uspto.gov

GLOSSARY

alpha decay – alpha decay occurs when a nucleus emits an alpha particle. An alpha particle is also known as a helium nucleus, and is made up of two protons and two neutrons.

alternating current (AC) – electrical current that regularly reverses its direction of flow. The frequency of the change in direction is measured in Hertz (Hz) or cycles per second. In the UK and Europe AC is 50 Hz, while in the United Sates the standard is 60 Hz. So in the UK, for example, this means that the current goes from positive to negative and back to positive (one full cycle) fifty times each second.

alternator – a device for converting motive energy into alternating current (AC) electricity.

battery – a device for storing electrical energy.

beta decay – beta decay can take a number of forms, but is most commonly characterized by an emission of an electron from an element's nucleus.

brushes – contacts which allow a 'sliding contact' between the coils in a motor and the cables or wires which provide the electric current.

capacitor/condenser – a device for storing electrical charge.

capacitance – a measure of a capacitor's ability to store electrical charge.

charge – an electrical charge can be positive or negative, depending on whether an atom has lost an electron (and become positive) or gained an electron (and become negative).

commutator – the part of an electric motor which allows the motor's rotor to rotate continuously as the magnetic forces in the rotating coil change direction.

condenser – *see* capacitor.

cosmic rays – a collective term for forms of radiation or radiated energy which travel through space. They are mostly formed of sub-atomic particles and nucleii of elements stripped of electrons. Some are electrically charged, such as protons, and their velocities are affected by magnetic fields. Others such as neutrons and neutrinos are not affected by magnetic fields, which means that their sources can be more easily determined.

direct current (DC) – direct current means that the flow of electrons in a circuit is always in the same direction.

dynamo – a device for converting motive energy into direct current (DC) electrical energy.

electromagnet – current flowing through a coil causes a magnetic field around the coils of the wire. The magnetic field in the coil interacts with other adjacent magnetic fields to cause repulsion and attraction.

electromotive force – electromotive force is another term for potential difference, and measures the pushing strength of electricity in volts.

electron – a small, negatively charged particle which orbits the nucleus of any element. In a normal state the number of electrons orbiting the nucleus is equal to the number of protons in the nucleus.

element – originally viewed as an indivisible form, elements – such as hydrogen, iron, carbon, uranium, etc. – are substances which cannot be spilt chemically into simpler substances. Elements sometimes occur in a number of isotopes (see isotopes).

entropy – the tendency of a system or process to end in heat energy, and/or increasing levels of disorder.

gamma decay – gamma decay, or gamma radiation, is an emission (from an element's nucleus) of gamma rays, which are an electromagnetic radiation of very short wavelengths and high penetrating power. These occur spontaneously in conjunction with the other forms of decay.

generator – a general term for a device which turns motive energy into electrical power.

half-life – the time period taken by a radioactive element to reduce its level of radioactive emissions to half its original value.

heavy water – also known as deuterium oxide or D_2O, heavy water occurs naturally in sea and river water and is safe and relatively easy to extract. It is called 'heavy' water as it is the oxide of deuterium or 'heavy' hydrogen. Heavy hydrogen atoms contain a neutron as well as a proton in their nucleus.

isotope – elements can exist in different forms, or isotopes, depending on the number of neutrons in the atom's nucleus. Carbon, for instance, occurs as carbon-12, carbon-13, carbon-14, meaning that as well as 6 protons, the nucleus contains 6, 7 and 8 neutrons respectively. Larger elements, such as uranium, can exist in radioactive isotopes, which vary in their radioactive stability. This stability is measured by the half-life (*see* half-life).

Leyden jar – a device for capturing electrostatic charge.

linac (linear accelerator) – a device formed of a straight, evacuated tube for accelerating sub-atomic particles to high velocities and high-energy states.

magnet – it has been known for over two thousand years that certain materials exhibit an invisible force known as magnetism. The origins of magnetism within materials is still something of a mystery, although it is now believed that it is connected to groups of atoms known as 'domains'. These domains, while randomly structured in other materials, are more ordered in one direction in magnetic materials, and can thus exert a force.

motor – a device for turning electrical power into motive power.

multiphase (also polyphase) – 'phasing' is a term used to describe the wave pattern of AC current as it moves from positive to negative and back again. In multiphase equipment there are a number of wave patterns, which, while occurring simultaneously, are out of synchronization with each other by a specific degree.

negentropy – a 'special situation' within a system or process in which order increases; a local breaking of the second law of thermodynamics. It has been postulated that natural biological systems – such as plants and animals – and some geological systems including the mineral strata in the earth's crust have the ability to perform 'negentropic' transformations in which they are able to increase order. It has also been suggested that negentropic reactions could be involved in energy technologies which claim to take energy from the zero-point vacuum.

neutron – a neutral, uncharged particle forming part of an atomic nucleus.

nuclear – pertaining to the nucleus of atoms.

nuclear fission – the process of liberating energy by splitting large atoms such as uranium into smaller atoms.

nuclear fusion – the process of liberating energy by bringing together small atoms such as hydrogen and deuterium (heavy hydrogen) to fuse into heavier elements such as helium.

paradigm shift – a phrase invented by philosopher of science Thomas S. Kuhn to denote a fundamental change in a science's model of the universe.

periodic table – the periodic table, or table of elements, categorizes elements according to their atomic number and their reactivity. The atomic number of an element is the number of protons in the element's nucleus. Elements can also be categorized according to their atomic weight – the sum of the protons and neutrons in the element's nucleus. There are currently 112 elements in the periodic table, although it is possible that further, 'heavier', unstable radioactive elements may yet be artificially created.

plasma – plasma is sometimes known as the 'fourth state' of matter (the other three being solid, liquid and gas). In some ways plasma is like gas, except that plasma is formed when gas atoms lose electrons and become positively charged. Plasma, simply put, is ionized gas. Its interest to scientists lies in its ability to act as a conductor of electricity with greatly varying amounts of resistance. (Some scientists define plasma as a gas in which at least

50 per cent of its particles are electrically charged.) Plasmas can only exist in high temperature conditions such as in containment vessels for nuclear experiments. It is also present in the sun and in stars, and can occur in lightning discharges.

plasma discharger – a high frequency electrical device for creating a plasma by dislodging electrons from gas molecules.

potential difference – the 'pushing strength' of electricity, measured in volts.

proton – a positively charged elementary particle forming an atomic nucleus.

resistor – a device to provide an electrical resistance in a circuit.

rotating magnetic field – first utilized by Nikola Tesla, a rotating magnetic field is at the heart of an AC generator or motor. Rather than simply generating an electrical current by rotating a coil in a magnetic field – as with a DC motor/generator – Tesla realized that by rotating a alternately segmented magnetic or electromagnetic field on a rotor, he could 'induce' an AC current in the windings of surrounding adjacent coils forming the generator's 'stator'. The fact that the current is produced by induction – 'at a distance' – does away with the conventional motor/generator's need for a commutator or brushes.

rotor – the moving, rotating part of an electrical motor, normally a coil.

static electricity – static electricity can be contrasted with current electricity. Whereas current electricity involves the flow of electrons along wires, static electricity involves the build-up and discharge of electron charges in air, or on the outside surfaces of materials.

stator – the static part of an electrical motor, normally a magnet.

transmutation – occurs when one element changes into at least one other element through a nuclear process.

vacuum – in physics: an absence not just of gases, but also of heat, in which quantum fluctuations – the creation and annihilation of fundamental physical particles – can still be measured to be taking place.

X-rays – X-rays are a form of artificial gamma rays produced by a high-voltage X-ray tube.

zero-point energy – energy resulting from the quantum fluctuations of the vacuum. Some scientists regard zero-point energy as a potential energy source in its own right.

Units of Measurement

Amp (A) – the standard unit for measuring the quantity of electrical current.

Electronvolt (eV) – a measure of energy when referring to subatomic particles and nuclear processes.

Farad (F) – the standard measurement of charge or capacitance.

Horsepower (HP) – a measure of power. One horsepower equals 745 watts.

Joule (J) – a measure of energy.

Kelvin (K) – an absolute measure of temperature employing units the same size as Celsius units but based on absolute zero (minus 273.15 Celsius).

Ohm (Ω) – a measure of resistance to the flow of electricity in an object or substance.

Volt (V) – the standard unit for the 'pushing strength' of electricity.

Watt (W) – a standard measurement of power, including electrical power.

REFERENCES

Chapter 1: Introduction

1 'Climate Change in America', US Govt Report, June 2000.
2 'Energy – The Changing Climate', Royal Commission on Environmental Pollution, June 2000. Available at http://www.rcep.org.uk.
3 Ibid.
4 Tesla, Nikola, 'The Problem of Increasing Human Energy', *Century Illustrated Monthly Magazine*, June 1900.
5 Ibid.

THE SEARCH FOR FREE ENERGY
Email: info@thesearchforfreeenergy.com
Web: www.thesearchforfreeenergy.com
The website of this book where you can read the most recent news, follow links to key sites, purchase books, etc.

Chapter 2: Nikola Tesla – Electricity's Hidden Genius

1 US Patent Nos 1,061,142 and 1,061,206: http:www// delphion.com.
2 Cheney, Margaret, *Man Out of Time*, (New York: Dell,1981), p 31.
3 Tesla, Nikola, 'My Inventions', *Electrical Experimenter*. May, June, July, October 1919, republished by Skolska Knjiga, Zagreb, Yugoslavia, 1977, p 41.
4 Cheney, Margaret, op cit, p 31.

5. Tesla, 'My Inventions', p 41.

6 Cheney, op cit, p 31.

7 O'Neill, John J., *Prodigal Genius* (New York: David McKay Co., 1944), pp 146–9.

8 Philadelphia *North American* 'Tesla Thinks Wind Power Should be Used More Now', 18 May 1902, Mag Sec V.

9 Tesla, 'The Problem of Increasing Human Energy'.

10. Tesla, 'My Inventions', p 51.

11. Tesla, 'The Problem of Increasing Human Energy'.

12 Tesla, Nikola, letter to J.P.Morgan, 3 July 1903, US Library of Congress.

13 Morgan, J.P., letter to Nikola Tesla, 14 July 1903, US Library of Congress.

14 Tesla, Nikola, lecture to American Institute of Electrical Engineers (AIEE), 1892.

15 Tesla, 'The Problem of Increasing Human Energy'.

16 Ibid.

17 Tesla, Nikola, US Patent No. 685,957, 'Apparatus for the Utilization of Radiant Energy', filed on 21 March 1901, granted on 5 November 1901.

18 Tesla, 'The Problem of Increasing Human Energy'.

19 Ibid.

20 Ibid.

21 Ibid.

22 Ibid.

Chapter 3: T. Henry Moray – Capturing the Energy of the Universe

1 Moray, T.H., *The Sea of Energy in Which the Earth Floats*, Fourth Edition (Salt Lake City: Cosray, P.O. Box 58141, Salt Lake City, UT, USA 84158-0141,1960).

2 Wilton H. Welling (Former Secretary of State of Utah), letter, February 1930.

3 Moray, T.H., notes, Harvey Fletcher Files, Brigham University,

Salt Lake City.

4 Ibid.

5 Ibid.

6 Ibid.

7 Ibid.

8 Ibid.

9 Ibid.

10 Ibid.

11 Ibid.

12 Eyring, Carl, letter to Robert L. Judd, 6 February 1926, Harvey Fletcher Files.

13 Jensen, E.C., letter to R.L. Anderberg, 8 October 1928, Harvey Fletcher Files.

14 Moray, op cit.

15 Jensen, op cit.

16 Fletcher, Harvey, letter to Robert L. Judd, 16 October 1928, Harvey Fletcher Files.

17 Ibid.

18 Fletcher, Harvey, letter to Robert L. Judd, 5 November 1928, Harvey Fletcher Files.

19 Yates, T.J., open letter, 16 March 1929, Harvey Fletcher Files.

20 Hayes, Dr Murray O., letter to W.H. Lovesy, 24 October 1929, Harvey Fletcher Files.

21 Ibid.

22 Moray, *The Sea of Energy in Which the Earth Floats*, p 155.

23 Ibid, p 156.

24 Ibid, p 157.

25 Lovesy, W.H., letter to T.H. Moray, 29 June 1932.

26 Moray, op cit, p 165.

27 Ibid, p 166.

28 Ibid, p 166.

29 Ibid, p 167.

30 Ibid, p 170.

31 Moray, *The Sea of Energy in Which the Earth Floats*, Fifth Edition (Salt Lake City: Cosray 1978).

32 Moray, J., E.E. Dahl Associates, US Air Force Systems

Command, Contract #F42600-75-2212, final report, 15 April 1977, p 10.

33 Fletcher, Harvey, letter to Professor Orin Tugman, 19 April 1940, Harvey Fletcher Files.

34 Perreault, Bruce A., lecture at 1999 Exotic Research Conference, Mesa, Arizona, 21 July 1999.

35 Ibid.

36 Ibid.

37 Ibid.

38 Brown, Paul M. Ph.D., 'The Moray Energy Device: Operational Parameters, Design Criteria, and Considerations', (Nashville: Aztec Publishing, 1997).

39 Ibid.

40 Brown, Paul M., open letter, 1 November 1991.

Cosray
John E. Moray
P.O. Box 58141
Salt Lake City,
UT 84158-0141
Tel: (801) 582 9281
John E. Moray is the son of T. Henry Moray, and still supplies copies of synopses of *The Sea of Energy in Which the Earth Floats*.

Nu Energy Technologies, Inc.
Bruce Perreault
P.O. Box 22
Rumney, NH 03266-0022
Tel: (603) 786-9316
Web: www.nuenergy.org
Website looking at the research work of Bruce Perreault, including his work to replicate the Radiant Energy Device of T. Henry Moray.

GlobalAtomics
Paul M. Brown
E-mail: brown@globalatomics.com

Web: www.globalatomics.com
Dedicated to developments in the 'photodeactivation' (photo-remediation) technology of Paul M. Brown.

Chapter 4: The N-machine – Michael Faraday's Mysterious Legacy

1 *New York Times*, 20 June 1931.

2 Faraday, Michael, *Experimental Researches in Electricity*, 3 vols, (London: Richard and John Edward Taylor, 1839-1855).

3 Tesla, Nikola, 'Notes on a Unipolar Dynamo', *The Electrical Engineer*, 2 September 1891.

4 DePalma, Bruce, 'Pendulum Experiment Data (The Force Machine)', DePalma Institute, 1975.

5 Ibid.

6 DePalma, Bruce, report #92, 'The Secret of the Faraday Disc', DePalma Institute, 1995.

7 DePalma, Bruce, report #62, 'Simularity Institute', 16 July 1979.

8 DePalma, interview quoted in *News-Press*, Santa Barbara, 30 March 1980.

9 Wilhelm, Timothy, *Wilhelm Report: The Stelle Homopolar Machine (built to DePalma's specifications)*, (Stelle, Illinois: The Stelle Group, 1981).

10 DePalma, Bruce, 'Critique of the N-machine Constructed by Trombly and Kahn', DePalma Institute, 11 October 1985.

11 White, Dr D.C., report on N-Machine, M.I.T. Energy Lab, 9 March 1981.

12 Satellite News, 'Researchers See Long-Life Satellite Power Systems in 19th Century Experiment', *Phillips Publishing*, 15 February 1981.

13 Valone, T., 'The Real Story of the N-Machine', *Extraordinary Science*, April/May/June 1994, re-quoted in *The Homopolar Handbook* (Washington DC: Integrity Research Institute, 1994), p 72.

14 Ibid, p 70.
15 Inomata, Shiuji, letter to Thomas Valone, 15 June 1998.
16 Kincheloe, Robert, report on the Sunburst N-Machine, 1986.
17 Manning, Jeane, *The Coming Energy Revolution* (New York: Avery Publishing Group, 1996), p 86.
18 DePalma, Bruce, 'Free Energy – The Political, Social and Economic Implications', DePalma Institute.

Bruce DePalma – The Home of Primordial Energy
Web: www.depalma.pair.com

Integrity Research Institute
Thomas Valone
1220 L Street NW, Suite 100-232
Washington, DC 20005
Tel: (202) 452 7674
    (800) 329 8416
E-mail: iri@erols.com
Web: www.integrity-research.org
Independent research body focusing on lobbying for new energy technologies. Founded by Tom Valone.

Chapter 5: A Secret in the Swiss Mountains – Paul Baumann and the Thesta-Distatica

1 Kelly, Don, 'Swiss M-L Converter – A Masterpiece of Craftsmanship and Electronic Engineering', private report, 1988.
2 Ibid.
3 Hauser, Albert, private report, 14 February 1986.
4 Methernitha video narration.
5 Methernitha website: http://www.methernitha.com.
6 Ibid.
7 Marinov, Stefan, suicide note, 15 July 1997.
8 Bass, Dr Robert W., open letter, 13 October 1997.

9 Schneeberger, Erwin, open letter, 12 August 1997.
10 Interview with Hans Holzherr, first reported on Stefan Hartmann's website: http://www.overunity.com.
11 Ibid.
12 Ibid.
13 Potter, Paul, 'The Back-engineered Thesta-Distatica', unpublished article, 1999.
14 Ibid.

Methernitha
Web: www.methernitha.com

Overunity Website
Stefan Hartmann
Web: www.overunity.com

Chapter 6: The Life and Premature Death of Cold Fusion

1 Lidsky, Professor. Lawrence M., 'The Trouble with Fusion', *MIT Technology Review*, October 1983.
2 Fleischmann, Prof. Martin, *On the Ropes*, interview on BBC Radio 4, 21 May 1997.
3 Ibid.
4 Ibid.
5 Aspden, Dr H., letter to author, 28 August 2000.
6 Mallove, Eugene F., 'Why MIT and "Cold Fusion"?', *Infinite Energy Magazine*, Issue 24, p 65.
7 Parker, Prof. Ronald, news conference, 1 May 1989.
8 Tate, Nick, interviewed for WBUR Radio, 9 August 1991.
9 Transcription of interview with Professor Ronald Parker and Professor Richard Ballinger, conducted by Nick Tate, *Boston Herald* journalist, 28 April 1989.
10 Tate, Nick, retrospective article, 8 June 1991, quoted in *Infinite Energy Magazine*, Issue 24, p 72.
11 Mallove, op cit, p. 66.

12 Ibid, p 75.

13 Fox, Hal, interview in *Infinite Energy Magazine*, Issue 24, p 17.

14 Bush, B.F., Miles, M.H. and Lagowski, J.J., 'Anomalous Effects Involving Excess Power, Radiation, and Helium Production During D_2O Electrolysis Using Palladium Cathodes', *Fusion Technology*, Vol. 25, July 1994, pp. 478–486.

15 Dufour, Jacques, 'Cold Fusion by Sparking in Hydrogen Isotopes', *Fusion Technology*, Vol. 24, September 1994, pp. 205–228.

16 Arata, Yoshiaki and Zhang, Yue-Chang, 'Solid State Plasma Fusion ("Cold Fusion")', *Journal of the High Temperature Society of Japan*, Vol. 23, January 1997.

17 Chubb, Scott R., 'Naval Research Laboratory', *Infinite Energy Magazine*, Issue 24, p 7.

18 Storms, Edmund, *Infinite Energy Magazine*, Issue 31, p 10.

19 McKubre, Michael C.H., interview with author, 6 July 2000.

20 McKubre, Michael C.H., 'The Works', interview with BBC World Service, 13 January 2000.

21 Rothwell, Jed, comments on the Tenth Anniversary Contributions, *Infinite Energy Magazine*, Issue 24, p 24.

22 Bockris, John O'M., interview, *Infinite Energy Magazine*, Issue 24, p 21.

23 Fox, Hal, interview, *Infinite Energy Magazine*, Issue 24, p 22.

24 McKubre, Michael C.H., *Today* programme, interview on BBC Radio 4, 20 October 1998.

JET (Joint European Torus)
Web: www.fusion.org
Home of the UK's hot fusion research.

Cold Fusion Times
Ed. Dr Mitchell R. Swartz,
P.O. Box 81135,
Wellesley Hills,
MA 02181
USA

Infinite Energy
c/o Eugene Mallove
P.O. Box 2816
Concord NH 03302-2816
Tel: (603) 228 4516
Fax: (603) 224 5975
Email: subscribe@infinite-energy.com
Web: www.infinite-energy.com
Infinite Energy magazine is probably the most comprehensive magazine in the new energy field. Many detailed and technical articles about advances in cold fusion/LENR research, as well as most other new energy topics, including renewables.

Chapter 7: Cold Fusion Comes of Age

1 Cravens, Dr Dennis, 'Flowing Electrolyte Calorimetry', report (Vernon, Texas: ENECO, May 1995).
2 Platt, Charles, 'What if Cold Fusion is Real?', *Wired*, November 1998.
3. Bishop, Jerry E, *The Wall Street Journal*, 29 January 1996.
4 US Department of Energy – Energy Assessments Division, letter to CETI, 29 May 1997.
5 CETI press release, 1996.
6 Mallove, op cit, p 68.
7 Appelee brief from the Board of Patent Appeals and Interferences, re: Mitchell R. Swartz, (00-1107, Serial No. 07/371,937), 30 May 2000, p 13.
8 Case, Dr Leslie C., 'Progress in Catalytic Fusion', *Infinite Energy Magazine*, Issue 23, p 9.
9 Ibid, p 10.
10 Mallove, Eugene F., 'Reproducible Catalytic Fusion Process', *Infinite Energy Magazine*, Issue 19, p 32.
11 McKubre, Michael C.H., 'Progress in Catalytic Fusion', *Infinite Energy Magazine*, Issue 23, p 15.
12 McKubre, Michael C.H., 'Proceedings of ICCF-7', quoted in

Infinite Energy Magazine, Issue 20, p 34.

13 Case, op cit, p 12.

14 McKubre, 'Progress in Catalytic Fusion', p 14.

15. McKubre, Michael C.H., article, *Infinite Energy Magazine*, Issue 24, p 8.

16 Storms, Edmund, quoted in *Excess Heat*, Charles Baudette (South Bristol, Maine: Oak Grove Press, 2000), pp 44–45.

17 Storms, Edmund, open letter accompanying paper, 1998.

18 Storms, Edmund, article, Infinite *Energy Magazine*, Issue 24, p 19.

19 Ibid.

20 Chubb, op cit, p 7.

Fusion Information Center
P.O. Box 58639
Salt Lake City UT 84158-8639
Tel: (801) 583 6232
Fax: (801) 583 6245
Publishes *Fusion Facts*, monthly newsletter on fusion topics. The editor is Hal Fox.

The Journal of New Energy
Published by Emerging Energy Marketing Firm, Inc.
3084 E. 3300 South,
Salt Lake City,
Utah 84109.
Tel: (801) 466 8680
Fax: (801) 466 8668.
Published by Hal Fox, *The Journal of New Energy* examines a wide range of new energy technologies.

Future Technology Intelligence Report
P.O. Box 2903A
Sacramento,
CA 95812-2903
USA

Monthly newsletter on 'over-unity' technologies, their economic implications, low energy transmutations etc.

ICCF8
8th International Conference on Cold Fusion
Web: www.frascati.enea.it/iccf8/

Chapter 8: Randell Mills – BlackLight's Power Struggle

1 Celente, Gerald C., *Trends 2000* (New York: Warner Books, 1997), p 305.
2 Blake, David, interviewed by Erik Baard, *Village Voice*, 22–28 December 1999.
3 Haldeman, Dr Charles, interviewed by Erik Baard, *Village Voice*, 22–28 December 1999.
4 Jacox, Michael, interviewed by Erik Baard, *Village Voice*, 22–28 December 1999.
5 BlackLight website: http://www.blacklightpower.com.
6 Mills, Randell, L., interview with Art Rosenblum, printed in *Infinite Energy Magazine*, Issue 17, p 21.
7 BlackLight website, op cit.
8 Mills, op cit, p 34.
9 Ibid.
10 Ibid, p 23.
11 Ibid, p 30.
12 Ibid.
13 Baard, Erik, 'The Empire Strikes Back', *Village Voice*, March 2000.
14 Park, Dr Robert L., *Voodoo Science: The Road from Foolishness to Fraud*, (New York: Oxford University Press, 2000).
15 Ibid.
16 Baard, Erik, op cit.
17 BlackLight Power, Complaint Case Number 1:00CV00422, US District Court, DC.
18 Ibid.

19 Ibid.
20 Melcher, Jeffreys, letter to Esther Kepplinger, USPTO, March 2000.
21 Ibid.

Blacklight Power Inc.,
Dr. Randell Mills
Web: www.BlacklightPower.com

What's New?
Dr. Robert Park
Web: www.aps.org/WN

Village Voice
Erik Baard
Web: www.villagevoice.com

Chapter 9: Zero Point Physics and the Cosmic Free Lunch

1 Kuhn, Thomas S., *The Structure of Scientific Revolutions*, second edition (Chicago: University of Chicago Press, 1970).
2 Ibid, p 109.
3 Pagels, Prof. Heinz R., *The Cosmic Code* (London: Michael Joseph, 1983).
4 Boyer, Timothy, 'The Classical Vacuum', *Scientific American*, 253(2), August 1985.
5 Puthoff, Dr Harold, *Quantum Fluctuations of Empty Space – A New Rosetta Stone of Physics?* (Austin, Texas: Institute for Advanced Studies, 1989).
6 Podolny, R., *Something Called Nothing* (Moscow: Mir Publishing, 1986).
7 'Does Jupiter Have New Bolts?', *The Economist*, 14 October 1989, p 99.
8 Puthoff, op cit.
9 King, Moray B., 'Vortex Filaments, Torsion Fields and the

Zero-Point Energy', article in *Infinite Energy Magazine*.
10 Forward, Dr R., 'The Extracting of Electrical Energy from the Vacuum by Cohesion of Charge-foliated Conductors', *Physical Review B*, 30, 4, 1984.
11 US Patent No. 5,590,031: http:www//patent.delphion.com.
12 'Energy Unlimited', *New Scientist*, 22 January 2000, pp 32–34.

ALSO:
Valone, T., 'Inside Zero Point Energy', *Infinite Energy Magazine*, Issue 26, pp 53–57.
Bohm, David, *Wholeness and the Implicate Order* (London: Routledge & Kegan Paul. 1980), pp 190–91.

Institute for Advanced Studies
Dr Hal Puthoff
4030 Braker Lane W., #300
Austin, Texas 78759-5329
USA
Tel: (512) 346 9947
Web: www.earthtech.org
A pioneering experimental laboratory with an excellent record in producing high-level, peer-reviewed articles on the implications of zero-point energy.

Sabberton Publications
P.O. Box 35
Southampton SS09 7BU
England
Web: www.energyscience.co.uk
Publisher of articles and books by Dr. Harold Aspden, author of *Modern Aether Science.*

Chapter 10: Significant Others

1 Peregrinus, P., originally found amongst the Pallips Manuscripts, dated 1269 (reprinted 1902 by Charles Wittingham & Co, Chiswick Press, London).

2 Curtis, Henry, report, http:www.//keelynet.com.

3 Report, 4 March 1998, http:www//keelynet.com.

4 British Intelligence Report, 1946.

5 Smokhin, Andrei, 'Vacuum Energy – a breakthrough', *NOVOSTI* press release : 03NTO-890717CM04, 17 July 1989.

6 Ibid.

7 Hindley, Dr. Keith B., *Summary of New Information from A.V. Chernetskii's Papers* (York, England: Technology Detail, 1989).

8 Puthoff, Dr Harold, interviewed in *It Runs on Water*, TV documentary, Channel 4, 17 December 1995.

9 Press release, BTA Sofia, 28 November 1988.

10 Labofex press release, 1996.

11 Carrell, Mike, 'The Correa Invention', *Infinite Energy Magazine*, Issue 8, p 10.

12 Correa, Paulo N., 'Usages of Physics and the Inventor's Health', lecture quoted in *Infinite Energy Magazine*, Issue 23, p 35.

13 Feynman, Prof. Richard, personal letter to Kenneth Shoulders, 31 January 1986.

14 Shoulders, K., 'Charge Clusters in Action', *Proceedings of COFE*, April 1999.

15 http://www.hydrodynamics.com.

16 *The Sciences*, magazine, July/August 1993.

KeelyNet – Order Out of Chaos
P.O. Box 570309,
Dallas, TX 75357-0309
Tel: (214) 324 8741
Fax: (214) 324 3501
Web: www.keelynet.com
A combination of alternative and scientific topics, including 'free

energy'. Includes a comprehensive archive section.

US Patent Office
Web: www.uspto.gov
A comprehensive site for all US patents.

Delphion
Web: www.delphion.com
Search patents worldwide through this site.

Correas
Web: www.globalserve.net/~lambdac/ListContents.html
Information on the work of Paulo and Alexandra Correa.

K.R.Shoulders
EV – A Tale of Discovery
P.O. Box 243
Bodega,
CA 94922-0243
An historical sketch of early EV work.

Hydro Dynamics Inc.
James Griggs
Web: www.hydrodynamics.com

Chapter 11: Of Charlatans, Conspiracies and Sceptics

1 Project Alpha tape, 1988.
2 Kingdom-Age Technologies and Project Alpha Information for Investors, 1988.
3 Interview with the author, September 2000.
4 Ibid.
5 Project Alpha tape, 1988.
6 Edwards, Dr Denis, email to author, 13 November 2000.

7 Kingdom-Age Technologies and Project Alpha Information for Investors, 1998.

8 Ibid.

9 Krieg, Eric, report on Dennis Lee at Philadelphia, 1996, Phact website: http://www.phact.org.

10 Ibid.

11 Ibid.

12 Krieg, op cit.

13 Ibid.

14 Newman, Joseph Westley, press release, 18 September 1999.

15 Newman, Joseph Westley, *The Energy Machine of Joseph Newman*, Eighth Edition (Scottsdale, Arizona: The Joseph Newman Publishing Company, 1999).

16 Hastings, Roger, statement to the Subcommittee on Energy, Nuclear Proliferation and Government Processes, 30 July 1986.

17 Everett, Milton, affidavit, 7 September 1999.

18 Newman, Joseph, report on demonstration, 14 August 1999, http://www.josephnewman.com.

19 Biss, Norm, posting to http://www.phact.org.

20 website: www.josephnewman.com.

21 Ibid.

Philadelphia Association for Critical Thinking
Eric Krieg
Web: www.phact.org or www.syc.org/e/skeptic/

The Energy Machine of Joseph Newman
Joseph Newman
Web: www.josephnewman.com

Chapter 12: Envisaging a New Energy Future

1 UN Framework Convention on Climate Change, 9 May 1992.

2 US Energy Information Administration, *Annual Energy Review*, 1997, p xxxii.

3 Global Warming International Center, news, 30 August 1999, http://www.globalwarming.net/news/news08301999-2.html.

4 Global Warming International Center, http://www.globalwarming. net/ news/news9.html.

5 EPRI figures (cost figures include operating, maintenance, capital generating expense), quoted at http://www. blacklightpower.com.

6 Hieronimus, Bob, radio programme, 21st Century Radio, Hieronimus and Co., 23 June 1996.

7 Zimmerman, Peter, 'Science, Junk Science and Pseudoscience', APS meeting, 22 March 1999, Atlanta, Georgia.

8 Ibid.

9 Zimmerman, Peter, e-mail mistakenly sent to Integrity Research Institute, 25 March 1999.

10 Zimmerman, Peter, e-mail sent to Integrity Research Institute (on purpose), 16 March 1999.

Royal Commission on Environmental Pollution
Web: www.rcep.org.uk
UK organisation which advises government on actions to be taken to reduce threats from climate change.

Unit Energy Ltd (Unit [e] united kingdom)
16 Avon Reach
Monkton Hill
Chippenham
Wiltshire SN15 1EE
Tel: 0044 1249 705550
Fax: 0044 1249 445374
Email: enquiries@unit-energy.co.uk
A supplier of wind energy to homes in UK. Any home can change to wind energy through Unit [e] without disruption of services or maintenance. The system works purely through a change in billing – the National Grid buys wind energy from Unit [e] to balance demand from customers.

APPENDIX 1: An Energy Primer

1 Steinmetz, Charles P., 'The Second Law of Thermodynamics and the "Death" of Energy, with Notes on the Thermodynamics of the "Atmosphere"', *General Electric Review*, Vol. 15, July 1912.
2 Ibid.
3 Rauen, Ken, review of 'The Refrigerator and the Universe' by Goldstein, Martin and Golstein, Inge F., (Cambridge, Mass: Harvard University Press, 1993) *Infinite Energy Magazine*, Vol. 5, Issue 29, p 46.
4. Aspden, H., letter to author, 28 August 2000.

PERMISSIONS

All photos of T. Henry Moray, courtesy of Cosray
Bruce De Palma, courtesy of 'The Home of Primordial Energy'
Randell Mills, courtesy of Robin Holland
Joint European Tours (JET), courtesy of UKAEA
Professors Pons and Fleischmann, courtesy of Infinite Energy Archives
Eugene F. Mallove, courtesy of *Infinite Energy* magazine
Edgar Mitchell, courtesy of Integrity Research Institute
Michael H. McKubre, courtesy of Michael H. McKubre
Dr Leslie C. Case, courtesy of *Infinite Energy* magazine
Dr Hal Puthoff, courtesy of the Institute for Advanced Studies

Index